DYNAMICS OF RIGID BODIES

By

A.K. Sharma

DISCOVERY PUBLISHING HOUSE
NEW DELHI-110002

First Published - 2007

Reprinted - 2018

ISBN: 978-81-8356-234-8

Dynamics of Rigid Bodies

Published by:

DISCOVERY PUBLISHING HOUSE PVT. LTD.
4383/4B, Ansari Road, Darya Ganj
New Delhi-110 002 (India)
Phone: +91-11-23279245, 43596064-65
Fax: +91-11-23253475
E-mail: discoverypublishinghouse@gmail.com
sales@discoverypublishinggroup.com
web: www.discoverypublishinggroup.com

Printed at:
Infinity Imaging Systems
Delhi

Preface

There are number of books on "Dynamics of Rigid Bodies" in the market for the use of degree students in various universities in India. An efforts has been made in this book to put the matter in a very lucid and simple way to that even a beginner has no difficulty in grasping the subject. Each chapter for this book contains complete theory and a fairly large number of solved examples. The answer to almost all unsolved problems have been checked and every care has been taken to avoid printing and other mistakes.

Suggestions for improvement from all corners will be thankfully acknowledge.

Author

CONTENTS

1

CONSERVATION OF MOMENTUM AND ENERGY

PRINCIPLE OF CONSERVATION OF LINEAR MOMENTUM (UNDER FINITE FORCES)

If the forces acting on a system be such that they have no component along a certain fixed straight line, throughout the motion, then the motion is such that the linear momentum resolved along this line is constant.

Let (x, y, z,) be the coordinates of any particle m of a body at time t, referred to fixed axes where the fixed straight line has been taken as the axis of x. Let X be the resolved part parallel to fixed line of the external forces acting on the particle, then

$$\text{or } \frac{d}{dt}\Sigma m\frac{dx}{dt} = \Sigma X.$$

But from the given conditions $\Sigma X. = 0$, **hence** $\frac{d}{dt}\Sigma m\frac{dx}{dt} = 0$

$$\textit{i.e. } \Sigma m\frac{dx}{dt} = \text{constant}$$

$$\Rightarrow M\frac{d\overline{x}}{dt} = \text{constant} \qquad \left(\because \overline{x} = \frac{\Sigma mx}{M}\right) \qquad \ldots(1)$$

where $\overline{x}$ **is the x - coordinate of the centre of gravity of body and M its total mass.**

From (1), we observe that the total momentum of the body parallel to the axis of x is constant throughout the motion.

PRINCIPLE OF CONSERVATION OF ENERGY

If a system moves under the action of finite forces and if the geometrical equations of the system do-not contain time explicity the change in the kinetic energy of the system in passing from one configuration to any other is equal to the corresponding work done by the forces.

Let (x, y, z) be the coordinates of a particle of mass m at the time t, and let the resolved parts of the external forces parallel to the axes at that time be X, Y, Z.

Then, by D' Alembert's principle, the forces $X - m\ddot{x}, Y - m\ddot{y}, Z - m\ddot{z}$ acting at the point (x, y, z) and the similar forces acting at other particles of the system, form a system of forces in equilibrium.

If dx, dy, dz denote arbitrary small displacements of the particle of mass m at (x, y, z) consistent with geometrical conditions at any time t, then by the principle of virtual work, we have

$$\Sigma[X - m\ddot{x})\,\delta x + (Y - m\ddot{y})\,\delta y + (Z - m\ddot{z})\delta z] = 0 \qquad ...(1)$$

If the geometrical conditions are expressed by the equations which do not contain time explicity, then the conditions which hold at time t, will also hold through the time δ t. Therefore, we can take the arbitrary displacements $\delta x, \delta y, \delta z$ as the actual displacements $\frac{dx}{dt}\delta t, \frac{dy}{dt}\delta t, \frac{dz}{dt}\delta t,$

Replacing δx by $\frac{dx}{dt}\delta t, \delta y$ by $\frac{dz}{dt}\delta t, \delta z$by $\frac{dz}{dt}\delta t$ in (1), we have

$$\Sigma\left[(X - m\ddot{x})\frac{dx}{dt} + (Y - m\ddot{y})\frac{dy}{dt} + (Z - m\ddot{z})\frac{dz}{dt}\right]\delta t = 0$$

$$\text{or } \Sigma m\left[\ddot{x}\frac{dx}{dt} + \ddot{y}\frac{dy}{dt} + \ddot{z}\frac{dz}{dt}\right] = \Sigma\left[X\frac{dx}{dt} + Y\frac{dy}{dt} + Z\frac{dz}{dt}\right]$$

On integration w. r.t. "t" we get

$$\Sigma\frac{1}{2}m\left[\dot{x}^2 + \dot{y}^2 + \dot{z}^2\right]_{t_1}^{t_2} = \Sigma\int_{t=t_1}^{t=t_2}(xdx + ydy + Zdz)$$

Thus we see that change kinetic energy of the system from time t_1 to t_2 equal to the work done by the external forces on the body from the configuration of the body at time t_1 to the configuration at time t_2.

PRINCIPLE OF CONSERVATION OF ANGULAR MOMENTUM (MOMENT OF MOMENTUM UNDER FINITE FORCES)

If the forces acting on a system be such that they have no moment about a certain fixed straight line, throughout the motion then the angular momentum about this straight line is constant.

Let the co-ordinates of a particles of mass m at time t referred to fixed axes be (x, y, z) where the fixed straight line has been taken as the axis of x. Let X, Y, Z be the resolved parts paralle! to the axis of the external forces acting on

particle m. The sum of the moments of the external force about the given fixed line is Σ (yZ - zY). By D- Alembert's principle, we have

$$\Sigma m\left(y\frac{d^2z}{dt^2}-z\frac{d^2y}{dt^2}\right)=\Sigma(yZ-zY).$$

But from the given condition that throughout the motion, the sum of the moments of the external forces about the axis of x is zero.

i.e. $\Sigma(yZ-zY)=0$

$$\therefore \Sigma m\left(y\frac{d^2z}{dt^2}-z\frac{d^2y}{dt^2}\right)=0 \text{ throughout the motion}$$

i.e. $$\frac{d}{dt}\Sigma m\left(y\frac{dz}{dt}-z\frac{dy}{dt}\right)=0$$

i.e. $$\Sigma m\left(y\frac{dz}{dt}-z\frac{dy}{dt}\right)=\text{constant.} \qquad ...(2)$$

From (2), we observe that total moment of moment of momentum of the body about x - axis is constant throughout the motion.

PRINCIPLE OF CONSERVATION OF LINEAR MOMENTUM (IMPULSIVE FORCES)

If the sum of the impulsive forces parallel to a certain fixed line vanishes, the total momentum in that direction remains the same just before and after the application of impulses.

Let us take the fixed line as the axis of x, then

$$\Sigma.m\frac{d^2x}{dt^2}=\Sigma X \;\; i.e. \;\; \frac{d}{dt}\left[\Sigma.m\frac{dx}{dt}\right]=\Sigma X. \qquad ...(1)$$

If τ be the time (small during which the impulsive forces act on the body, then on integration (1),

$$\text{we get } \left[\Sigma\frac{dx}{dt}\right]_0^\tau=\Sigma\int_0^\tau X dt=\Sigma x_1$$

i.e. $$\Sigma m(v-u)=\Sigma X_1, \text{ when } X_1=\int_0^\tau X dt \qquad ...(2)$$

where u value are the velocities before and after the impulse and X_1 is the impulse of the forces parallel to the x–axis . But if $\sum X_1=0$, we have from (2) $\sum m(v-u)=0$ *i.e.* $\sum mv=\sum mu$),

i.e. **total momentum after impulse = the total momentum before impulse**

PRINCIPLE OF CONSERVATION OF ANGULAR MOMENTUM [IMPULSIVE FORCES]

If the sum of the moments of the impulses about a certain line vanishes then the angular momentum about it remains the same before and after the application of the impulse.

Let us take the fixed line as axis of x. Let t be the time (small) during which the impulses act on the body. By taking moments about the fixed axis, we have

$$\Sigma m(y\ddot{z}-z\ddot{y})=\Sigma(yZ-zY). \qquad ...(1)$$

integrating it w.r.t. "t" we have

$$\int_0^\tau \Sigma m(y\ddot{z}-z\ddot{y})dt=\int_0^\tau \Sigma(yz-zY)dt$$

$$\Rightarrow [\Sigma m(y\dot{z}-z\dot{y})]_0^\tau=\Sigma(yZ_1-zY_1)$$

$$\text{where } Z_1=\int_0^\tau Zd \text{ and } Y_1=\int_0^\tau Ydt. \qquad ...(2)$$

L.H.S. of (2) is angular momentum after the impulse minus angular momentum before impulse.

R.H.S. of (2) is the sum of the moments of the impulses about x – axis. In case the sum of the moments of impulses about x – axis is zero

i.e., $\Sigma(yZ_1-zY_1)=0$, we have

Angular momentum after impulse = angular momentum before impulse.

CONSERVATIVE FORCES

If the forces acting on the body are such that $\Sigma(xdx+Ydy+Zdz)$ *is the complete differential of some quantity say V, then the forces are said to be conservative.*

Thus we see, If the forces are conservative, then

$$\Sigma(Xdx+Ydy+Zdz)=\int_{t_1}^{t_2}\{\Sigma(Xdx+Ydy+Zdz)\}$$

$$=\int_{t_1}^{t_2} dV=Vt_2-V_{t_1} \qquad ...(1)$$

which implies that the potential of forces is V. Thus we note that L.H.S. of (1) is independent of the path followed by the body in moving from one position to the other and depends only on the configuration of the body at time t_1 and t_2.

Thus if A is the configuration at time t_1 and B the configuration at time t_2, then have K.E. at time t_2 – K.E. at time t_1 = V_t-V_t *i.e.* K.E. at B – K.E. at A = V_B-V_A

When a body moves under the action of a system of Conservative faces, the sum of its kinetic and potential energies is constant throughout the motion. (Conservation of energy)

In the last article, we have shown that if A and B are the configuration of the body at times t_1 and t_2 then

K.E. at time t_2 *i.e.* at the position B – K.E. at t_1 *i.e.* at the position A

$$= \int_{t_1}^{t_2} dV = VB - V_A \qquad ...(1)$$

The potential energy of the body in any position A is the work done by the forces in moving the body form position A to some standard position C (say)

$\therefore$ Potential energy at time t_1

$$= \Sigma \int_A^C (Xdx + Ydy + Ydz) = \int_A^C dV = V_C - V_A \qquad ...(2)$$

and potential energy at time

$$t_2 = \Sigma \int_A^C (Xdx + Ydy + Ydz)$$

$$= \int_A^C dV = V_C - V_B \qquad ...(3)$$

Combining (2) and (3), we have P.E. at time t_1 – P.E. at time t_1

$$= V_C - V_A - (V_C - V_B) = V_B - V_A \qquad ...(4)$$

Comparing (1) and (4), we have P.E. at time t_1 – P.E. at time t_2

= K.E. at time t_2 – K.E. at time t_1

i.e. K.E. at time t_1 + P.E. at time t_1

= K.E. at time t_2 + P.E. at time t_2.

i.e. sum of the potential energy and kinetic energy is constant at all times.

The kinetic energy of a rigid body, moving in any manner, is at any instant equal to the kinetic energy of the whole mass, supposed to be collected at its centre of inertia and moving with it, together with the kinetic energy of the whose mass relative to its centre of inertia.

Consider a particle of mass m of the body. Let (x, y, z) be the coordinates of this particle at any time t. Let $(\bar{x}, \bar{y}, \bar{z})$ be the co-ordinates of G, the centre of gravity of the body. If (x', y', z') are the co-ordinates of some particle relative to G then, we have $x = \bar{x} + x', y = \bar{y} + y', z = \bar{z} + z'$ and $*Smx' = 0$, $Smy' = 0$, $\Sigma mz' = 0$

so that $\Sigma m\frac{dx'}{dt} = 0, \Sigma m\frac{dy'}{dt} = 0; \Sigma m\frac{dz'}{dt} = 0$

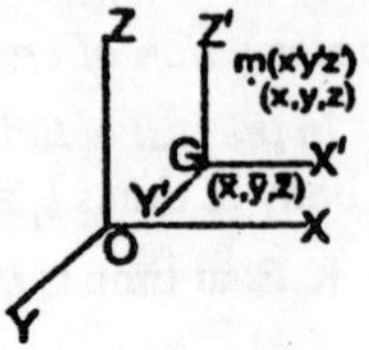

The total K.E. of the body

$$= \frac{1}{2}\Sigma m\left[\left(\frac{dx}{dt}\right)^2 + \left(\frac{dy}{dt}\right)^2 + \left(\frac{dz}{dt}\right)^2\right]$$

Fig. 1.1

$$= \frac{1}{2}\Sigma m\left[\left(\frac{d\bar{x}}{dt} + \frac{dx'}{dt}\right)^2 + \left(\frac{d\bar{y}}{dt} + \frac{dy'}{dt}\right)^2 + \left(\frac{d\bar{z}}{dt} + \frac{dz'}{dt}\right)^2\right]$$

$$= \frac{1}{2}\Sigma m\left[\left(\frac{d\bar{x}}{dt}\right)^2 + \left(\frac{d\bar{y}}{dt}\right)^2 + \left(\frac{d\bar{z}}{dt}\right)^2\right] + \frac{1}{2}\Sigma m\left[\left(\frac{dx'}{dt}\right)^2\right.$$

$$\left. + \left(\frac{dy'}{dt}\right)^2 + \left(\frac{dz'}{dt}\right)^2\right] + \Sigma m\left[\frac{d\bar{x}}{dt}\frac{dx'}{dt'} + \frac{d\bar{y}}{dt}\frac{dy'}{dt} + \frac{d\bar{z}}{dt}\frac{dz'}{dt}\right]$$

$$= \frac{1}{2}\Sigma m\left[\left(\frac{d\bar{x}}{dt}\right)^2 + \left(\frac{d\bar{y}}{dt}\right)^2 + \left(\frac{d\bar{z}}{dt}\right)^2\right]$$

$$+ \frac{1}{2}\Sigma m\left[\left(\frac{dx'}{dt}\right)^2 + \left(\frac{dy'}{dt}\right)^2 + \left(\frac{dz'}{dt}\right)^2\right]$$

$$+ \frac{d\bar{x}}{dt}\Sigma m\frac{dx'}{dt} + \Sigma m\frac{dy'}{dt}\Sigma m\frac{dy'}{dt} + \frac{d\bar{z}}{dt}\Sigma m\frac{dz'}{dt}$$

$$= \frac{1}{2}\left[\left(\frac{d\bar{x}}{dt}\right)^2 + \left(\frac{d\bar{y}}{dt}\right)^2 + \left(\frac{d\bar{z}}{dt}\right)\right]^2 \Sigma m$$

$$+ \frac{1}{2}\Sigma m\left[\left(\frac{dx'}{dt}\right)^2 + \left(\frac{dy'}{dt}\right)^2 + \left(\frac{dz'}{dt}\right)\right]^2$$

$= \frac{1}{2}$ (velocity of centre of gravity G)^2 Σm

$+ \frac{1}{2}$ (velocity of G)^2 $\times \Sigma m + \frac{1}{2}\Sigma m$

$= \frac{1}{2}Mv^2 + \frac{1}{2}\Sigma m$ (velocity of m relative to G)^2

Taking G as the origin the co-ordinates of general point are (x', y', z'). Then co-ordintes of the C.G. of the body are given as x coordinate of C.G $= \frac{\Sigma mx'}{Zm}$

But x coordinate of G = 0 (since G is the origin) $\therefore$ $\Sigma mx' = 0$ Similarly $\Sigma my' = 0$ $\Sigma mz' = 0$. where M is the total mass of the body and v is the velocity of the centre of gravity G. *To sum up:*

Total K.E. of the body = K.E. of mass M supposed to be collected at G + K. E. of the body relative to G.

VIS-VIVA

Vis-Viva of a particle is the product of its mass and the square of its velocity.

If a particle of mass m is moving with velocity v, then its

Vis-Viva $= mv^2 = 2\cdot\left(\frac{1}{2}mv^2\right)$ = Twice its kinetic energy.

PRINCIPLE OF VIS-VIVA

If a system moves under the action of finite forces and if the geomertical conditions of the parts of the system be expressed by equations which do not contain time explicity, the change in the Vis - Viva of the system in passing from one position to any other is equal to twice the corresponding work done by the forces.

Note: Proof is the same as that of principle of conservation of energy

SOLVED EXAMPLES

Example 1:

A uniform plane of thickness 2h rests across the top of a fixed circular cylinder of radius a whose axis is horizontal. prove that if it be set in motion, the equation of energy is

$$\frac{1}{2}[k^2 + h^2 + a^2\theta^2]\theta^2 + g[a\theta\sin\theta - (a+h)(1-\cos\theta)] = \text{const.}$$

on the assumption that the motion is of pure rolling. Hence show that if a>h, horizontal position is stable and period of small oscillation is the same as for a simple pendulum of length $\frac{k^2 + h^2}{a - h}$.

Solution:

The figure is the vertical cross section of the system through the centre of gravity G of the plank. From G drawn GB perpendicular to the edge of the plank, so GB = h. Initially the point B of the plank coincided with the highest point A of the fixed cylinder. Let ω be the initial angular velocity. After time t, the edge of the plank make an angle θ with the horizontal. Since it is given that there is no slipping between the plank and the cylinder, therefore arc AP = BP *i.e.* BP = aθ. With O as origin OX and OY as axes, the co-ordinates of G are given by

$$x = MP - PL + BD = a\sin\theta - a\theta\cos\theta + h\sin\theta$$

$$y = OM + BL + GD = a\cos\theta + a\theta\sin + h\cos\theta$$

$$\therefore \dot{x} = a\cos\theta\dot{\theta} + h\cos\theta\dot{\theta} - a(\cos\theta\dot{\theta} - \theta\sin\theta\dot{\theta})$$

$$= (a\theta\sin\theta + h\cos\theta)\dot{\theta}$$

and $\dot{y} = -a\sin\theta\dot{\theta} - h\sin\theta\dot{\theta} + a(\theta\dot{\theta} - \sin\theta\dot{\theta})$

$$= (a\theta\cos\theta - h\sin\theta)\dot{\theta}$$

$\therefore$ velocity of G at time t $= \sqrt{\dot{x}^2 + \dot{y}^2}$

$$= \theta\sqrt{[(a\theta\sin\theta + h\cos\theta)^2 + (a\theta\cos\theta - h\sin\theta)^2]}$$

$$= \dot{\theta}\sqrt{(a^2\theta^2 + h^2)}$$

K.E. at time $t = \frac{1}{2}m[k^2 + \dot{\theta}^2 + h^2\dot{\theta}^2] = \frac{1}{2}m\dot{\theta}^2[k^2 + a^2\theta^2 + h^2]$

Initial K.E. $= \frac{1}{2}m\omega^2[k^2 + h^2]$

[since in the beginning, $\theta = 0$, and $\dot{\theta} = \omega$]

Hence energy equation gives

$$\frac{1}{2}m[k^2 + a^2\theta^2 + h^2]\dot{\theta}^2 - \frac{1}{2}m(k^2 + h^2)\omega^2$$

$$= mg(a + h) - (a\cos\theta + a\theta\sin\theta + h\cos\theta)]$$

or $(k^2 + a^2\theta^2 + h^2)\dot{\theta}^2 - [(k^2 + h^2)\omega^2 = 2g(a + h) - (a + h)\cos\theta - a\theta\sin\theta]$

or $(k^2 + a^2\theta^2 + h^2)\dot{\theta}^2 - 2g[(a + h)(1 - \cos\theta) - a\theta\sin\theta]$

$$= (k^2 + h^2)\omega^2 = \text{const.}$$

or $\frac{1}{2}(k^2 + h^2 + a^2\theta^2)\dot{\theta}^2 + g[a\theta\sin\theta - [a + h)(1 - \cos\theta)]\text{const.}$

Small oscillations: We take q to be small then from the above equation,

we have $\frac{1}{2}(k^2 + h^2)\dot{\theta}^2 + g\left[\theta^2 - (a + h).\frac{2\sin^2(\theta/2)}{(\theta/2)^2}\left(\frac{\theta}{2}\right)^2\right] = \text{const}$

$$\left[\therefore \theta\sin\theta = \theta.\frac{\sin\theta}{\theta}\theta = \theta^2 \text{ approx.}\right]$$

$$\text{or } \frac{1}{2}(k^2+h^2)\dot{\theta}^2 + ga\theta^2 - 2ga(a+h).\left(\frac{\sin\frac{1}{2}\theta}{\frac{1}{2}\theta}\right)^2 \frac{\theta^2}{4} = \text{const.} = 0$$

$$\text{or } \frac{1}{2}(k^2+h^2)\dot{\theta}^2 = g(a+h)\theta^2 - 2ga\theta^2 = -g(a-h)\theta^2$$

$$\text{or } \dot{\theta}^2 = -\frac{g(a-h)}{(k^2+h^2)}2\theta\dot{\theta}$$

Differentiating it, we get

$$2\dot{\theta}\ddot{\theta}^2 = -\frac{g(a-h)}{(k^2+h^2)}2\theta\dot{\theta}$$

$$\text{i.e. } \ddot{\theta} = -\frac{g(a-h)}{(k^2+h^2)}\theta$$

which is a simple harmonic motion implying that the horizontal position of equilibrium is stable.

The length of the simple equivalent pendulum $= \frac{k^2+h^2}{a-h}$.

Example 2:

A heavy circular disc is revolving in a horizontal plane about the centre which is fixed. An insect of mass $\frac{1}{n}$ th that of the disc walks from the centre along a radius and then flies away. Show that the final angular velocity is $\frac{n}{n+2}$ times the original angular velocity of the disc.

Solution:

Let ω be the initial angular velocity of the disc. The insect flies away when it reaches the edge of the disc, let at this time ω′ be the angular velocity of the disc.

The forces acting on the system are either vertical or pass through O; thus their moments vanish about the vertical through O; so moment of, momentum about the vertical through O remains constant the motion

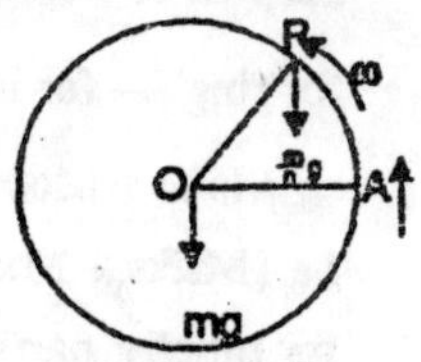

Fig. 1.2

$$\therefore m0.\omega' + m\frac{a^2}{2}\omega' + \frac{m}{n}a^2\omega' = m.0.\omega + m\frac{a^2}{2}\omega$$

Example 3:

A circular ring of mass M and radius a, lies on a smooth horizontal plane and an insect of mass m, resting on it starts and walks round it with uniform velocity v relative to the ring. Show that the centre of the ring describes a circle with angular velocity $\frac{m}{M+2m} \cdot \frac{v}{a}$.

Solution:

Let O be the centre of the ring and G the common centre of gravity of the ring and the insect resting at A.

If OG = x and GA = y, we have Mx = my

$$\Rightarrow \frac{x}{m} = \frac{y}{m} = \frac{x+y}{m+M} = \frac{a}{m+M}$$

$$\Rightarrow x = \frac{ma}{m+M'}\, y = \frac{Ma}{m+M}$$

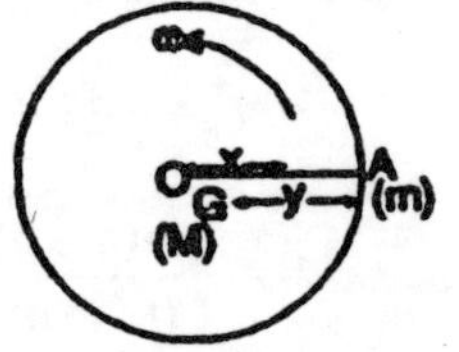

Fig. 1.3

where m is the mass of the insect and M the mass of ring.

So there is no horizontal force on the system throughout the motion, the horizontal momentum remains constant throughout the motion, which implies that the velocity of G (common C. G. of ring and the insect) in the horizontal plane will be zero throughout the motion because of its initial velocity being zero. In other words G remains fixed.

Hence the point O will describe a circle of radius $\frac{ma}{m+M}$ about G.

Now let ω be the angular velocity of the ring about G. Since all the forces [weight of the ring, weight of the insect] acting on the system are vertical, therefore their moments vanish about the vertical through G, hence moment of momentum about the vertical through G remains constant throughout the motion.

i.e. $(Mk^2\omega + M\, x\, \omega.\, GO) + (m\, \omega\, G\, A.\, G\, A + m\, v.\, G\, A) = 0$

for ring ← for insect →

$\Rightarrow Ma^2\omega + M\omega x^2 + (m\omega y^2 + mv\, y) = 0$

i.e. $\{Mk^2\omega_1 + Mx\omega_1.GO\} + m\omega_2 GA.GA = 0 + mu.GA$

for tubefor particle [tube] [practical]

$\therefore M(a^2 - x^2)\omega + my^2\omega + mv(a-x) = 0 (\because y = a - x)$

$\Rightarrow \omega[Ma^2 + Mx^2 + My^2] = -mv(a-x)$

$$\Rightarrow \omega[Ma^2 + \frac{Mm^2a^2}{(m+M^2} + \frac{mM^2a^2}{(m+M^2}] = -mv\left[a - \frac{ma}{m+M}\right]$$

$$\Rightarrow \frac{Ma^2}{(m+M)^2}[(m+M)^2 + m^2 + mM]\omega = -\frac{amMv}{(m+M)}$$

$$\Rightarrow \frac{Ma^2}{(m+M)^2}[(m+M)^2 + m(m+M)]\omega = -\frac{amMv}{(m+M)}$$

$$\Rightarrow \frac{a(m+M)(2m+M)\omega}{m+M} = -mv \Rightarrow \omega = -\frac{m}{M+2m}.(v/a)$$

Negative sign shows that disc will turn in a direction which is opposite of the direction of v

Example 4:

A particle of mass m, moves within a rough circular tube of mass M lying on a horizontal plane and initially the tube is at rest while the particle has an angular velocity round the tube. Show that by the time the relative motion ceases, the fraction $\frac{M}{M+2m}$ *of the initial kinetic energy has been dissipated by friction.*

Solution:

Let O be the centre of the circular tube; the common C.G. of m and M where m = mass of the particle and M = mass of the tube. If OG = x and GA = y, then M x = my.

$$\Rightarrow \frac{x}{m} = \frac{y}{m} = \frac{x+y}{m+M} = \frac{a}{M+m}$$

$\Rightarrow x = ma/(M+m)$, $y = Ma/M + m)$.

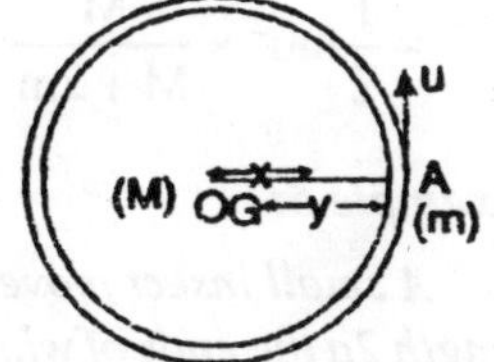

Fig. 1.4

Let u be the initial of the particle when the tube is at rest and v the velocity with which G, the common C.G. begins to move.

Now there being no force acting on the system in the horizontal plane throughout the motion, the horizontal momentum remains unchanged throughout the motion.

$$\therefore (M+m)v = mu \Rightarrow v = \frac{mu}{M+m}$$

When the system begins to move, let ω_1 and ω_2 be the angular velocities of the tube and the particle about G. Since the forces acting on the system are all vertical, therefore their moments vanish about the vertical axis through G throughout the motion, which implies that the moment of momentum about G remains the same throughout the motion.

i.e. $muy = M(a^2\omega_1 + x^2\omega_1) + my^2\omega_2$

The relative motion will cease when $\omega_1 = \omega_2$, then from (1), we have.

$$\omega_1 = \frac{muy}{M(a^2+x^2)+my^2} \qquad ...(2)$$

At this time, the kinetic energy of the system is

$$= \frac{1}{2}(M+m)v^2 + \frac{1}{2}M(a^2+x^2)\omega_1^2 + \frac{1}{2}my^2)\omega_1^2$$

[particle] [Tube] [K.E. of G.]

$$= \frac{1}{2}(M+m)\frac{m^2u^2}{(M+m)^2} + \frac{1}{2}(my^2+Ma^2)\times\frac{m^2u^2y^2}{(my^2+Ma^2+Mx^2)^2}$$

$$= \frac{1}{2}m^2u^2\left[\frac{1}{M+m} + \frac{y^2}{(my^2+Ma^2+Mx^2)}\right]$$

$$= \frac{1}{2}mu^2 - \frac{1}{2}mu^2\,\frac{M}{M+2m}$$

[by putting the values of x and y]

$$\therefore \text{ Loss of K.E.} = E\cdot = \frac{1}{2}mu^2 - \left[\frac{1}{2}mu^2 - \frac{1}{2}mu^2\frac{M}{M+2m}\right]$$

$$= \frac{1}{2}mu^2 \times \frac{M}{M+2m} = \frac{M}{M+2m} \text{ of the initial K.E.}$$

Example 5:

A small insect moves along a uniform bar; of mass equal to itself and of length 2a the ends of which are constrained to remain on the circumference of a fixed circle whose radius is $(2a/\sqrt{3})$. *If the insect starts from the middle point of the bar and moves along the bar with relative velocity V, show that the bar in time t will turn through an angle.*

$$\frac{1}{\sqrt{3}}\tan^{-1}\left(\frac{Vt}{a}\right)$$

Solution:

Let θ be the angle through which the bar AB turn in time t, the dotted line through A represents the original position. Let P be the position of insect time t.

$$\therefore CP = Vt \text{ and} OC = \left[\left(\frac{2a}{\sqrt{3}}\right)^2 - a^2\right]^{1/2} = \frac{a}{\sqrt{3}}$$

$$\therefore OP = \sqrt{[OC^2 + CP^2)]} = \sqrt{\left[(\frac{1}{3}a^2 + V^2t^2)\right]}$$

Since the moment of external forces [weights, reaction about vertical axis through O vanishes throughout the motion so the moment of momentum about this line remains unchanged.

i.e. $0 = (OC\dot{\theta}.OC + \frac{1}{3}a^2\dot{\theta}) + m(VOC + OP\dot{\theta}.OP)$

$$\Rightarrow \frac{1}{3}a^2\dot{\theta} + \left(\frac{1}{3}a^2 + V^2t^2\right)\dot{\theta} + \frac{a}{\sqrt{3}}V = O$$

$$\Rightarrow a^2\dot{\theta} + V^2t^2\ \dot{\theta} + \frac{a}{\sqrt{3}}V = O$$

$$\Rightarrow \dot{\theta} + (a^2 + V^2t^2) + \frac{a}{\sqrt{3}}V = 0 \Rightarrow \theta = -\frac{Va}{\sqrt{3(a^2 + V^2t^2)}}$$

$$\therefore \theta = \frac{Va}{\sqrt{2}}\int_0^1 \frac{dt}{V^2t^2 + a^2} = -\frac{Va}{\sqrt{3}}\frac{1}{V^2}\int_0^1 \frac{dt}{t^2 + (a^2/V^2)}$$

$$= -\frac{Va}{\sqrt{3}\cdot}\frac{1}{V^2}\frac{V}{a}\left[\tan^{-1}\frac{Vt}{a}\right]_0^1 = -\frac{1}{\sqrt{3}}\tan^{-1}\left(\frac{Vt}{a}\right)$$

Negative sign shows that the rod turns in a direction opposite to that of the insect.

Example 6:

A uniform circular wire of radius a, lies on a smooth horizontal table and is movable about a fixed point O on its circumference. An insect of mass equal to that of the wire, starts from the other end of the diameter through O and crawls along the wire with a uniform velocity v relative to the wire. Show that at the end of time t, the wire has turned through an angle

$$\left(\frac{vt}{2a}\right) - \left(\frac{1}{\sqrt{3}}\right)\tan^{-1}\left[\left(\frac{1}{\sqrt{3}}\right)\tan\left(\frac{vt}{2a}\right)\right]$$

Solution:

Let in time t the diameter O A have turned through an angle ϕ from its initial position OA_0, let the insect be at P such that

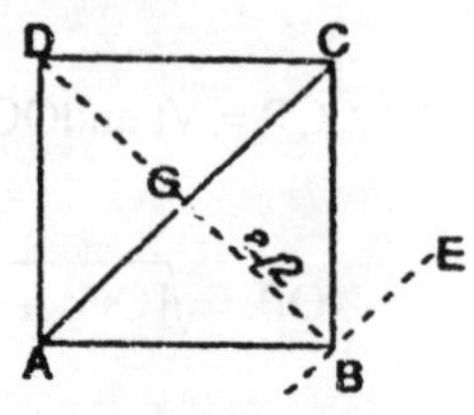

Fig. 1.5

$\angle ACP = \theta \therefore OP = 2a\cos(\theta/2)$.

Let O N be perpendicular on the tangent at P

$\therefore ON = OP\cos(\theta/2) = 2a\cos^2(\theta/2)$

The forces acting on the system are (i) Reaction at the point O (ii) Weight of the insect vertically downwards. (iii) Weight of the wire acting vertically down wards. Since the forces acting on the system are either vertical or pass through O, therefore moment of all forces about the vertical axis through O vanishes throughout the motion. Thus the moment of momentum of the system about this axis remains unchanged throughout the motion. The insect at P has a velocity v along the tangent at P and a velocity OP perpendicular to OP ϕ due to rotation of the circular wire.

So the moment of momentum of the insect about a vertical through

$$O = m(v.ON + OP\phi.OP = m\left[2av\cos^2\frac{\theta}{2}. + \left(2a\cos\frac{\theta}{2}\right)^2\phi\right]$$

$$= m\left[2av\cos^2\frac{\theta}{2} + 4a^2\cos^2\frac{\theta}{2}.\phi\right]$$

Also the moment of momentum of the circular wire about the vertical axis though O.

= moment of momentum of the mass m moving with the C.G + moment of momentum about the C.G.

$$= m[a\phi.a + a^2\phi]$$

$= 2ma^2\phi$ [C.G. describes a circle of radius a with velocity a $\dot{\phi}$]

Hence the total moment of momentum at time t

$$= m\left[2av\cos^2\frac{\theta}{2} + 4a^2\cos^2\frac{\theta}{2}.\phi\right] + 2ma^2\phi$$

But the moment of momentum of the system remains unchanged and initial the body was at rest, therefore we have

$$m\left[2av\cos^2\frac{\theta}{2} + 4a^2\cos^2\frac{\theta}{2}.\phi\right] + 2ma^2\phi$$

$$\Rightarrow 2a^2\left(1 + 2\cos^2\frac{\theta}{2}\right)\phi = -2av\cos^2\frac{\theta}{2}$$

$$\Rightarrow 2a^2\left(1 + 2\cos^2\frac{\theta}{2}\right)\phi = -2av\cos^2\frac{\theta}{2}$$

$$\Rightarrow \dot{\phi} = -\frac{v\cos^2(\theta/2)}{a\{1+2\cos^2(\theta/2)\}} \qquad ...(1)$$

Now the arc AP is covered by the insect in time moving with uniform velocity v.

$\therefore$ arc AP = vt, also arc AP = aθ $\therefore$ $a\theta = vt \Rightarrow \theta = \left(\frac{vt}{a}\right)$

putting this value of θ in (1), we get

$$= -\left(\frac{\pi}{4}\right) + \left(\frac{72}{3\sqrt{7}}\right)\tan^{-1}\left(\frac{\sqrt{7}}{3}\right) = \left(\frac{24}{\sqrt{7}}\right)\tan^{-1}\left(\frac{\sqrt{7}}{3}\right) - (\pi/4).$$

Hence the angle turned by the diameter OA in time t is given by

$$\theta = \int_o^t \frac{-v\cos^2(vt/2a)}{a[1+2\cos^2(vt/2a)}dt = -\frac{v}{a}\int_o^t \frac{\cos^2(vt/2a)}{1+2\cos^2(vt/2a)}dt$$

$$= -\frac{v}{a}\int_o^t \frac{1}{2}\left[1 - \frac{1}{1+2\cos^2(vt/2a)}\right]dt$$

$$= -\frac{v}{2a}\int_o^t \left[1 - \frac{\sec^2(vt/2a)}{\sec^2(vt/2a)+2}\right]dt$$

$$= -\frac{v}{2a}\int_o^t \left[1 - \frac{\sec^2(vt/2a)}{3+\tan^2(vt/2a)}\right]dt$$

$$= -\frac{v}{2a}\int_o^t \left[t - \frac{2a}{v}\frac{1}{\sqrt{3}}\tan^{-1}\left(\frac{1}{\sqrt{3}}\tan\frac{vt}{2a}\right)\right]$$

$$= -\left[\frac{vt}{2a} - \frac{1}{\sqrt{3}}\tan^{-1}\left(\frac{1}{\sqrt{3}}\tan\frac{vt}{2a}\right)\right].$$

Negative sign shows that wire moves in a direction opposite to that of the insect.

Example 7:

A circular disc is moving with an angular velocity ω about an axis through its centre perpendicular to its plane. An insect alights on its edge and crawls along a curve drawn on the disc in the form of lemniscale with uniform relative angular velocity $\frac{1}{8}\omega$, the curve touching the edge of the disc. The mass of the in sect being $\frac{1}{16}$ th of that of the disc. Show that the angle turned through by the disc when the insect gets to the centre is

$$\left(\frac{24}{\sqrt{7}}\right)\tan^{-}\left[\frac{\sqrt{7}}{3}\right]-\left(\frac{\pi}{4}\right)$$

Solution:

Let the disc turn through an angle ϕin time t and the distance of insect from 0, the centre of the circle, be than r (OP = r) at an angle θ with the axis of the lemniscate, then equation of leminiscate is

$$r^2 = a^2 \cos 2\theta$$

Moment of momentum before insect alights of the disc $= M\frac{1}{2}a^2\omega$,

and moment of momentum of the system about O after time t

$$= \frac{1}{2}Ma^2\dot{\phi} + \frac{1}{16}M\left(r^2\dot{\phi} + r^2.\frac{1}{8}\omega\right)$$

Since all forces acting on the system are vertical or pass through the centre O, therefore the moment of all the forces about a vertical axis through O. vanishes, thus the moment of momentum about this axis through O remains unchanged throughout the motion.

$$\therefore M.\frac{1}{2}a^2\dot{\phi} + \frac{1}{16}M\left(r^2\dot{\phi} + \frac{1}{8}r^2\omega\right) = \frac{1}{2}Ma^2\omega$$

$$\text{or } Ma^2\dot{\phi} - \frac{1}{8}M\left(\dot{\phi} + \frac{1}{8}\omega\right)a^2\cos 2\theta = Ma^2\omega\left[\because r^2 = a^2\cos 2\theta\right]$$

$$\text{or } 64\dot{\phi} + \left(8\dot{\phi} + \omega\right)\cos 2\theta = 64\omega$$

$$\text{or } (64 + 8\cos 2\theta)\dot{\phi} = 64\omega - \omega\cos 2\theta$$

$$\text{or } \dot{\phi} = \frac{d\theta}{dt} = \frac{(64-\cos 2\theta)\omega}{64 + 8\cos 2\theta.} \text{ or } \frac{d\phi}{d\theta}\cdot\frac{d\theta}{dt} = \frac{(64-\cos 2\theta)\omega}{64 + 8\cos 2\theta}$$

$$\text{or } \frac{d\phi}{d\theta}\cdot\frac{1}{8}\omega = \frac{(64-\cos 2\theta)\omega}{8(8+\cos 2\theta)} \qquad \left[\because \frac{d\theta}{dt} = \frac{1}{8}\omega\right]$$

$$\text{or } d\phi = \frac{64-\cos 2\theta}{8+\cos 2\theta}d\theta.$$

If ϕ be the angle turned by the disc when the insect reaches the centre of the circle (*i.e.* when $\theta = \pi/4$), then

$$\phi = \int_0^{\pi/4}\frac{64-\cos 2\theta}{8+\cos 2\theta}d\theta = \int_0^{\pi/4}\left[-1 + \frac{72}{8+\cos 2\theta}\right]d\theta$$

$$= \int_0^{\pi/4}\left[-1+\frac{72}{8+\left(2\cos^2\theta-1\right)}\right]d\theta$$

$$= \int_0^{\pi/4}\left[-1+\frac{72}{(7+2\cos^2\theta}\right]d\theta = \int_0^{\pi/4}\left[-1+\frac{72\sec^2\theta}{7\sec^2\theta+2}\right]d\theta$$

$$= \int_0^{\pi/4}\left[-1+\frac{72\sec^2\theta}{(9+7\tan^2\theta}\right]d\theta = \int_0^{\pi/4}\left[-1+\frac{72}{7}\frac{\sec^2\theta}{\left(\frac{9}{7}\right)+\tan^2\theta}\right]d\theta$$

$$= \left[-\theta+\frac{72}{3\sqrt{7}}\tan^{-1}\left(\frac{\sqrt{7}}{3}\tan\theta\right)\right]_0^{\pi/4}$$

$$= -\left(\frac{\pi}{4}\right)+\left(\frac{72}{3\sqrt{7}}\right)\tan^{-1}\left(\frac{\sqrt{7}}{3}\right)=\left(\frac{24}{\sqrt{7}}\right)\tan^{-1}\left(\frac{\sqrt{7}}{3}\right)-(\pi/4).$$

Example 8:

A rod OA can turn freely in a horizontal plane about the end O and lies at rest. An insect, whose mass is one third that of the rod alights on the end A and commences crawling along the rid with uniform velocity V, at the same instant the rod is set in rotation about O in such a way that the initial velocity of A is V, when the insect reaches O, prove that the rod has rotated through a right angle and that the angular velocity of the rod is then twice the initial angular velocity.

Solution:

Let OA be the initial position of the rod, when the insect is at A. Let the rod turn through an angle θ time t, also let the insect reach the point p in this time. since the insect moves along the rod will uniform velocity V so the distance moved in time t.

AP = Vt, and OP = 2a –t where 2a is length of the rod.

Since the rod moves about 0 with initial velocity V so its angular velocity in its initial position

$$= \frac{V\cdot 2a}{(a)^2} = \frac{V}{2a} \qquad \left[\therefore \text{angular velocity} = \frac{pV}{r^2}\right]$$

Moment of momentum of the system about 0, when the insect is at A

$$= \frac{1}{3}M.V.2a + M\left(a\frac{V}{2a}a+\frac{1}{3}a^2\frac{V}{2a}\right) = \frac{4}{3}MVa$$

also moment of momentum after time t

$$=\frac{1}{3}M(2a-vt)\theta(2a-Vt)+M\left(a\theta a+\frac{1}{3}a^2\dot{\theta}\right)$$

[formula $mvp + mk^2\dot{\theta}$]

[since now the angular velocity of rod is θ and that of insect due to rotation of the rod is $(2a-Vt)\theta$]

$$=\frac{M}{3}(2a-Vt)^2+\frac{4}{3}Ma^2 \qquad ...(ii)$$

The moment of all the forces about the vertical through 0 vanishes, so the moment of momentum about 0 remains unchanged throughout the motion. therefore we have from (i) and (ii)

$$\frac{M}{3}(2a-Vt)^2\dot{\theta}+\frac{4}{3}Ma^2\dot{\theta}=\frac{4}{3}MVa$$

or $$[(2a-Vt)^2+4a^2]\dot{\theta}=4Va$$

or $$\frac{d\theta}{dt}=\frac{4Va}{(2a-Vt)^2+4a^2}$$

Now the insect will reach the point 0 (moving with uniform velocity V) in time (2a/V). If θ be the angle described by the rod in this time, then

$$\int_0^{2a/v}\frac{4Va}{\left(2a-Vt^2\right)+4a^2}dt \text{ Put } 2a-Vt=z, \therefore -Vdt=dz$$

$$i.e.\ \theta=\int_{2a}^{0}\frac{4Va}{z^2+2a^2}\cdot\frac{-dz}{V}=\int_{2a}^{0}\frac{4a}{z^2+(2a^2)}dz$$

$$=4a\int_0^{2a}\frac{dz}{z^2+(2a)^2}=4a\cdot\frac{1}{2a}\left[\tan^{-1}\frac{z}{2a}\right]_0^{2a}=\left(\frac{\pi}{4}-0\right)=(\pi/2).$$

Hence the rod has turned through a right angle in this time the angular velocity of the rod $\dot{\theta}$ when the insect reaches 0 is obtained by putting $t=\left(\frac{2a}{V}\right)$ in (iii), i.e., $\dot{\theta}=\left(\frac{V}{a}\right)=2\left(\frac{V}{2a}\right)$ = twice the initial angular velocity

Example 9:

A uniform square plate ABCD of mass M and side 2a, lies on a smooth horizontal plane, it is struck a A by a particle of mass m moving with velocity V in the direction of AB, the particle remaining attached to the plate. Determine subsequent motion of the system and show that its angular velocity is $\frac{m}{M+4m}\cdot\frac{3v}{2a}$

Solution:

Let O be the centre of the square ABCD of mass M and G the centre of gravity of the system.

$$\therefore M.O.G = m.AG$$

$$\text{or } \frac{OG}{m} = \frac{Ag}{M} = \frac{OG++AG}{m+M} = \frac{AO}{m+M}$$

$$\therefore OG = \frac{ma\sqrt{2}}{m+M} \text{ or } AG = \frac{Ma\sqrt{2}}{m+M}$$

$$\because AO = \frac{1}{2}AC = \frac{1}{2}\sqrt{\left[(2a)^2 + (2a)^2\right]} = 2\sqrt{2}.$$

The external forces acting on the system *i.e. (i)* the weight of the square (ii) the weight of the particle and (iii) the reaction of the smooth plane, are all vertical, thus there is no horizontal component of the force throughout the motion. Hence the total horizontal momentum of the system will remain constant throughout the motion. Le V′ is the velocity of the system after impact, then we have (M + m) = mV′ + M.O or V′ mV/M +m)

Again the moment of the external forces (acting vertically) about the vertical axis through G is zero, so the angular momentum of the system about this vertical axis through G remains constant throughout the motion. Let w is the angular velocity of the system after impact, then we have

$$\therefore \{Mk^2\omega + M.OG\} + mAG.\omega.AG = mV.GL$$

(for square) (for particle)

$$\text{or } \frac{2}{3}Ma^2\omega + M\omega.\left(\frac{ma\sqrt{2}}{m+M}\right)^2 + m\omega\left(\frac{Ma\sqrt{2}}{m+M}\right)^2 = mV.\frac{Ma\sqrt{2}}{m+M}\sin 45^\circ$$

$$\because GL = AG\sin 45^\circ$$

$$\text{or } 2a^2\left[\frac{1}{3} + \frac{m(m+M)}{(m+M)^2}\right]\omega = \frac{mVa}{m+M}$$

$$\text{or } \frac{2a^2}{3}\left(\frac{m+M+3m}{m+M}\right)\omega = \frac{mVa}{m+M}$$

$$\text{or } \omega = \frac{m}{M+4m}\cdot\frac{3V}{2a}$$

Example 10:

A circular plate rotates about an axis through its centre perpendicular to its plane with angular velocity ω. This axis is set free and a point, in the circumference of the plate is fixed, show that the resulting angular velocity is $\frac{1}{3}\omega$.

Solution:

In this case centre C is set free and a point A on the circumference is suddenly fixed. Let ω′ be the angular velocity just after the fixture. The impulse is at A, so the moment of the impulse about A will be zero. Hence moment of momentum about the axis through A remains the same before and after the fixture. *i.e.*

$$m\left[a^2\omega' + \frac{a^2}{2}\omega'\right] = \frac{ma^2}{2}\omega \text{ or } \omega' = \frac{1}{3}\omega.$$

Example 11:

A circular plate is turning in its own plane about a point A on its circumference. Suddenly A is freed and a point B on the circumference is fixed. Show that the plate will be reduced to rest if the arc AB is one third of the circumference.

Solution:

Consider a circular plate with centre C turning in its own plane about a point A on its circumference. A is set free and B is suddenly fixed. Let w¢ be angular velocity just after the fixture. Let . Since the impulse is at B, so the moment of the impulse about B is zero, hence moment and momentum about B will remain the same before and after fixture

$$i.e.\quad m\left[\frac{a^2}{2}\omega + a^2\omega'\right] = \left[\frac{a^2}{2}\omega + a\omega a\cos\theta\right]$$

$$\text{or}\quad \omega' = \frac{1}{3}(1 + 2\cos\theta)\omega.$$

The plate will reduced to rest if $\omega' = 0$

i.e. if $1 + 2\cos\theta = 0$ or $\cos\theta = -\frac{1}{2}$ i.e. $\theta = \frac{2\pi}{3}$

or a $\theta = \frac{1}{3}(2\pi a)$ *i.e.* are AB is $\frac{1}{3}$ of the circumference.

Example 12:

A uniform circular disc is spinning with angular velocity ω about a diameter, when a point P on its rim is suddenly fixed. If the radius vector to P makes an angle α with this diameter, show that the angular velocities after the fixing, about the tangent and normal at P are $\frac{1}{5}\omega \sin \alpha$ and $\omega \cos \alpha$.

Solution:

Consider a circular plate with centre C, rotating with angular velocity ω about the diameter ACB. The resolved part of ω about the normal at P *i.e.* about PC = ω cos α.

The resolved part of ω about the tangent at P = ω sin α.

Now the diameter AB is set free and the point P is suddenly fixed. Let ω_1 and ω_2 be the angular velocities about the tangent and normal at P just after the fixture.

The impulse is at P, therefore moment of the impulse about P is zero.

Hence the moment of momentum about the tangent at P remains unchanged after the fixture.

i.e. $m\left(\frac{a^2}{4}\right)\omega_1 + ma^2\omega_1 = m\left(\frac{a^2}{4}\right)\omega \sin a$. *i.e.* $\omega_1 = \left(\frac{1}{5}\right)\omega \sin \alpha$. Similarly the moment of momentum about the normal must be the same before and after the fixture.

$$m\left(\frac{a^2}{4}\right)\omega_2 = m\left(\frac{a^2}{4}\right)\omega \cos a \text{ i.e. } \omega_2 = \omega \cos \alpha.$$

Example 13:

An equilateral triangular lamina is rotating in its plane with uniform angular velocity about an axis through one vertex. If this vertex is released and one of the other vertices fixed. Show that the new angular velocity is 1/5 of its former value.

Solution:

Let the vertex C be released and the vertex B be suddenly fixed. Let ω and ω′ be the angular velocities just before and after the fixture. If m is the mass of the triangular lamina, then it is equivalent to three particles each of mass m/3 placed at the mid - points of the sides.

The moment of momentum about axis through B remains unchanged *i.e.*

$$\left(\frac{m}{3}\right)a^2\omega + 0 + 0 = \left(\frac{m}{3}\right)a^2\omega' + \frac{m}{3}a^2\omega' + \left(\frac{m}{3}\right)a^2\omega'$$

$$\text{i.e. } 5\omega' = \omega \text{ i.e } \omega' = \frac{1}{5}\omega.$$

Example 14:

A rod of length 2a is moving about one end with uniform angular velocity upon a smooth horizontal plane. Suddenly this end is set free and a point distant b from this end is fixed; find the motion, considering the case when b> = < $\frac{4a}{3}$.

Solution:

Let AB be the rod, moving with uniform angular velocity ω about the end A. The end A is set free and a point O of the rod is suddenly fixed, where AO = b. Let the angular velocity, of the rod after the fixture be ω′. The impulse is at O, thus moment of impulse about O will be zero, hence the moment of momentum about the axis through O will remain unchanged before and after the fixture *i.e.*

$$i.e.\ m\frac{a^2}{3}\omega' + m(a-b)^2\omega' = m\frac{a^2}{3}\omega + ma(a-b)\omega$$

$$\text{or}\quad \left[\frac{a^2}{3} + (a-b)^2\right]\omega' = \left[\frac{a}{3} + (a-b)\right]\omega$$

$$\text{or}\quad [a^2 + 3(a-b)^2\ \omega' = a(4a-3b)\omega$$

$$i.e.\ \omega' = \frac{a(4a-3b)}{a^2+3(a-b)^2}\omega.$$

(i) If $b < \frac{4a}{3}$ then $\omega' = \frac{3\left(\frac{4}{3}a - b\right)}{a^2+3(a-b)^2}$ is positive which implies that the rod will rotate in the same direction after the fixture as before.

(ii) If $b = \frac{4a}{3}$, then ω′ = 0, the rod is reduced the rest after the fixture.

(iii) If $b < \frac{4a}{3}$, then ω′ is negative, which implies that the rod will move in opposite sense after the fixture.

Example 15:

A lamina in the form of an ellipse is rotating in its own plane about one of its foci with angular velocity ω. This focus is set free and other focus, at the same time is fixed, show that the ellipse now rotates about it with angular velocity $\omega\frac{2-5e^2}{2+3e^2}$.

Solution:

Consider an ellipse, rotating with angular velocity ω about the focus S. If O is the midpoint of the major axis then OS = OS′ = ae, where length of the major axis AA′ = 2a. The focus S is set free and suddenly the other focus S ′ fixed.

Let the angular velocity after the fixture be ω¢ the impulse is at S ′, therefore the moment of the impulse about S′ is zero. Hence moment of momentum about this axis remains unaltered before and after the fixture

$$i.e.\ m\frac{a^2+b^2}{4}\omega' + ma^2e^2\omega' = m\frac{a^2+b^2}{4}\omega - ma^2e^2\omega$$

$$\text{or}\quad \left(\frac{a^2+b^2}{4}+a^2e^2\right)\omega' = \left(\frac{a^2+b^2}{4}-a^2e^2\right)\omega$$

$$\text{or}\quad \left(a^2+b^2+4a^2e^2\right)\omega' = \left(a^2+b^2-4a^2e^2\right)\omega$$

$$\text{or}\quad \omega' = \frac{a^2+b^2-4a^2e^2}{a^2+b^2+4a^2e^2}\cdot\omega$$

$$\text{or}\quad \omega' = \frac{a^2+a^2(1-e^2)-4a^2e^2}{a^2+a^2(1-e^2)+4a^2e^2}\omega \qquad \{\because b^2 = a^2(1-e^2)\} = \frac{2-5e^2}{2+3e^2}\omega.$$

Example 16:

An elliptic area, of eccentricity e is rotating with angular velocity ω about one latus rectum; suddenly this latus rectum is loosened and the other fixed. Show that the new angular velocity is $\frac{1-4e^2}{1+4e^2}\omega.$

Solution:

Consider the ellipse rotating with angular velocity ω, about its latus rectum L S L′.

Let this latus- rectum be set free and suddenly the other latus rectum L″S′L‴ be fixed. Let the angular velocity be ω′ just after the fixture. The impulse is at L″S′L‴ . Hence the moment of the impulse about the rectum L¢¢S¢L¢¢¢ remains the same before and after the fixture.

$$i.e.\ m\frac{a^2}{4}\omega' + ma^2e^2\omega' = m\frac{a^2}{4}\omega - ma^2e^2\omega$$

$$\text{i.e}\ \left(a^2+4a^2e^2\right)\omega' = \left(a^2-4a^2e^2\right)\omega$$

$$i.e.\ \omega' = \frac{1-4e^2}{1+4e^2}\omega.$$

Example 17:

An elliptic lamina is rotating about its centre on a smooth horizontal table. If $\omega_1, \omega_2, \omega_3$ be its angular velocities when the extremity of its major axis its focus and the extremity of its minor axis respectively become fixed prove that

$$\left(\frac{7}{\omega_1}\right)=\left(\frac{6}{\omega_2}\right)+\left(\frac{5}{\omega_3}\right)$$

Solution:

Initially the lamina was rotating with angular velocity ω about its O.

(i) **Let the centre O be set free and the end A of the major axis suddenly fixed.** The impulse is at A, therefore moment of the impulse about the axis through A (perpendicular to the plane of motion) is zero, therefore the moment of momentum about this axis remains the same before and after the fixture. If ω1 is the angular velocity just after the fixture, we have

$$\Rightarrow mk^2\omega + o = mk^2\omega_1 + ma\omega_1 \cdot AOm\frac{a^2+b^2}{4}\omega_1 + ma^2\omega_1$$

$$\text{or } \left(a^2+b^2\right)\omega = \left[\left(a^2+b^2\right)+4a^2\right]\omega_1 \text{ } i.e. \text{ } \omega_1 = \frac{a^2b^2}{5a^2+b^2}\omega \qquad ...(1)$$

(ii) **Let the centre O be set free and the focus S be suddenly fixed.**

Again the impulse will be at S and the moment of the impulse about S is zero. Therefore the moment of momentum about the axis through S will remain the same before and after the fixture

$$i.e. \text{ } m\frac{a^2+b^2}{4}\omega = m\frac{a^2+b^2}{4}\omega_2 + ma^2e^2\omega_2$$

$$\text{or } \left(a^2+b^2\right)\omega = \left(a^2+b^2+4a^2e^2\right)\omega_2$$

$$i.e. \text{ } \omega^2 = \frac{a^2+b^2}{a^2+b^2+4a^2e^2}\omega$$

$$\text{or } \omega_2 = \frac{a^2+b^2}{a^2+b^2+4(a^2-b^2)}\omega \qquad \left[\because b^2 = a^2\left(1-e^2\right)\right] = \frac{a^2+b^2}{5a^2+3b^2}\omega$$

(iii) **Let the centre be set free and the end B of the minor axis be suddenly fixed.** In this case, we have

$$m\frac{a^2+b^2}{4}\omega = m\frac{a^2+b^2}{4}\omega_3 + mb^2\omega_3$$

$$\text{or } \left(a^2+b^2\right)\omega = \left(a^2+b^2+4b^2\right)\omega_3$$

i.e. $\omega_3 = \frac{a^2+b^2}{a^2+5b^2}\omega$ ...(3)

from (1), (2) and (3), we have

$$\frac{7}{\omega_1}-\frac{6}{\omega_2}-\frac{5}{\omega_3}=\frac{35a^2+7b^2}{(a^2+b^2)\omega}-\frac{30a^2-18b^2}{(a^2+b^2)\omega}-\frac{5a^2+25b^2}{(a^2+b^2)\omega}$$

$$=\frac{[35a^2+7b^2-30a^2+18b^2-5a^2-25b^2]}{(a^2+b^2)\omega}=0 \Rightarrow \frac{7}{\omega_1}=\frac{6}{\omega_2}=\frac{5}{\omega_3}.$$

Example 18:

A uniform square lamina, of mass M and side 2a, is moving freely about a diagonal with uniform angular velocity where one of the corners not in that diagonal becomes fixed, show that the new angular velocity is $\frac{1}{7}\omega$ and that the impulse of the force on the fixed point is $\frac{\sqrt{2}}{7}Ma\omega$.

Solution:

Initially the square ABCD is revolving about the diagonal AC with angular velocity ω; this diagonal AC is set free and the corner B is suddenly fixed. The square will begin to turn about the line BE through B parallel to AC. Let ω′ be angular velocity about BE. The impulse is at B, thus the moment of the impulse about BE zero. Therefore the moment of momentum about BE remains the same before and after the fixture,

i.e. $Mk^2\omega' + M(\overline{BG})^2\omega' = Mk^2\omega$ ...(1)

But k^2 about AC $=\frac{a^2}{3}\cos^2\frac{\pi}{4}+\frac{a^2}{4}\sin^2\frac{\pi}{4}=\frac{a^2}{3}$

and BG $= a\sqrt{2} \therefore M\frac{a^2}{3}\omega' + M2a^2\omega' = M\frac{a^2}{3}\omega$ *i.e.* $\omega'=\frac{\omega}{7}$.

After the fixture, the velocity of G, the centre of gravity of the square is $a\sqrt{2}\omega'$ at right angles to BG.

$$= M\left(a\sqrt{2}\omega' - O\right) = Ma\sqrt{2}\omega' = Ma\sqrt{2}.\frac{1}{7}\omega = \frac{\sqrt{2}}{7}Ma\omega.$$

Example 19:

A cube is turning with angular velocity ω about a diagonal, when suddenly the diagonal is let go and of the edges which does not meet this diagonal is fixed; show that the resulting angular velocity about this edge is $\left(\frac{\omega\sqrt{3}}{12}\right)$

Solution:

Let 2a be the side of the cube. Take OA, OB, OC as the axes of x,y,z, respectively. Then the direction cosines of the diagonal OP are $\frac{1}{\sqrt{3}}, \frac{1}{\sqrt{3}}, \frac{1}{\sqrt{3}}$. Let the cube revolve about the diagonal OP with angular velocity ω. Obviously the resolved parts of this angular velocity about OA, OB, OC will be $\frac{\omega}{\sqrt{3}}, \frac{\omega}{\sqrt{3}}, \frac{\omega}{\sqrt{3}}$ respectively.

Let the diagonal OP be set free and edge LA be suddenly fixed. Let ω′ be the angular velocity about the edge. The distance of the edge from the centre is

Since the moment of momentum remains the same before and after the fixture, therefore we have $M\left(\frac{2a^2}{3}\omega' + 2a^2\omega'\right) = m.o + m\frac{2a^2}{3}\frac{\omega}{\sqrt{3}}$

[∵ For the cube about any axis through its centre, $k^2 = \frac{2a^2}{3}$]

or $\frac{8a^2}{3}\omega' = \frac{2a^2}{3\sqrt{3}}\omega$ *i.e.* $\omega' = \frac{\omega}{4\sqrt{3}} = \frac{\sqrt{3}\omega}{12}$.

Example 20:

A uniform cube is spinning freely with angular velocity w about a diagonal through a corner O, when suddenly the diagonal through O′ of one of the faces through O becomes fixed, show that the new angular velocity is $\frac{2\sqrt{3}}{5\sqrt{3}}\omega$.

Solution:

Let the side of cube be 2a, so the length of its diagonal

$= \sqrt{[(4a^2 + 4a^2 + 4a^2)]} = 2a\sqrt{3}$

and the length of the diagonal of a face $= \sqrt{[(4a^2 + 4a^2)]} = 2a\sqrt{2}$.

∴ inclination of the diagonal of the cube to the diagonal of the face

$$= \cos^{-1}\frac{2a\sqrt{2}}{2a\sqrt{3}} = \cos^{-1}\sqrt{\left(\frac{2}{3}\right)}$$

Initially the cube was revolving about its diagonal with angular velocity ω, resolved part of this angular velocity along diagonal of the face is $\omega\sqrt{\left(\frac{2}{3}\right)}$.

The distance of the centre of gravity of the cube from the diagonal of the face equal to a. Since the diagonal of the face is suddenly fixed the impulse is at this diagonal, so moment of the impulse about this diagonal is zero, therefore the moment of momentum about this diagonal of the face is the same before and after the fixture.

$$\text{i.e } m\left(\frac{2a^2}{3}\omega' + a^2\omega'\right) = m\left[\left(\frac{2a^2}{3}\omega\right)\sqrt{\left(\frac{2}{3}\right)}\right]$$

$$5\omega' = 2\sqrt{\left(\frac{2}{3}\right)}\omega \text{ or } 5\omega' = \left(\frac{2\sqrt{2}}{5\sqrt{3}}\right)\omega.$$

Example 21:

A heave ring of radius a is moving in its own plane which is vertical. At a certain instant when its velocity is V horizontally from left to right and the angular velocity is (V/2a) clockwise, the highest point of the ring is suddenly fixed. Prove that the ring will describe a complete revolution about the point of fixing, if $V^2 > 32$ ag

Solution:

Consider a ring of radius am moving in its own plane with velocity V. Let its angular velocity be ω, τηεν $\omega = \frac{V}{2a}$ (given).

Just after fixing at the highest point of A, let the angular velocity be ω′. Τηε velocity of the centre will be = aω′.

Obviously the impulse is at A, therefore the moment of the impulse about the axis through A (which is horizontal) is zero thus moment of momentum about A will remain unaltered just before and after the fixture at the point

A *i.e.* $mk^2\omega' + ma\omega'.a = mk^2\omega - m.\,a = mk^2\omega - mVa$

$$\text{or } mk^2\omega' + ma\omega'.a = mk^2\omega - mVa$$

$$\text{or } (a^2\ a^2)\omega' = a^2\left(\frac{V}{2a}\right) - Va \text{ i.e. } \omega' = -\left(\frac{V}{4a}\right)$$

When the ring is turning about A, let the radius through A make an angle θ with the vertical. Also the energy equation gives

$$\frac{1}{2}m\{a^2\dot{\theta}^2 + \dot{\theta}^2\} - \frac{1}{2}m\left(a^2 + \omega'^2 +\right) = mg(a - a\cos\theta)$$

$$\text{or } \dot{\theta}^2 - \omega'^2 = -\left(\frac{g}{a}\right)(a - \cos\theta)$$

$$\text{or } \dot{\theta}^2 - \omega'^2 - \left(\frac{g}{a}\right)(1 - \cos\theta) = \left(\frac{V^2}{16a^2}\right) - \frac{g}{a}(1 - \cos\theta)$$

Now the ring will make a complete revolution if θ is greater than or equal to zero when $\theta = \pi$.

When $\theta = \pi$, $\quad \theta = \pi.\,\dot{\theta}^2 = \left(\frac{V^2}{16a^2}\right) - \frac{g}{a}(1 - \cos\pi) = \frac{2g}{a}$

it is positive only when $\left(\frac{V^2}{16a^2}\right) > \left(\frac{2g}{a}\right)$ i.e. $V^2 > 32ag$.

Example 22:

Three equal uniform rods placed in a straight line are freely jointed and move with a velocity v perpendicular to their lengths. If the middle point of the middle rod be suddenly fixed, show that the ends of the other two rods will meet in time (4 π a)/(9v), *where a is the length of each rod.*

Solution:

Let AB, BC, CD be the three rods each of length a and mass m. Freely jointed at B and C, and placed in a straight line. Let these rods move with velocity v in a direction perpendicular to their lengths. Let G_1, the middle point of the BC be suddenly fixed.

Consider the motion of the rod AB, the impulsive action acts at B with the result the moment of the impulsive force at B vanishes. Hence the angular momentum of AB about the end B remains unaltered before and after the fixture.

$$\therefore mv\left(\frac{a}{2}\right) = m(a/2)^2\,\omega + (m/3)(a/2)^2\omega = \left(\frac{ma^2\omega}{3}\right)$$

(where ω is the angular velocity of AB just after the fixture)

i.e. $\omega = \left(\frac{3v}{2a}\right)$

Similarly, considering the motion of the rod CD, we can prove that its angular velocity after the fixture $= \left(\frac{3v}{2a}\right)$

The end A and D of the rods will meet in E and in that position the triangle CBE will be an equilateral triangle so that ∠ABE = ∠DCE = 120°. Now $(d\theta/dt) = \omega$. *i.e.* $\theta = \omega t$.

$$\therefore \text{Required time} = \frac{\theta}{\omega} = \frac{120^\circ}{(3v/2a} = \frac{2\pi}{3}\cdot\frac{2a}{3v} = \frac{4\pi a}{9v}.$$

Example 23:

If an actant of ellipsoid bounded by three principal planes be rotating about the axis of "a" with angular velocity ω and if this axis suddenly becomes free when the axis of "b" becomes suddenly fixed at the same instant, show that the new angular velocity is $\left(\frac{2abw}{\pi(a^2+c^2}\right)$.

Solution:

Let the axis of "a" be taken as the axis of x. Let $\omega_{x'}, \omega_{y'}, \omega_z$ be the angular velocities about the axes just before the fixture, then we have $\omega_x = \omega$ given $\omega_y = 0$, $\omega_{z'} = 0$.

Let $\omega'_{x'}, \omega'_{y'}, \omega'_{z'}$ be the angular velocities about the same axis after the fixing of the axis b. *i.e.* y – axis.

$\therefore\ \omega'_{x'} = 0,\ \omega'_{z'} = 0$ and $\omega'_{y'}$ is to be determined.

Now as y – axis is suddenly fixed, the impulse is at y – axis and moment of the impulse about y – axis vanishes, therefore the moment of momentum about y – axis remains unaltered before and after the fixture.

i.e. $B\ (\omega'_{y'} - \omega_y) - D\,(\omega'_z - \omega_z) - (\omega'_x - \omega_x) = 0$

where B, D, F have their usual meaning in moments of inertia.

Now substituting the values of $\omega_{x'}, \omega_{y'}, \omega_{z'}$ and $\omega'_x\, \omega'_{z'}$ we get $B\ \omega'_{y'} = -F$

ω But $B = M\left[\frac{c^2+a^2}{5}\right]$, therefore, we have

$$M\frac{c^2+a^2}{5}\omega'y = -\omega F = -\omega\iiint p.xydxdydz$$

the integration being taken throughout the region bounded by

$x > 0, y > 0, z > 0$ and $\frac{x^2}{a^2}+\frac{y^2}{b^2}+\frac{z^2}{c^2}\le 1,$

and M is the mass of the octant. Let $dx = \frac{1}{2}aX^{-\frac{1}{2}}dX$

Similarly, $dy = \frac{1}{2}bY^{-1/2}$ $dZ = \frac{1}{2}cZ^{-1/2}dZ.$

making these substituting in (1), we get

$$M\frac{c^2+a^2}{5}\omega'y$$

$$= -\omega p\iiint aX^{1/2}bY^{1/2}\frac{1}{2}aX^{-1/2}\frac{1}{2}bY^{-1/2}\frac{1}{2}cZ^{-1/2}\ dXdYdZ$$

$$= -\frac{a^2b^2c}{8}\omega\rho\iiint X^{\circ}Y^{\circ}Z^{-1/2}dXdYdZ \text{ where } X+Y+Z\le 1$$

$$= -\frac{a^2b^2c}{8}\omega\rho\iiint X^{1-1}Y^{1-1}Z^{(1/2)^{-1}}\,dXdYdZ$$

$$= -\frac{a^2b^2c}{8}\frac{1.1.\Gamma(1)\Gamma\left(\frac{1}{2}\right)}{\frac{5}{2}\cdot\frac{3}{2}\cdot\frac{1}{2}\cdot\Gamma\left(\frac{1}{2}\right)}\omega\rho = \frac{6M}{\pi abc\cdot}$$

$$M\frac{(c^2+a^2)}{5}\omega'y = \frac{a^2b^2c}{15}\cdot\omega\frac{6M}{\pi abc}\text{ i.e. }\omega'y = \frac{2abc\omega}{\pi(c^2+a^2)}$$

Example 24:

Two like rods AB and BC, each of length 2a are freely jointed at B; AB can turn round the end A, and C can move freely on a vertical straight line through A and they are then released. Initially the rods are held in a horizontal line, C being in coincidence with A and they are then released. Show that when the rods are inclined at an angle θ to the horizontal, the angular velocity of either is

$$\sqrt{\left(\frac{3g}{a\cdot}\frac{\sin\theta}{1+3\cos^2\theta}\right)}$$

Solution:

Take the fixed point A as origin, the lines AX and AY as the axes. Let G_1 and G_2 be the centres of gravity of the rods AB and BC respectively. Then Co-ordinates of G_1 are (a cos θ, a sin θ). Hence the energy equation gives

$$\frac{1}{2}m\left[\frac{a^2}{3}\dot{\theta}^2 + (-a\sin\theta\dot{\theta})^2 + (a\cos\theta\dot{\theta})^2\right]$$

$$\frac{1}{2}m\left[\frac{a^2}{3}\dot{\theta}^2 + (-a\sin\theta\dot{\theta})^2\right.$$

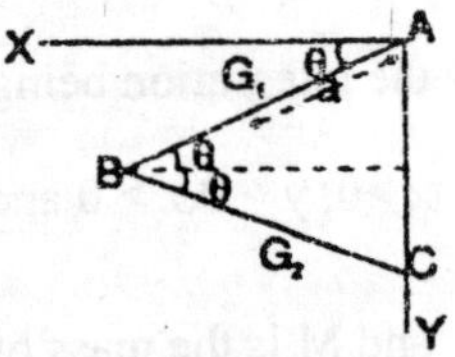

$$= mg\ a\ sing\ \theta + mg.\ 3\ a\sin\theta$$

X, A, G_1, θ, a, B, θ, θ, G_2, C, Y

Fig. 1.6

$$\text{Or } \frac{1}{2}m\left[\frac{4}{3}a^2\dot{\theta}^2\right] + \frac{1}{2}m\left[\frac{1}{3}a^2\dot{\theta}^2 + a^2\sin^2\dot{\theta}\theta^2 + 9a^2\cos^2\theta\dot{\theta}^2\right]$$

$$= 4g\ a\sin\theta$$

$$\text{Or } \left[\frac{4}{3}a^2\dot{\theta}^2 + a^2\dot{\theta}^2 + 8a^2\cos^2\theta\dot{\theta}\right] = 8g\ a\sin\theta$$

$$\text{Or } \frac{8}{3}(a^2\dot{\theta}^2 + a^2\cos^2\theta\dot{\theta}^2 = 8ga\sin\theta$$

Or $(a^2\dot{\theta}^2 + 3a^2\cos^2\theta\dot{\theta}^2) = 3ga\sin\theta$

Or $a\dot{\theta}^2(1+3\cos^2\theta) = 3g\sin\theta$ or $\dot{\theta} = \sqrt{\left(\dfrac{3g}{a}\dfrac{\sin\theta}{1+3\cos^2\theta}\right)}$.

Example 25:

A uniform straight rod of length 2a. has two small rings at its ends which can respectively slide on thin smooth horizontal and vertical wires OX and OY. The rods starts at an angle α, to the horizontal with angular velocity [{3g (1 – sin α)}/2a]$^{1/2}$ and downwards. Show that it will strike the horizontal wire at the end of time

$$2\sqrt{\left(\frac{a}{3g}\right)}\log\left[\left\{\cot\left(\frac{\pi}{8}-\frac{\alpha}{4}\tan\right)\right\}\frac{\pi}{8}\right].$$

Solution:

At any time t, let the rod AB be inclined at an angle θ to the horizontal al. If G be the C.G. of the rod AB, then co-ordinates of G are given by $x = a\cos\theta$, $y = a\sin\theta$, so that

$\dot{x} = -a\sin\theta\dot{\theta},\ \dot{y} = a\cos\theta\dot{\theta},$

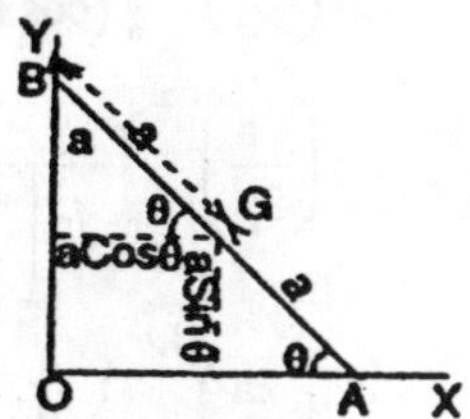

Fig. 1.7

∴ velocity of $G = \sqrt{\{(\dot{x}^2 + \dot{y}^2)\}}$

$= \sqrt{[(-a\sin\theta\dot{\theta})^2 + (a\cos\theta\ddot{\theta}^2]} = \dot{\theta}$

∴ kinetic energy of the rod at time t

$$= \frac{1}{2}m\left[\frac{a^2}{3}\dot{\theta}^2 + a^2\dot{\theta}^2\right] = \frac{2}{3}ma^2\dot{\theta}^2 \qquad ...(1)$$

Initial angular velocity is

$$= \left[\frac{3a}{2a}(1-\sin\alpha)\right]^{1/2} \quad \text{(given)}$$

∴ Initial kinetic energy $= \dfrac{2}{3}ma^2 \cdot \dfrac{3g}{2a}(a - \sin\alpha)$

[from (1)] = mga (1 – sin α).

Hence energy equation gives

$$\frac{2}{3}ma^2\dot{\theta}^2 = mga(1-\sin\alpha) = mg(a\sin\alpha) - mg(a\sin\theta)$$

i.e. $\dfrac{2}{3}a^2\dot{\theta}^2 - ga(1-\sin\alpha) = ga(\sin\alpha - \sin\theta)$

i.e. $\frac{2}{3}a^2\dot{\theta}^2 = ga\,(1-\sin\theta)$

or $\dot{\theta} = \frac{d\theta}{dt} = -\sqrt{\left(\frac{3g}{2a}\right)}\sqrt{(1-\sin\theta)}$

(negative sign is taken with radical sign, since θ decreases)

or $dt = -\left(\frac{2a}{3g}\right)^{1/2}\frac{1}{\sqrt{1-\sin\theta}}d\theta.$

Hence the required time

$$= -\left(\frac{2a}{3g}\right)^{1/2}\int_{\alpha}^{0}\frac{1}{\sqrt{1-\sin\theta}}d\theta = \left(\frac{2a}{3g}\right)^{1/2}\int_{0}^{\alpha}\frac{1}{\sqrt{(1-\sin\theta)}}d\theta$$

$$= \left(\frac{2a}{3g}\right)^{1/2}\int_{a}^{\alpha}\frac{d\theta}{[\{\cos^2(\theta/2)+\sin^2(\theta/2)-2\sin(\theta/2)\cos(\theta/2)]^{1/2}}$$

$$= \left(\frac{2a}{3g}\right)^{1/2}\int_{0}^{\alpha}\frac{d\theta}{\{\cos(\theta/2)-\sin(\theta/2)\}}$$

$$= \left(\frac{2a}{3g}\right)^{1/2}\int_{0}^{\alpha}\frac{d\theta}{\sqrt{2}\left[\frac{1}{\sqrt{2}}\cos(\theta/2)-\frac{1}{\sqrt{2}}\sin(\theta/2)\right]}$$

$$= \left(\frac{2a}{3g}\right)^{1/2}\frac{1}{\sqrt{2}}\int_{0}^{\alpha}\frac{d\theta}{\sin\left(\frac{\pi}{4}-\frac{\theta}{2}\right)} = \left(\frac{a}{3g}\right)^{1/2}\int_{9}^{\alpha}\operatorname{cosec}\left(\frac{\pi}{4}-\frac{\theta}{2}\right)d\theta$$

$$= -2\sqrt{\left(\frac{a}{3g}\right)}\left[\log\tan\left(\frac{\pi}{8}-\frac{\theta}{4}\right)\right]_0^{\alpha}$$

$$= 2\sqrt{\left(\frac{a}{3g}\right)}\left[\log\tan(\pi/8)-\log\tan\left(\frac{\pi}{8}-\frac{\alpha}{4}\right)\right]$$

$$= 2\sqrt{\left(\frac{a}{3g}\right)}\frac{\tan(\pi/8)}{\tan[(\pi/8)-(\alpha/4)]}$$

$$= 2\sqrt{\left(\frac{a}{3g}\right)}\log\left[\tan\frac{\pi}{8}\cot\left(\frac{\pi}{8}-\frac{\alpha}{4}\right)\right].$$

Example 26:

A uniform rod of length 2a, is placed with one end in contact with a smooth horizontal table and is then allowed to fall, if α be its initial inclination to the vertical, show that its angular velocity when it is inclined at an angle θ is

$\left[\frac{6g}{a}\cdot\frac{\cos\alpha-\cos\theta}{1+3\sin^2\theta}\right]^{1/2}$ *find also the reaction of the table.*

Solution:

Let AB be the rod such that AB = 2a. Let G be the C.G. of the rod AB. Since there is no horizontal force on the rod AB, therefore its centre of gravity G moves down a vertical line through G Let this vertical line through G cut the horizontal table at the point O, then O is fixed point.

Taking O as the origin and the line OX and OY as the axes, the co-ordinates of G are (0, a cos θ).

i.e. $x_G = 0, y_G = a\cos\theta$

$\Rightarrow \dot{x}_G = 0.\dot{y}_G = -a\sin\theta\dot{\theta} \Rightarrow v_{G^2} = \dot{x}_{G^2} + \dot{y}_{G^2} = a^2\sin^2\theta\dot{\theta}^2$

Hence the energy equation gives

$$\frac{1}{2}m\left[v_G^2 + k^2\dot{\theta}^2\right] = \frac{1}{2}m\left[\frac{a^2}{3}\dot{\theta}^2 + a^2\sin^2\theta\dot{\theta}^2\right] = m\,ga\cos\alpha - mga\cos\theta$$

i.e., $\frac{a^2\dot{\theta}^2}{6}[1+3\sin^2\theta] = ga(\cos\alpha - \cos\theta)$

i.e. $\dot{\theta}^2 = \frac{6g}{a}\frac{\cos\alpha - \cos\theta}{1+3\sin^2\theta}$

$$i.e.\ \dot{\theta} = \sqrt{\left(\frac{6g}{a}\right)}\sqrt{\left(\frac{\cos\alpha-\cos\theta}{1+3\sin^2\theta}\right)} \qquad ...(1)$$

To find the reaction R, take moments about G.

$$R\,a\sin\dot{\theta} = m\frac{a^2}{3}\theta\ddot{\theta}\ \ i.e.,\ R = \frac{m}{3}a\,\mathrm{cosec}\,\theta\ddot{\theta} \qquad ...(2)$$

To find the value of $\ddot{\theta}$, we differentiate $\dot{\theta}^2$ found above

$$2\dot{\theta}\ddot{\theta} = \frac{6g}{a}\frac{[(1+3\sin^2\theta)\sin\theta - (\cos\alpha - \cos\theta).6\sin\theta\cos\theta]\dot{\theta}}{(1+3\sin^2\theta)^2}$$

$$\Rightarrow \ddot{\theta} = \frac{3g}{a}\frac{\sin\theta[1+3\sin^2\theta - 6\cos\theta(\cos\alpha - \cos\theta)]}{(1+3\sin^2\theta)^2}$$

$$= \frac{3g\sin\theta}{a(1+3\sin^2\theta)^2}[1+3\sin^2\theta+\cos^2\theta-6\cos\theta\cos\alpha]$$

$$= \frac{3g\sin\theta}{a(1+3\sin\theta)^2}[1+3(\sin^2\theta+\cos^2\theta)+3\cos^2\theta-2\cos\theta\cos\alpha]$$

$$= \frac{3g\sin\theta}{a(1+3\sin^2\theta)^2}[4+3(\cos^2\theta-2\cos\theta\cos\alpha)-3\cos^2\alpha]$$

$$= \frac{3g\sin\theta}{a(1+3\sin^2\theta)^2}[4-3\cos+3(\cos\theta-\cos\alpha)^2].$$

Substituting this value of $\ddot{\theta}$ in (2), we get

$$R = \frac{ma}{3\sin\dot{\theta}} = \frac{3g\sin\theta}{a(1+3\sin^2\theta)^2}[4-3\cos^2\alpha)+3(\cos\theta-\cos\alpha)^2]$$

$$= \frac{ma}{(1+3\sin^2\theta)^2}[4-3\cos^2\alpha+3(\cos\theta-\cos\alpha)^2]$$

we observe that value of the reaction is positive for all values of θ, hence the lower end of the rod will never leave the horizontal table.

Example 27:

A straight uniform rod, of mass m, is placed at right angles to smooth plane of inclination α with one end in contact with it; the rod is then released. Show that when its inclination to the plane is ϕ, the reaction of the plane will be

$$mg\frac{3(1-\sin\phi)^2+1}{(3\cos^2\phi+1)^2}\cos\alpha.$$

Solution:

Let at any time t, the rod AB make an angle ϕ with the inclined plane. Then the equation of motion of the C.G. of the rod

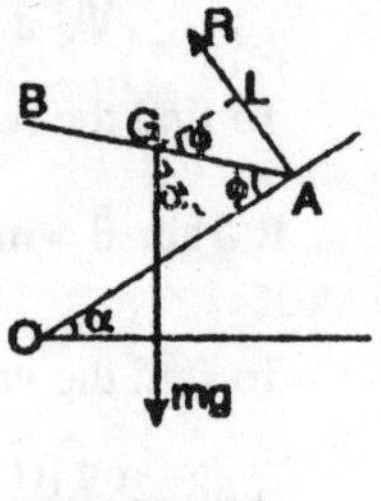

$$\text{AB} \quad m\frac{d^2}{dt^2}(a\sin\phi) = R - mg\cos\alpha \qquad \text{...(i)}$$

$$m\frac{a^2}{3}\ddot{\phi} = -R\,a\cos\phi \qquad \text{...(ii)}$$

Fig. 1.8

Substituting the value of R from (ii) in (i),

$$\text{we get } m\frac{d^2}{dt^2}(a\sin\phi) = -mg\cos\alpha - \frac{ma}{3}\sec\phi.\ddot{\phi}$$

$$\text{or } \frac{d}{dt}(a\cos\phi.\dot{\phi}) = -g\cos\alpha - \frac{1}{3}a\sec\phi.\ddot{\phi}$$

$$\text{or } \left(a\cos\phi + \frac{a}{3}\sec\phi \right)\ddot{\phi} - a\sin\phi\dot{\phi}^2 = -g\cos\alpha$$

$$\text{or } a\left(\frac{1}{3} + \cos^2\phi \right)\ddot{\phi} - a\sin\phi\cos\phi\dot{\phi}^2 = -g\cos\alpha\cos\phi$$

Multiplying by 2 $\dot{\phi}$ throughout, we get

$$2a\left(\frac{1}{3} + \cos^2\phi \right)\dot{\phi}\ddot{\phi} - 2a\sin\phi.\dot{\phi}^3 = -2g\cos\alpha\cos\phi\dot{\phi}$$

$$\text{or } \frac{d}{dt}\left[a\left(\frac{1}{3} + \cos^2\phi \right)\dot{\phi}^2 \right] = -2g\cos\alpha\cos\phi\dot{\phi}.$$

Integrating it we get a $a\left(\frac{1}{3} + \cos^2\phi \right).\dot{\phi}^2 = -2g\cos\alpha\sin\phi + C.$

Initially $\phi = (\pi/2)$ and $\dot{\phi} = 0$ $\therefore C = 2g\cos\alpha$.

Hence $a\left(\frac{1}{2} + \cos^2\phi \right).\dot{\phi}^2 = 2g\cos\alpha(1 - \sin\phi)$

$$\text{or } \dot{\phi}^2 = \frac{2g\cos\alpha(1 - \sin\phi)}{a\left(\frac{1}{3} + \cos^2\alpha \right)}$$

Substituting the value of $\dot{\phi}^2$ in (iii), we get

$$a\left(\frac{1}{3} + \cos^2\phi \right)\ddot{\phi} - a\sin\phi\cos\phi.\frac{2g\cos\alpha(1 - \sin\phi)}{a\left(\frac{1}{3} + \cos^2\phi \right)} = -g\cos\alpha\cos\phi$$

$$\text{or } a\left(\frac{1}{3} + \cos^2\phi \right)^2\ddot{\phi} - 2g\cos\alpha\sin\phi\cos\phi(1 - \sin\phi)$$

$$= -g\cos\alpha\cos\phi\left(\frac{1}{3} + \cos^2\phi \right)$$

$$\text{or } a(1 + 3\cos^2\phi)^2\ddot{\phi} - 3g\cos\alpha\cos\phi[6\sin\phi - 6\sin^2\phi - 1 - 3\cos^2\phi)]$$

$$= 3g\cos\alpha\cos\phi[6\sin\phi - 3\sin^2\phi - 3(\sin^2\phi + \cos^2\phi) - 1]$$

$$= 3g\cos\alpha\cos\phi[-3(\sin^2\phi - 2\sin\phi + 1) - 1]$$

$$= 3g\cos\alpha\cos\phi[-3(1 - \sin\phi)^2 - 1]$$

$$= -3g\cos\alpha\cos\phi[3(1 - \sin\phi)^2 + 1]$$

$$\text{or } \ddot{\phi} = -\frac{3g\cos\alpha\cos\phi[3(1 - \sin\phi)^2 + 1]}{a(11 + 3\cos^2\phi)^2}$$

putting this value of $\ddot{\phi}$ in (ii), we get R = m g cos `

$$\alpha \frac{3(1-\sin\phi)^2 + 1}{(1+3\cos^2\phi)^2}.$$

Example 28:

A hemisphere of mass M and radius a is placed with its plane base on a smooth table, and a heavy rod of mass m is constrained to move in a vertical line with one end p on the curved surface of the hemisphere. If at any time t, the radius to p makes an angle θ with the vertical, show that

$$a\dot{\theta}^2[M\cos^2\theta + m\sin^2\theta] = 2mg(\cos\alpha - \cos\theta).$$

Solution:

Let pQ (= 2a) be the rod moving in a vertical line, with its one end p in contact with the curved surface of the hemisphere. Let G_1 be the C.G. of the hemisphere and G_2 the C.G. of the rod pQ.

Let the vertical line along which the rod move cut the table at O, then O is a fixed point. Take O as the origin and horizontal line OA as - axis and vertical line through O as y-axis. Then the co - ordinate of G_2 are

(0, a + a cosθ) and co-ordinates of G_1 are $\left(a\sin\theta, \frac{3a}{8}\right)$

Hence the energy equation gives

$$\frac{1}{2}k\left(-a\sin\theta\dot{\theta}\right)^2 + \frac{1}{2}M\left(a\cos\theta\dot{\theta}\right)^2 = mg\left(a\cos\alpha - a\cos\theta\right)$$

or $a\dot{\theta}(M\cos^2\theta + m\sin^2\theta) = 2mg\left(\cos\alpha - \cos\theta\right)$.

Example 29:

A uniform rod, of length 2a is freely jointed at one end to a small ring, whose mass is equal to that of the rod. The ring is free to slide on smooth wire and initially is at rest and the rod is vertical and below the ring rotating with angular velocity $\sqrt{}(3g/a)$ in a vertical plane passing through the wire. When the rod is inclined at an angle θ to the vertical, show that its angular velocity is $\sqrt{\left(\frac{3g}{a}\frac{1+\cos\theta}{8-3\cos^2\theta}\right)}$ and find the velocity of the ring.

Solution:

Let A′ B′ be the initial position of the rod.

At time t, let q be the angle through which the rod A B has turned and the ring has moves a distance x from its initial position A ′ along the smooth horizontal wire.

Now taking A′ as the origin and the lines, A′A,A′B′ as axes of x and y repetitively , the co-ordinates of G are (X + a sinθ, a cos θ).

∴ Its velocity components are $\left(\dot{x} + a\cos\theta\dot{\theta}\right)$ and $\left(-a\sin\theta\dot{\theta}\right)$ and velocity of the ring is $\dot{x}$ .Thus the horizontal momentum at time t is

$$= m\dot{x} + m\left(\dot{x} + a\cos\theta\dot{\theta}\right)$$

Initial horizontal momentum $= m\left[0 + a\left(\frac{3g}{a}\right)^{1/2}\right] = m\sqrt{(3ag)}$

$$\{\text{since initially } \theta = 0, \theta = (\frac{3g}{a})^{1/2} \text{ and } x = 0\}$$

Since there is no horizontal force on the system, therefore the horizontal momentum remains unaltered throughout the motion.

$$\therefore m\ddot{x} + m(\dot{x} + a\cos\theta\dot{\theta}) = m\sqrt{(3ag)}$$

$$\text{or } \; 2\dot{x} + a\cos\theta\dot{\theta}) = \sqrt{(3ag)} \text{ i.e.} \dot{x} = \frac{1}{2}[\sqrt{(3ag)} - a\cos\theta\dot{\theta}] \quad ...(1)$$

Kinetic energy at time t

$$= \frac{1}{2}m[\dot{x}^2 + \frac{1}{2}m[\dot{x} + a\cos\theta.\dot{\theta})^2 + (-a\sin\theta.\dot{\theta})^2 + \frac{1}{3}a^2\dot{\theta}^2]$$

$$= \frac{1}{2}m[\dot{x}^2 + \dot{x}^2 + a^2\dot{\theta}^2 + 2a\dot{x}\dot{\theta}\cos\theta + \frac{1}{3}a^2\dot{\theta}^2]$$

$$= \frac{1}{2}m[2\dot{x}^2 + \frac{4}{3}a^2\dot{\theta}^2 + 2a\dot{x}\dot{\theta}\cos\theta]$$

Initial kinetic energy

$$\frac{1}{2}m\left\{0 + \frac{4}{3}a^2 \cdot \frac{3g}{a} + 0\right\}\left(\text{since initially } \dot{x} = 0, \theta = 0 \text{ and } \dot{\theta}^2 = \frac{3g}{a}\right)$$

$$= 2mga$$

Thus the energy equation gives

$$\frac{1}{2}m[2\dot{x}^2 + \frac{4}{3}a^2\dot{\theta}^2 + 2a\dot{x}\dot{\theta}\cos\theta] - 2mga = -mg(a - a\cos\theta)$$

$$\text{or } \; \dot{x}^2 + \frac{2}{3}a^2\dot{\theta}^2 + a\dot{x}\dot{\theta}\cos\theta - 2ga + ga\cos\theta)$$

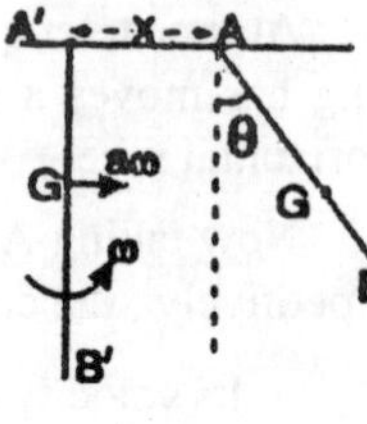

or $\dot{x}^2 + \frac{2}{3}a^2\dot{\theta}^2 + a\dot{x}\dot{\theta}\cos\theta = ga(1+\cos\theta)$

Substituting the value of $\dot{x}$ from (1), we get

$$\left\{\frac{\sqrt{(3ag)} - a\cos\theta\dot{\theta}}{2}\right\}^2 + \frac{2}{3}a^2\dot{\theta}^2 + a\dot{\theta}\cos\theta \times$$

$$\times\left\{\frac{\sqrt{(3ag)} - a\cos\theta\dot{\theta}}{2}\right\} = ga(1+\cos\theta)$$

Fig. 1.9

or $\frac{1}{4}[3ag + a^2\cos^2\theta\dot{\theta}^2 - 1\sqrt{(3ag)}.a\cos\theta\dot{\theta} + \frac{2}{3}a^2\dot{\theta}^2$

$+\frac{1}{2}a\dot{\theta}\cos\theta\sqrt{(3ag)} - \frac{1}{2}a^2\cos^2\theta\dot{\theta}^2 = ga(1+\cos\theta)$

or $\left(\frac{2}{3}a^2 - \frac{1}{4}a^2\cos^2\theta\right)\dot{\theta}^2 = \frac{ga}{4} + ga\cos\theta$

or $(8a^2 - 3a^2\cos^2\theta)\dot{\theta}^2 = 3ga(1+4\cos\theta)$ $\dot{\theta} = \sqrt{\left\{\frac{3g(1+4\cos\theta)}{a(8-3\cos^2\theta)}\right\}}$

Example 30:

A uniform rod, of length 2a, hangs in a horizontal position being supported by vertical strings, each of length 1, attached to its ends, the other extremities being attached to fixed points. The rod its given an angular velocity ω about a vertical axis through its centre; find its angular velocity when it has turned through an angle, and show that it will rise through a distance $(a^2\omega^2)/(6g)$. prove also that the time of a small oscillation about the position of equilibrium is $2\pi\sqrt{(1/3g)}$.

Solution:

Let A'B' be the initial position of the rod, supported by two vertical strings DA', CB, such that DA′ = CB′ = 1. The rod is then turned in such a way that its middle point moves in a vertical through O′. Let AB be the position of the rod when it has turned through an angle θ. Let O′O = x and ϕ is the angle which either string makes with the vertical.

Let the horizontal plane through AB cut CB′, DA′ in N and M respectively.

Obviously $\angle AMD = \angle BNC = \pi/2$. and $x = OO' = CB' - CN = 1 - l\cos\phi$ where t is the length of the vertical string

$\therefore \dot{x} = l\sin\phi\dot{\phi}$

From the right angle Δ CBN we have BN = l sin φ Also from isosceles triangle OBN, we have BN = 2a sin (θ/2)

$\therefore l\sin\phi = 2a\sin(\theta/2)$

so that l cos $\phi\dot{\phi} = a\cos(\theta/2).\dot{\theta}$

i.e. $\dot{\phi} = \dfrac{a\cos(\theta/2}{l\cos\phi}\dot{\theta}$

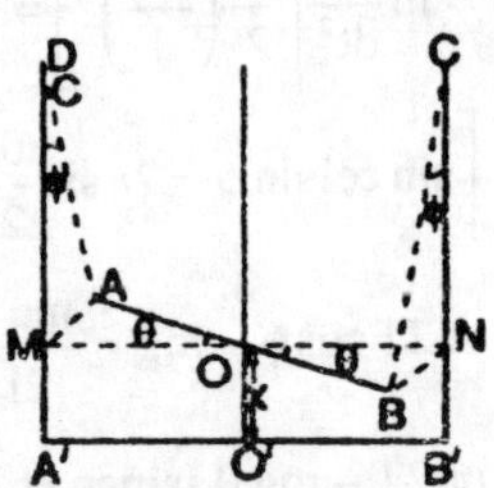

Fig. 1.10

Therefore form (2), we have

$$\dot{x} = l\sin\phi.\frac{a\cos(\theta/2)}{l\cos\phi}\dot{\theta}$$

$$= 2a\sin\frac{\theta}{2}a\cos\frac{\theta}{2}\frac{1}{\sqrt{l^2 - 4a^2\sin^2\theta/2}}\dot{\theta}\sin\text{cel}\sin\phi = 2a\sin(\theta/2)$$

$$= \frac{la^2\sin\theta\dot{\theta}}{[l^2 - 4a^2\sin^2(\theta/2)]\cdot}$$ Now energy equation gives

$$\frac{1}{2}m\dot{x}^2 + \frac{1}{2}mK^2\dot{\theta}^2 - \frac{1}{2}k^2\omega^2 = -mgx \qquad ...(3)$$

$$\Rightarrow \frac{1}{2}m\left(\dot{x}^2 + \frac{a^2}{3}\dot{\theta}^2\right) - \frac{1}{2}m\frac{a^2}{3}\omega^2 = -mgx$$

$$\Rightarrow \frac{1}{2}m\left[\frac{l^2a^4\sin^2\theta\dot{\theta}^2}{[l^2 - 4a^2\sin^2(\theta/2)]^2} + \frac{a^2\dot{\theta}^2}{3}\right] - \frac{1}{2}m\frac{a^2}{3}\omega^2 = -mgx$$

$$\Rightarrow a^2\dot{\theta}^2\left[\frac{la^2\sin^2\theta}{[l^2 - 4a^2\sin^2(\theta/2)]^2}\right] - \frac{1}{3}a\omega^2 = 2gx \qquad ...(4)$$

This equation gives the angular velocity of the rod in any position. The rod will come to instantaneous rest when $\dot{\theta} = 0$.

Thus putting $\dot{\theta} = 0$. in (4), we get $2gx = \frac{1}{3}a^2\omega^2$ i.e. $x = \dfrac{a^2\omega^2}{6g}$

For finding the time of small oscillation, we consider the motion of AB in the vertical direction.

$$\therefore 2T\cos\varphi - mg = mx$$

$$= m\frac{d^2}{dt^2}(l - l\text{oc}\phi)) = m\frac{d^2}{dt^2}[l(1 - \cos\phi)]$$

$$= m\frac{d^2}{dt^2}\left[l.2\sin^2\frac{\phi}{2}\right] = m\frac{d^2}{dt^2}\left[l.2.\frac{[\sin(\phi/2]^2}{(\phi/2)^2}\left(\frac{\phi}{2}\right)\right]$$

$$= m\frac{d^2}{dt^2}\left[\frac{1}{2\cdot}\left(\frac{a\theta}{1}\right)^2\right] = m\frac{d^2}{dt^2}\left[\frac{a^2\theta^2}{2l}\right]$$

$$\left[\sin\text{cel}\sin\phi = 2a\sin\frac{\theta}{2}\therefore\frac{l\sin\phi}{\phi}\cdot\phi = 2a\frac{\sin\theta/2}{(\theta/2)}\cdot(\theta/2\text{i.e.}l\phi = a\theta\right]$$

$$\therefore 2T\cos\phi - mg = \frac{ma^2}{2l}\frac{d}{dt}(2\theta\dot{\theta}) = \frac{2ma^2}{2l}[\theta\ddot{\theta} + \dot{\theta}^2] = \frac{ma^2}{l}[\theta\ddot{\theta} + \dot{\theta}^2]$$

or $2T - mg\ 0$ [since $\dot{\theta}\ \ddot{\theta}$ and are small so they could be neglected ϕ being small $\dot{\phi} = 1$].

Now taking moments about the vertical axis through O, we have

$$m\frac{a^2}{3}\ddot{\theta} = -2T\sin\phi \text{ [perpendicular from O on BN]}$$

$$= -2T\sin\phi.a\cos\frac{\theta}{2} = -2a\cos\frac{\theta}{2\cdot}T\sin\phi$$

$$= -2T\cos\frac{\theta}{2\cdot}\frac{2a}{l}\sin\frac{\theta}{2} = -\frac{2a^2}{l}T\sin\theta$$

Now since $2T = mg$ i.e $T = \frac{1}{2}mg$. putting this value above, we get

$$m\frac{a^2}{3}\ddot{\theta} = -\frac{2a}{l\cdot}\frac{2a}{l}\sin\frac{\theta}{2} = -\frac{2a^2}{l}T\sin\theta$$

or $\ddot{\theta} = -\frac{3g}{l}\sin\theta$, when θ is small.

$\therefore \ddot{\theta} = -\frac{3g}{l}\theta$, which is simple harmonic motion. Hence time of small oscillation $= 2\pi\sqrt{\left(\frac{l}{3g}\right)}$

Example 31:

If the earth, supposed to be a uniform sphere, had in a certain period contracted slightly so that its radius was less by (1/n) th than before, show that the length of the day would have shortend by (48/n) hours.

Solution:

Let a be the radius, m be the mass and ω the angular velocity of the earth. Supposed to be a uniform sphere, about its axis of rotation which is its diameter.

$\therefore$ The length of a day $= l_1 = 2\pi/\omega = 24$ hours.

Now when the earth contracted slightly, let a_1 be its new radius then a_1 be its new radius then $a_1 = a - a/n = a\,(1 - 1/n)$. ...(1)

If ω_1 is the angular velocity of the earth in this position, then shortened length of a day $= l_2\ 2\pi/\omega_1$.

$$\therefore \frac{\text{Decrease in the length of a day}}{\text{Length of a day}} = \frac{l_1 - l_1}{l1} = 1 - \frac{l_2}{l_1} = 1 - \frac{\omega}{\omega_1}$$

i.e. Decrease in the length of a day $= \left(1 - \dfrac{\omega}{\omega_1}\right)$

Length of a day $= \left(1 - \dfrac{\omega}{\omega_1}\right)$. 24 hours. ...(2)

The moment of the external forces (*i.e.* weight o the earth and the reaction on the axis of rotation) about the axis of rotation (*i.e.* diameter) of the earth is zero. Therefore the moment of the momentum about the axis of rotation (*i.e.* diameter) of the earth will remain constant.

$\therefore mk^2\omega = mk_1{}^2\omega_1$

or $\quad \dfrac{1}{5}ma^2\omega = \dfrac{2}{5}ma^2\ \omega_1$ or $\dfrac{\omega}{\omega_1} = \left(1 - \dfrac{1}{n}\right)^2$,

$$= 1 - \frac{2}{n'}\left(\text{Neglecting } \frac{1}{n^{2'}} \text{ etc. being small quantities}\right)$$

Putting in (2), we have

the decrease in the length of a day $= \left\{1 - \left(1 - \dfrac{2}{n}\right)\right\} 24 = \dfrac{48}{n}$ hours.

i.e. the length of the day is shortened by (48/n) hours.

Example 32:

A sphere of radius b, rolls without slipping down the cycloid $x = a\,(\theta + \sin\theta)$; $y = a\,(1 - \cos\theta)$. *It starts from rest with its centre on the horizontal line* $y = 2a$. *Show that velocity v of its centre when at its lowest point is given by*

$$v^2 = \frac{10}{7}g(2a - b).$$

Solution:

Initially, let the point A′ of the sphere be at the cusp A. Let C be the centre of this sphere, then the radius CA′ is a fixed line in the sphere.

Let at time t the line CA make an angle ϕ with the vertical and tangent at the point of contact P, make an angle ψ with the horizontal line OX.

Let the arc OP = s and arc OA = c.

$\therefore$ are AP = c – s.

But we are given that sphere rolls without slipping.

$\therefore$ arc AP = arc A′ P *i.e.* $c - s = b\,(\phi - \psi)$

[since $\angle A¢CP = \phi - \psi$]

Differentiating it, we get $-s = b\,(\dot\phi - \psi)$ ...(1)

Let the centre C of the sphere move with the velocity v, then

v = velocity of P + velocity of C relative to P.

or $v = \dot s - b\dot\psi = -b(\dot\phi - \dot\psi) - b\dot\psi = -b\dot\phi$ ...(2)

Now energy equation gives $\frac{1}{2}m\left[v^2 + \frac{2b^2\dot\phi^2}{5}\right] = mg(2a - b)$

or $\left[v^2 + \frac{2b^2}{5}\cdot\frac{v^2}{b^2}\right] = 2g(2a - b)$ [from (2)]

or $\frac{7}{5}v^2 = 2g(2a - b)$ *i.e.* $v^2 = \frac{10g(2a - b)}{7}$

Example 33:

A sphere of radius a, and of radius of gyration k about an axis through its centre, rolls with linear velocity v on a horizontal plane, the direction of motion being perpendicular to a vertical face of a fixed rectangular block are perfectly rough and perfectly elastic. Show that the sphere will surmount the block if $(a^2 - ah + k^2)v^2 > 2gha^2(a^2 + k^2)$.

Solution:

Let O be the centre of the sphere and AB vertical face of the fixed block; AB = h. The sphere strikes the block at A, therefore the impulse is at the point A. Let ω and ω′ be the angular velocities of the sphere just after the impulse. After striking at A, the sphere begins to turn about A so the velocity of the centre O after impulse is at right angles to OA and is equal to aw. Since the impulse is at the point A, therefore the moment of the impulse about A is zero, hence the moment of momentum about A remains unaltered before and after the impulse.

Moment of momentum about A before impulse = $mk^2\,\omega + mv\,(a - h)$

[$\therefore$ moment of momentum = $mk^2\,\dot\theta$ + mvp]

Moment of momentum about A after impulse = $mk^2\,\omega' + ma\omega'.a$

$\therefore mk^2 + mv\,(a - h) = mk^2\,\omega' + ma^2\omega'$ or $k^2\omega + (a - h) = (k^2 + a^2)\omega'$

$$\text{or } k^2\frac{v}{a} + v(a - h) = (k^2 + a^2)\omega' \qquad \text{[since } \omega = v/a]$$

$$\text{or } (k^2 + a^2)\,\omega' = \frac{v}{a}\left(a^2 - ah + k^2\right)$$

$$\text{or } \omega' = \frac{(a^2 - ah + k^2)}{(k^2 + a^2)}$$

Now the sphere will surmount the block if the sphere goes on turning about A till its lowest point L rises a height h, the height of the block. This can happen only if the sphere after impact acquires a kinetic energy, which is sufficient to take the sphere to a height h. It implies that the K.E. of the sphere must be more then that would be required for doing work of taking it upto a height h. But K.E. of the sphere after the impact

$$= \frac{1}{2}m\left(k^2\omega'^2 + a^2\omega'^2\right),$$

$$\therefore \frac{1}{2}m(k^2\omega'^2 + a^2\omega'^2) > mgh \text{ or } (k^2 + a^2)\omega'^2 > 2gh$$

$$\text{or } (k^2 + a^2)\frac{v^2(a^2 - ah + k^2)^2}{a^2(k^2 + a^2)^2} > 2gh \qquad \text{[from (1)]}$$

$$\text{or } (k^2 - ah + k^2)^2 v^2 > 2gha^2\,(k^2 + a^2)$$

REVISION AT A GLANCE

1. Principle of Conservation of Linear Momentum

(a) *Finite forces :* If a body moving under the action of external forces such that sum of the components of these forces parallel to a certain fixed direction is zero throughout the motion, then the linear momentum along this line is constant throughout the motion.

(b) *Impulsive Forces:* If the sum of impulsive forces parallel to a certain fixed direction is zero, then the total momentum in that direction remains unchanged before and after application of impulses.

2. Principle of Conservation of Moment of Momentum

(a) *Finite forces:* If a rigid body is moving under the action of external forces the sum of whose moments about a given line is zero throughout the motion, the angular momentum (or moment of momentum) of the body about that line remains unaltered throughout the motion.

(b) *Impulsive forces:* If thc sum of the impulsive forces about a certain line vanishes then angular momentum about it remains unchanged before and after the application of the impulses.

3. Principle of Conservation of Energy

If a system moves under the action of finite forces and if the geometrical equations of the system do not contain time explicitly, the change in the kinetic energy of the system in passing from one configuration to any other is equal to the corresponding work done by the forces.

Vis-Viva of a particle is the product of its mass and the square of its velocity.

4. Conservation Forces

(a) If the forces acting on the body are such that $\int(Xdx + Ydy + Zdz)$ is a complete differential of some quantity V, then the forces are said to be conservative.

(b) When a body moves under the action of a system of conservative forces, the sum of its kinetic and potential energies is constant throughout the motion.

(c) Total K.E. of the body = K.E. due to translation + K.E. due to rotation.

EXERCISES

1. A uniform circular board of mass M and radius a is placed on a perfectly smooth plane and free to rotate about a vertical axis through its centre; a man of mass 'M' walks round the edge of the board whose upper surface is rough enough to prevent his slipping ; when he has walked completely round the board to his starting point, show that the board has turned through an angle

$$\frac{4\pi M'}{M + 2M'}.$$

2. A right angled triangular lamina is turning about the side AC. suddenly AC is set free and BD fixed. If C be the right angle, prove that the angular velocity is 1/2 (BC/CA) of its former value.

3. A rectangular lamina whose sides are of lengths 2a and 2b is at rest on smooth horizontal plane. If one corner is caught and suddenly made to move with prescribed speed V in the plane of the lamina, then the greatest, angular velocity which can thus be imparted to the lamina is

$$\frac{3V}{4\sqrt{[(a^2 + b^2)]}}$$

4. An elliptic lamina is rotating about a diameter and a point p on the edge is suddenly fixed. Prove that the velocity of the centre immediately afterwards is 1/5 of the velocity of p before it was fixed.

5. A uniform rod AB of mass 3m has a small hoop at B and swings through an angle 60° on each side of the vertical about a fixed horizontal axis through the end A. When B is passing through its lowest point the hook picks up a particle of mass m. Show that the system will afterwards swing through an angle θ on each side of the vertical given by cos θ = $\frac{17}{20}$

Hint : Let ω be the angular velocity of the rod when B is in the lowest position *i.e.* when AB is vertical. Energy equation gives

$$\frac{1}{2}3m\frac{4a^2}{3}\omega^2 = 3mg(a - a\cos 60)$$

$$i.e. \quad \omega = \sqrt{\left(\frac{3g}{4a}\right)}$$

When mass m is picked up by the hook at B, the impulsive action is at A, let ω′ be angular velocity after impulse.

$$\therefore \quad 3m\left(\frac{a^2}{3}\omega' + a^2\omega'\right) + 4m^2\omega' = 3m\left(\frac{a^2}{3}\omega' + a^2\omega'\right).$$

$$i.e. \ \omega' = \frac{1}{2}\omega = \frac{1}{2}\sqrt{\left(\frac{3g}{4a}\right)}$$

Let θ be the angle through which the system rises the energy equation gives

$$\frac{1}{2}3m.\frac{4a^2}{3}\omega'^2 + \frac{1}{2}m.4a^2\omega'^2 = 3mg(a - a\cos\theta) + mg(2a - 2a\cos\theta)$$

$$\text{or } \ 8\omega^2 = \frac{10g}{a}(1 - \cos\theta) \text{ which gives } \cos\theta = \frac{17}{20}.$$

6. A uniform circular disc. of radius a is rolling without slipping along a smooth horizontal plane with velocity V when the highest point becomes suddenly fixed. Prove that the disc will make a complete revolution round the point if $V^2 > 24ag$.

7. Three uniform rods AB, BC, CD freely jointed at B and C lie on a smooth horizontal plane. They are originally moving as a rigid body with velocity V parallel to CB, A and B being on the same side of BC and the angles B and C being right angles, A is suddenly fixed, prove that if 2a, 2b, 2c are the lengths of rods and 3m, m, 2m their respective masses, the initial angular velocities $\omega_1 \omega_3$ of AB, CD are given by $5a\omega_1 = 20\ w = 3V$.

8. A horizontal lamina of mass M can rotate freely about an axis through O, some point of it and perpendicular to it. An insect of mass m alights on A, some point of it at distance a from O and crawls along a circle having OA as diameter and returns to the point of starting Initially if the insect and the lamina were at rest, Prove that the lamina has moved through an angle relative to the ground given by $\pi\sqrt{\{Mk^2/(Mk^2.ma^2)\}}]$ where k is radius of gyration of the lamina about its axis.

9. A uniform square plate A B C D of mass M and side 2a, lies on a smooth horizontal plane; it is struck at A by particle of mass m moving with velocity V in the direction of AB, the particle remaining attached to plate. Determine the subsequent motion of the system and show that its angular velocity is $\frac{m}{M+4m}\frac{3V}{2a}\cdot$

10. The ends of a straight uniform rod of mass m and length 2a slide on a smooth fixed horizontal circle of radius and an insect of mass m crawls along it at a constant rate V relative to the rod. If θ is the angle made by the rod at time t with a fixed direction, show that

$\dot{\theta}\left(2c^2 - \frac{5}{3}a^2 + V^2t^2\right) = \text{const}$ and if $c = \frac{2a}{\sqrt{3'}}$ the angle turned through by the rod in time t is $\frac{1}{\sqrt{3}}\tan^{-1}\left(\frac{Vt}{a}\right)$

11. A bead of mass M can slide on a smooth straight horizontal wire and a particle of mass m is attached to the body by a light string of length l, the particle is held in contact with the wire with the string taught and is then let fall. Prove that when the string is inclined to the wire at an angle θ, the bead will have slipped a distance along the wire $\frac{mgl(1-\cos\theta)}{M+m}$ and that the angular velocity ω of the string will be given by the equation

$(M + m\cos^2\theta)\, l\omega^2 = \omega\,(M + m)\, g\sin\theta$

12. A uniform rod moves in a vertical plane, its ends being in contact with the interior of fixed smooth sphere; when it is inclined at an angle θ to the horizontal, show that the square of its angular velocity is $\frac{6cg}{3c^2+a^2}[\cos\theta - \cos\alpha]$, where a is the initial value of θ, 2a is the length of the rod, and c is the distance of its middle point from the centre of the sphere.

13. A hoop of radius a rolling on a horizontal rod with the velocity v comes onto collision with a rough inalastic kerb of height h which is

perpendicular to the plane of the hoop. Show that if the hoop is to clear the kerb without the jumping then

$$\frac{2a}{2a-h}\sqrt{\{g(a-h)\}} > v > \frac{2}{2a-h}\sqrt{(gk)}.$$

14. A sphere of radius a rolling on a rough table comes to a slit of breadth b, perpendicular to its path; if V be its velocity, show that the condition it should cross the slit without jumping is

$$v^2 > \frac{100}{7} ga(1-\cos\alpha)\sin^2\alpha \frac{14-10\sin^2\alpha}{(7-10\sin^2\alpha)^2};$$

where b = 2a sin α and 17 gα cos α> 7V² + 10ga.

15. Discuss the principle of conservation of energy.

Lagrange's Equations (Conservative Field), Small Oscillations, Solved Examples, Revision at a Glance, Exercises.

2

MOTION OF TOP

MOTION OF A SPINNING TOP

Definition : An interesting example of rigid body motion occurs when a symmetrical rigid body having one point on the axis of symmetry fixed in space is set spinning in a gravitational field. A top is a *rigid body which is a solid of revolution about the axis of symmetry.* The adjoining figure shows such a top rotating about a fixed point O on its axis of symmetry., Thus we idealise the ordinary top by supposing it to terminate in a sharp point (or vertex) and to spin on a floor rough enough to prevent slipping.

EQUATION OF MOTION OF A TOP

(Derived from Euler's Equation) : Let us assume that a top spins with its vertex O fixed in contact with a floor rough enough to prevent slipping Fig. 10.01, Let OC be the axis of the top and G its centre of gravity such that OC = h.

Let OX, OY, OZ be the fixed axes and OA, OB, OC the principal axes at O.

Let C, A be the moments of inertia about OC and OA, since the top is symmetrical about OC, so B = A.

Let at zero time OC be in the plane ZOX and at time t it makes an angle θ to OZ and the plane ZOC makes the angle ϕ with the fixed plane ZOX. Let ω_1, ω_2, ω_3 be the angular velocities of the top about OA, OB and OC respectively and L, M, N be the moments of the external forces about OA, OB and OC respectively.

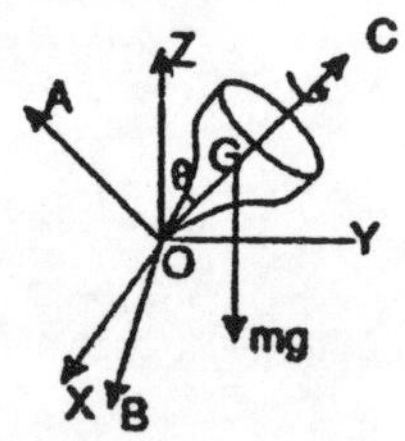

Fig. 2.1

Again the external forces acting on the top are its weight mg acting vertically downwards through G, the C.G. of the top in a direction parallel to OZ and the reactions at point O (0, 0, 0).

The direction cosines of OZ with respect to OA, OB and OC are. $-\sin\theta\cos\psi$, $\sin\theta\sin\psi$, $\cos\theta$

or $\quad -\sin\theta, 0, \cos\theta \quad$ ($\because$ In case of top $\psi = 0$)

Thus the weight – mg acting at G (0, 0, h) has the resolved parts mg sin θ; 0, –mg cosθ, parallel to OA, OB and OC respectively.

By $$L = \Sigma (y_1 Z_1 - z_1 Y_1) \text{ etc.,}$$

we have $$L = 0, M = hmg \sin\theta, N = 0$$

Therefore Euler's equations give

$$A\dot{\omega}_1 - (B - C)\omega_2\omega_3 = L = 0;$$

$$B\dot{\omega}_2 - (C - A)\omega_3\omega_1 = M = hmg\sin\theta$$

$$C\dot{\omega}_3 - (A - B)\omega_1\omega_2 = N = 0$$

Again Euler's geometrical relations are

$$\omega_1 = \dot{\theta}\sin\psi - \dot{\phi}\sin\theta\cos\psi, \omega_2 = \dot{\theta}\cos\psi + \dot{\phi}\sin\theta\sin\psi,$$

$$\omega_3 = \dot{\psi} + \dot{\phi}\cos\theta$$

which reduce to $\omega_1 = -\dot{\phi}\sin\theta.\ \omega_3 = \dot{\phi}\cos\theta, \omega_2 = \dot{\theta}$ since for top $\dot{\psi} = 0$.

Again B = A, thus the Euler's third equation gives

$\dot{\omega}_3 = 0$ or $\omega_3 = n$ (constant). or $\phi \cos\theta = n$

Putting the values of $\omega_1, \omega_2, \omega_3$.

Euler's first equation $A\omega_1 - (B - C)\omega_2\, \omega_3 = 0$

deduces to $A\dfrac{d}{dt}(-\dot{\phi}\sin\theta) - (A - C)\dot{\theta}\dot{\phi}\cos\theta = 0$ as B = A

or $-\ A\phi^2\sin\theta - 2A\dot{\theta}\dot{\phi}\cos\theta + C\dot{\theta}\dot{\phi}\cos\theta = 0$

or $-\ A\phi\sin\theta - 2A\dot{\theta}\dot{\phi}\cos\theta + Cn\dot{\theta} = 0$ ...(2)

And Euler's second equation $B\dot{\omega}_2 - (C - A)\omega_3\omega_1 = mgh \sin\theta$

reduces to $A\dfrac{d}{dt}(\dot{\theta}) + (C - A)\dot{\phi}^2 \sin\theta\cos\theta = mgh\sin\theta$ as B = A

or $A\ddot{\theta} - A\dot{\phi}^2\sin\theta + C\dot{\phi}^2\sin\theta\cos\theta = mgh\sin\theta$

$A\ddot{\theta} - A\dot{\phi}^2\sin\theta + Cn\dot{\phi}\sin\theta = mgh\sin\theta$

Equations (1) and (2) are the *equations of motion of the top* and are of second order.

Multiplying (1) by sin θ and integrating, we have

$A\dot{\phi}\sin^2\theta + Cn\cos\theta = D$ (cosnt.) ...(3)

Again multiply (1) by $2\dot{\phi}\sin\theta$ and (2) by $2\dot{\theta}$ and subtracting, we get

$$2A\ddot{\theta}\dot{\theta} + 2A\dot{\theta}\dot{\phi}^2\sin\theta\cos\theta + 2A\dot{\phi}\ddot{\phi}\sin^2\theta = 2mgh\sin\theta$$

Integrating, we get

$$A(\dot{\theta}^2 + \dot{\phi}^2 \sin^2 \theta) + 2mgh\cos\theta = E(\text{const.}) \quad ...(4)$$

Equations (3) and (4) are also the equations of motion of the top but are of first order. Equation (4) is called equation of Energy. The motion due to change in θ is called *mutation* and due to change in ϕ is called precision. The general motion of the top about its fixed vertex O is a combination of these two.

EQUATIONS OF MOTION OF A TOP

(Deduced from the Principle of Energy and Momentum) : Since for motion of top B = A and $\psi = 0$

$$\therefore \omega_1 = -\dot{\phi}\sin\theta, \omega_2 = \dot{\theta}, \omega_3 = n = \dot{\phi}\cos\theta$$

$$\therefore \text{K.E.} = \frac{1}{2}[A(\omega_1^2 + \omega_2^2) + C\omega_3^2] = \frac{1}{2}[A\,\dot{\phi}^2 \sin^2\theta + \dot{\theta}^2) + Cn^2] \quad (\because B = A)$$

Again potential energy = mgh cos θ where h is the distance of C.G. from the vertex O and θ inclination of OC to the vertical. By the principle of energy, the sum of the kinetic and the potential energy remains constant throughout motion. Thus by the principle of energy we have

$$\frac{1}{2}[A(\dot{\phi}^2 \sin^2\theta + \dot{\theta}^2) + Cn^2] + mgh\cos\theta = \text{const.}$$

$$\text{or } A(\dot{\theta}^2 + \dot{\phi}^2 \sin^2\theta) + mgh\cos\theta = E \quad ...(1)$$

Since the external force (weight) is parallel to OZ and the reactions at O cut OZ; so the sum of their moments about OZ is zero. Thus by the principle of momentum, the moment of momentum about OZ is constant throughout the motion.

Again A ω_1, Aω_2, Cω_3 are the moments of momentum of the top about OA, OB, OC respectively; and the direction cosines of OZ about these axes are given by – sin θ, 0 cos θ.

Resolving these momentums about OZ, we have moment of momentum about OZ –A ω_1 sinθ + Cω_3 cos θ.

Therefore by the principle of momentum, we have

$$-A\,\omega_1 \sin\theta + C\omega_3 \cos\theta = \text{const.}$$

$$\text{or } A\sin\theta\,(-\dot{\phi}\sin\theta) + Cn\cos\theta = D\ (\text{constant}). \quad ...(2)$$

Equations (1) and (2) ae same equations of motion of a top.

EQUATIONS OF MOTION OF A TOP

(Deduced from Lagrange's Equations) : For motion of a top, we have

$$B = A, \psi = 0 \text{ and } \omega_1 = -\dot{\phi}\sin\theta, \omega_2 = \dot{\theta}, \omega_3 = n = \dot{\phi}\cos\theta$$

∴ The kinetic energy is

$$\therefore T = \frac{1}{2}m[A(\omega_2^2 + \omega_2^2) + C\omega_3^2] \qquad (\because B = A)$$

$$= \frac{1}{2}m[A(\dot{\phi}^2 \sin^2\theta + \dot{\theta}^2) + C\dot{\phi}^2 \cos^2\theta]$$

And the work function W is W = – mgh cos θ where h is distance of C.G. form the vertex of O. and θ is inclination of OC to the vertical OZ.

Here the generalised co-ordinates are θ and φ.

Lagrange's θ- equation is $\frac{d}{dt}\left(\frac{\partial T}{\partial \dot{\theta}}\right) - \frac{\partial T}{\partial \theta} = \frac{\partial W}{\partial \theta}$ which gives

$$\frac{d}{dt}(mA\dot{\theta}) - \{mA\dot{\phi}^2 \sin\theta\cos\theta - C\dot{\phi}^2 \cos\theta\sin\theta\} = mgh \sin\theta$$

$$\text{or} \quad A\ddot{\theta} - A\dot{\phi}^2 \sin\theta\cos\theta + Cn\dot{\phi}\sin\theta = mgh\sin\theta \qquad ...(2)$$

And Lagrange's φ-equation is $\frac{d}{dt}\left(\frac{\partial T}{\partial \dot{\phi}}\right) - \frac{\partial T}{\partial \phi} = \frac{\partial W}{\partial \phi}$

which gives $\frac{d}{dt}(mA\dot{\phi}\sin^2\theta + C\dot{\phi}\cos^2\theta) = 0$

$$\text{or} \quad A\dot{\phi}\sin^2\theta + Cn\cos\theta = D \text{ (const.)} \qquad ...(2)$$

Equation (1) and (2) are same equations of the motion of a top.

STEADY MOTION

The motion of a top is said to be steady if it spins about is vertex O in such a way that its axis OC makes the same angle with the vertical OZ throughout the motion.

For steady motion θ = α (constant), *i.e.* the angular velocity about the vertical OZ is constant.

In this case the axis of the top describes a cone about the vertical with uniform angular velocity. Thus precessional velocity φ is constant.

In case the motion steady.

Put $\theta = \alpha, \ddot{\theta} = 0$ and $\dot{\phi} = \omega$ in equation

$$A\ddot{\theta} - A\dot{\phi}^2 \sin\theta\cos\theta + Cn\dot{\phi}\sin\theta - mgh\sin\theta = 0$$

Thus, we have $\omega^2 A \cos\alpha - Cn\omega + mgh = 0$ ...(1)

$$\text{or} \quad \omega \frac{Cn \pm \sqrt{(C^2n^2 - 4A\, mgh\cos\theta}}{2A\cos\theta}$$

i.e. there are in general two values of the precessional velocity ω; the two precessional velocities, call them ω_1, ω_2 ω_3; are real and distinct if

$$C^2n^2 > 4A\ mgh \cos\alpha$$

This is the necessary condition of steady motion.

Cor. If $\alpha = \frac{1}{2}\pi$, then from (1), $\omega = \left(\frac{mgh}{Cn}\right)$

Thus if the top is given an angular velocity n about OC when OC is horizontal and OC be then given an angular velocity (mgh/Cn) about OZ, then OC will continue to revolve uniformly in a horizontal plane round the vertical OZ.

If the top is set in motion in the usual manner. Then n is very great, thus

$$\omega = \frac{1}{2A\cos\alpha}\left[Cn \pm Cn\left\{1 - \frac{4Amgh\cos\alpha}{C^2n^2}\right\}^{1/2}\right]$$

$$= \frac{1}{2A\cos\alpha}\left[Cn \pm Cn\left\{1 - \frac{1}{2}.\frac{4Amgh\cos\alpha}{C^2n^2}\right\}\right]$$

$$= \frac{Cn}{2A\cos\alpha}\left[1 \pm \left\{1 - \frac{2Amgh\cos\alpha}{C^2n^2}\right\}\right]$$

$$= \frac{Cn}{A\cos\alpha} \text{ or } \frac{mgh}{Cn}$$

(by taking positive and negative signs respectively)

Thus $\omega = \frac{Cn}{A\cos\alpha}$ or $\frac{mgh}{Cn}$ approx. When n is very great. Obviously the first value of ω is large and second is very small, when n is very great.

STABLE MOTION

When axis is vertical : A top is executing steady motion with angular velocity n about its axis which is vertical; to show that the motion is stable.

If the body be disturbed in such a way that θ is very small whilst ψ is unaltered initially, so the general equations of motion of the top are

$$A\ddot{\theta} - A\dot{\phi}^2 \sin\theta\cos\theta + Cn\dot{\phi}\sin\theta = mgh\sin\theta$$

and $A\dot{\phi}^2 \sin^2\theta\cos\theta\ +\ Cn\cos\theta = D$

Since motion is steady with axis vertical; thus we have

$$\theta = 0, \ddot{\theta} = 0, \dot{\phi} = n, \therefore D = Cn$$

Also $C^2n^2 > 4A$ mgh is the condition for steady motion when $\alpha = 0$. Let the motion be slightly disturbed. The disturbed motion is a general motion of the top; hence its equations are

$$A\ddot{\theta} - A\dot{\phi}\sin\theta\cos\theta + Cn\dot{\phi}\sin\theta = mgh\sin\theta \qquad ...(1)$$

and $A\dot{\phi}\sin^2\theta + Cn\cos\theta = Cn$ ...(2)

Eliminating ϕ between (1) and (2), we have

$$A^2\ddot{\theta} - \frac{C^2n^2}{(1+\cos\theta)^2}\sin\theta\cos\theta + \frac{C^2n^2}{(1+\cos\theta)}\sin\theta = Amgh\sin\theta$$

Since θ is small, therefore, writing θ for $\sin\theta$ and 1 for $\cos\theta$ the above equation reduces to

$$A^2\ddot{\theta} - \frac{C^2n^2\theta}{4} + \frac{C^2n^2\theta}{2} = Amgh\,\theta \text{ or } \ddot{\theta} = -\left(\frac{C^2n^2 - 4Amgh}{4A^2}\right)\theta,$$

(the coefficient of q is negative, $\because C^2n^2 > 4Amgh$)

The above equation is simple harmonic motion.

i.e. the motion of the axis of the figure is simple Harmonic about the vertical OZ from which θ is measured. In other words, axis of the top, if disturbed slightly from its vertical position in steady motion, will tend to come back to its original position, *i.e.* the steady motion, in which axis of the figure is vertical, is stable.

The period of oscillation

$$= 2\pi\sqrt{\left(\frac{4A^2}{B^2n^2 - 4Amgh}\right)} = \frac{4\pi A}{\sqrt{(C^2n^2 - 4Amgh)}} \text{ (where axis is not vertical)}$$

STABLE MOTION

A top is executing steady motion, with its axis inclined at a constant angle α to the vertical, and precessional velocity ω; to show that motion is stable. Here, we shall show that, the axis of the top, when disturbed slightly, from its position in steady motion, will tend to come back to the original position.

Equations of motion of the top are

$$A\ddot{\theta} - A\dot{\phi}^2\sin\theta\cos\theta + Cn\dot{\phi}\sin\theta = mgh\sin\theta$$

and $A\dot{\phi}\sin^2\theta + Cn\cos\theta = D$

Since the motion, originally, is steady with $\theta = \alpha, \dot{\phi} = \omega$.

Thus the above equation reduces to

$$Cn\omega - A\omega^2\cos\alpha = mgh \text{ and } D = A\omega\sin^2\alpha + Cn\cos\alpha.$$

Let the steady motion be slightly disturbed, so that motion is then general one and so its equations are

$$A\ddot{\theta} - A\dot{\phi}^2 \sin\theta\cos\theta + Cn\dot{\phi}\sin\theta = mgh\sin\theta \qquad ...(1)$$

and $A\dot{\phi}\sin^2\theta + Cn\cos\theta = A\omega\sin^2\alpha + Cn\cos\alpha \qquad ...(2)$

Eliminating $\dot{\phi}$ between (1) and (2), we get

$$A^2\ddot{\theta}\sin^3\theta - \{A\omega\sin^2\alpha + Cn(\cos\alpha - \cos\theta)\}^2\cos\theta + Cn\sin^2\theta \times$$

$$\{A\omega\sin^2\alpha + Cn(\cos\alpha - \cos\theta)\} = Amgh\sin^4\theta$$

Putting $\theta = \alpha + X$ Where X is small, the above equation reduces to

$$A^2\ddot{X}\sin^3(\alpha + X) - [A\omega\sin^2\alpha + Cn\{\cos\alpha - \cos(\alpha + X)\}]^2\cos(\alpha + X)$$

$$+ Cn\sin^2(\alpha + X)[A\omega\sin^2\alpha + Cn\{\cos\alpha - \cos(\alpha + X)\}]$$

$$= Amgh\sin^4(\alpha + X)$$

Since X is small, neglecting quantities of second and higher orders of smallness, we have

$$A^2\ddot{X}(\sin\alpha + X\cos\alpha)^3 - (A\omega\sin^2\alpha + Cn\{\cos\alpha - (\cos\alpha -$$

$$X\sin\alpha)\}]^2(\cos\alpha - X\sin\alpha) + Cn(\sin\alpha + X\cos\alpha)^2[A\omega\sin^2\alpha$$

$$+ Cn\{\cos\alpha - (\cos\alpha - X\sin\alpha)\}] = Amgh(\sin\alpha + X\cos\alpha)^4$$

or $A^2\ddot{X}\sin^3\alpha - (A\omega\sin^2\alpha + CnX\sin\alpha)$

$$= A\,mgh(\sin^4\alpha + 4X\cos\alpha\sin^3\alpha)$$

or $A^2\ddot{X}\sin^3\alpha - (A^2\omega^2\sin^4\alpha + 2XA\,Cn\omega\sin^3\alpha)(\cos\alpha - X\sin\alpha)$

$$+ Cn(\sin^2 + 2X\sin\alpha\cos\alpha)(A\omega\sin^2\alpha + CnX\sin\alpha)$$

$$= A\,mgh(\sin^4\alpha + 4X\cos\alpha\sin^3\alpha)$$

or $A^2\ddot{X}\sin^3\alpha - (A^2\omega^2\sin^4\alpha + 2X\,ACn\omega\sin^3\alpha + XA^2\omega^2\sin^5\alpha)$

$$+ Cn(\sin^2\alpha + 2X\sin\alpha\cos\alpha)A\omega\sin^2\alpha + XC^2n^2\sin^3\alpha$$

$$= A\,mgh(\sin^4\alpha + 4X\cos\alpha\sin^3\alpha)$$

or $A^2\ddot{X} - A^2\omega^2\sin\alpha\cos\alpha + Cn\omega A\sin\alpha + XA^2\omega^2\sin^2\alpha + XC^2n^2$

$$= Amgh(\sin\alpha + 4X\cos\alpha)$$

or $A^2X - A^2\omega^2\sin\alpha\cos\alpha + (A\omega^2\cos\alpha + mgh)A\sin\alpha + XA^2\omega^2\sin^2\alpha$

$$+ X(A\omega^2\cos\alpha + mgh)^2(1/\omega^2) = Amgh(\sin\alpha + 4X\cos\alpha)$$

or $A^2\ddot{X}+X[A^2\omega^4(\sin^2\alpha+\cos^2\alpha)+2A\,mgh\omega^2\cos\alpha+m^2g^2h^2]$

$$\times[1/\omega^2]\,4XA\text{ mgh}\cos\alpha$$

or $A^2\ddot{X}+X[A^2\omega^4-2A\text{ mgh }\omega^2\cos\alpha+m^2g^2h^2](1/\omega^2)=0$

or $\ddot{X}=-\dfrac{A^2\omega^4-2Amgh\omega^2\cos\alpha+m^2g^2h^2}{A^2\omega^2}X$ [S.H.M]

(the coefficient of X is obviously negative)

This shows that the axis of the top, if disturbed slightly from its position in steady motion will tend to come back to the original (predisturbed), position, *i.e.* the steady motion, with axis inclined at α to the vertical, is stable.

The period of oscillation $=2\pi\dfrac{A\omega}{(A^2\omega^4-2Amgh\,\omega^2\cos\alpha+m^2g^2)^{(1/2)}}$

In case the top is set in motion in usual manner, then n is very large and two values of the precessional velocity are approximately given by

$$\omega=\frac{Cn}{A\cos\alpha.}\,\frac{mgh}{Cn}$$

When n is large, the first value is large and the second small. For first value of ω, the period of oscillation is given by

$$\frac{2\pi A\omega}{A\omega^2}\text{ (approx.) }=\frac{2\pi\cos\omega}{Cn}$$

And for second value of ω, the period of oscillation is given by

$$\frac{2\pi A\omega}{mgh}\text{ (approx.) }=\frac{2\pi A}{Cn}$$

LIMITS OF θ

A top is set spinning with angular velocity n about its axis. Initially he axis being instantaneously at rest and inclined at an angle i to the vertical. To show that in the subsequent motion, the angle θ between the axis and the vertical oscillates between

$$i\le\theta\le\cos^{-1}\{p-\sqrt{[(p^2-2p\cos i+1)]}\}\text{ where }p=\left(\frac{C^2n^2}{4Amgh}\right),$$

and the letters have their usual meanings.

By equation (3) and (4), the two equations of motion of top are

$$A\dot{\phi}\sin^2\theta+Cn\cos\theta=D\text{ and }A(\dot{\theta}^2+\dot{\phi}^2\sin^2\theta)+2mgh\cos\theta=E$$

where D and E are constants.

Initially $\theta = i, \theta = \dot{0}, \dot{\psi} = 0$,

$\therefore$ D = Cn cos i and E = 2 mgh cos i.

Thus the above equations reduce to

$$A\dot{\phi}\sin^2\theta + Cn\cos\theta = Cn\cos i \quad ...(1)$$

and $A(\dot{\theta}^2 + \dot{\phi}^2\sin^2\theta) + 2mgh\cos\theta = 2mgh\cos i \quad ...(2)$

Now eliminating ϕ. between (1) and (2), we get

$$A\dot{\theta}^2\sin^2\theta + C^2n^2(\cos i - \cos\theta)^2 + 2Amgh(\cos\theta - \cos i)\sin^2\theta = 0$$

or $A^2\dot{\theta}^2\sin^2\theta = -2Amgh(\cos\theta - \cos i)\sin^2\theta - C^2n^2(\cos\theta - \cos i)^2$

$= -2Amgh(\cos\theta - \cos i)\sin\theta - 4Amgh\,p(\cos\theta - \cos i)^2$

$= 2Amgh(\cos\theta - \cos i)[-\sin^2\theta - 2p(\cos\theta - \cos i)]$

$= 2Amgh(\cos i)\ [\cos^2\theta - 2p\cos\theta - 1 + 2p\cos i]$

$= 2Amgh(\cos\theta - \cos i)\ [(\cos\theta - p)^2 - (p^2 - 2p\cos i + 1])$

$= 2Amgh(\cos\theta - \cos i)\ \{\cos\theta - (p - \sqrt{[p^2 - 2p\cos i + 1]})\}$

$$\times\{\cos\theta - (p + \sqrt{[p^2 - 2p\cos i + 1]})\} \quad ...(3)$$

Now $\dot{\theta}$ will vanish when $\theta = i$ or θ_1 or θ_2

where $\cos\theta_1 = p - \sqrt{[(p^2 - 2p\cos i + 1)]}$

and $\cos\theta_2 = p + \sqrt{[(p^2 - 2p\cos i + 1)]}$

The second expression is greater than 1, *hence* θ_2 *is imaginary.*

But $\cos\theta_1 < \cos i$. $\therefore \theta_1 > i$=

Again from (2) θ^2 is negative if $\cos\theta > \cos i$ *i e.* $\theta < i$.

Hence possible values of θ are i and θ_1 where

$\cos\theta_1 = p - \sqrt{(p^2 - 2p\cos i + 1)}$

Again from (3) θ^2 is negative if

$\cos\theta > p - \sqrt{(p^2 - 2p\cos i + 1)}$ *i.e.* $\theta > \theta_1$

Thus, we conclude that top is never at a less inclination than i or at a greater inclination than θ_1, *i.e.* the motion is included between these two limits.

SOLVED EXAMPLES

Example 1:

A top consists of a thin uniform spherical shell of radius a and centre C and is free to move about a fixed point O of its surface. The radius OC makes an angle θ with upward down vertical Oz and φ is the angle between the plane zOC and a fixed vertical plane zOx.

Initially $\theta = \frac{1}{2}\pi, \dot{\phi} = \left(\frac{2n}{5}\right)$,

where $n = \sqrt{\left(\frac{15g}{2a}\right)}$

Show that at time t,

$\cos\theta = \tanh^2 \left\{\left(\frac{3g}{10a}\right)\right\}$.

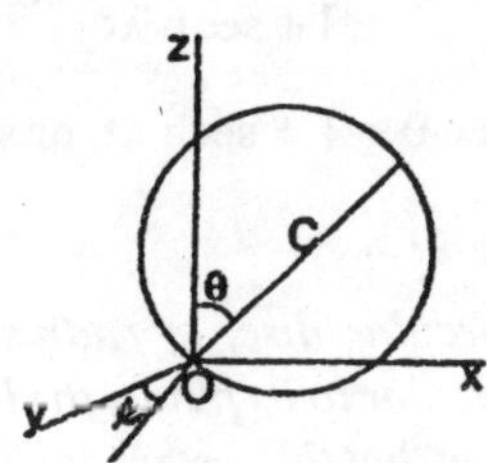

Fig. 2.2

Solution:

We have equations of motion of the top as

$$A(\dot{\theta}^2 + \dot{\phi}^2 \sin^2\theta) + 2mgh\cos\theta = E \quad \text{and} \quad A\dot{\phi}^2 \sin^2\theta + Cn\cos\theta = D$$

where D,E are constants to be determined by initial conditions.

Initially $\theta = \frac{1}{2}\pi, \theta = 0, \dot{\phi} = \frac{2n}{5}$.

Putting these in the above equations, we get

$$E = A\left(\dot{\theta} + \frac{4n^2}{25}\right) = (4n^2/25)A \text{ and } D = A\frac{2n}{5} = \frac{2n}{5}A$$

Thus the above equations can be written as

$$A(\dot{\theta}^2 + \dot{\phi}^2 \sin^2\theta) + 2mgh\cos\theta = \left(\frac{4n^2}{25}\right)A \quad \text{...(1)}$$

$$\text{and } A\dot{\phi}\sin^2\theta + Cn\cos\theta = (2n/5)A \quad \text{...(2)}$$

Again C = moment of inertia about OC

= moment of inertia of a hollow sphere about a diameter

= $(2ma^2/3)$

A = moment of inertia about OA

= moment of inertia of a hollow sphere about a line at ⊥ OC

$= (2ma^2/3) + ma^2 = (5ma^2/3)$

and $\quad h =$ distance of C.G. from O = a

or $u = \tanh\frac{\lambda t}{2} \Rightarrow u^2 = \frac{\sinh^2\frac{1}{2}\lambda t}{\cosh^2\frac{1}{2}\lambda t} = \frac{\cosh\lambda t - 1}{\cosh\lambda t + 1} = \frac{1 - \text{sech}\,\lambda t}{1 + \text{sech}\,\lambda t}$

$\therefore 1 + u^2 = \frac{2}{1 + \text{sech}\,\lambda t}$ *i.e.* $2\cos\theta = \frac{2}{1 + \text{sech}\,\lambda t}$

or $\sec\theta = 1 + \text{sech}\,\lambda t$, or $\sec\theta = 1 + \text{sech}\sqrt{(mgh/A)}\,t$.

Example 2:

A circular disc, of radius a, has a thin rod pushed through its centre perpendicular to its plane, the length of the rod being equal to the radius of the disc. Show that the system can not spin with the rod vertical unless the angular velocity is greater then $\sqrt{\left(\frac{20g}{a}\right)}$

Solution:

With usual notations, in this case

$$A = \left(\frac{Ma^2}{a}\right) + Ma^2 = \left(\frac{5Ma^2}{4}\right), C = \left(\frac{Ma^2}{2}\right) \text{ and } h = a$$

For the top to execute steady motion with axis vertical, the necessary condition is that

$$C^2n^2 > 4AMgh \quad \sqrt{\left(\frac{4AMgh}{C^2}\right)}$$

or $n > \sqrt{\left(\frac{20g}{a}\right)}$ putting for A, C and h.

Example 3:

If a top is made by running a thin pin through the centre of a circular disc, of radius 3 inches, so that length of the pin below the disc is 2 inches, prove that, for steady motion in which rim does not touch the ground, the number of revolutions per second about the axis must exceed $\frac{80}{3\pi(13)^{1/4}}$.

Solution:

In this case we shall discuss the steady motion when the rim of the disc just goes on touching the ground. Let axis OC of the top make an angle α with the vertical OZ, then it makes the angle $\frac{1}{2}\pi - \alpha$ with the horizontal OX. Again

$$\cos\left(\frac{\pi}{2}-\alpha\right)=\cos NOC=\frac{OC}{ON}=\frac{2}{\sqrt{(13)}}$$

$$i.e. \Rightarrow \sin\alpha=\frac{2}{\sqrt{(13)}}, \cos\alpha=\frac{3}{\sqrt{(13)}}$$

The condition for steady motion is $C^2n^2 > 4Amgh \cos\alpha$ ...(1)

where A and C have their usual meanings.

Here A = moment of inertia about OA

= moment of inertia about a line through O ⊥ to OC

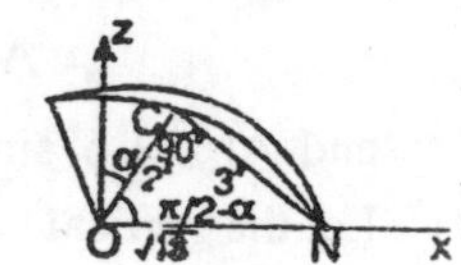

Fig. 2.3

$$=m\left\{\frac{1}{2}\left(\frac{1}{4}\right)^2+\left(\frac{1}{6}\right)^2\right\}$$ [∵ radius of the disc]

$$=3''=\frac{1}{4}\text{ft. and } CO=2''=\frac{1}{6}\text{ft.}=m\left(\frac{1}{64}+\frac{1}{36}\right)=\frac{25m}{576}$$

$$C=\text{moment of inertia about } OC=\frac{1}{2}m\left(\frac{1}{4}\right)^2=\frac{m}{32}$$

and h = distance of C.G. of the top from the vertex

$$=\text{distance of C.G. of the disc from } O=2''=\frac{1}{6}\text{ft.}$$

Putting these values in (1) the required condition is

$$\left(\frac{m}{32}\right)^2 n^2 > 4\left(\frac{25m}{576}\right)mg\left(\frac{1}{6}\right)\frac{3}{\sqrt{(13)}} \text{ or } n^2 > \frac{4.25.1.3}{576.0}, \frac{32.32}{\sqrt{(13)}}$$

$$\text{or } n^2 > \frac{25.32.32}{2(13)^{1/2}} \; n > \frac{160}{2(13)^{1/4}} \text{ or } \frac{n}{2\pi} > \frac{160}{3\pi(13)^{1/4}}$$

$$\text{or number of revolutions per second} > \frac{80}{3\pi(13)^{1/4}}$$

i.e. number of revolutions per second must exceed

$$=\frac{80}{3\pi(13)^{1/4}}=4.5 \text{ approx.}$$

Example 4:

Show that the vertical pressure of the top on the point of support is equal to its weight when the inclination of its axis to the vertical is given by the least root of the equation

$$3\,Amgh\cos^2\theta - \cos\theta\,(C^2n^2+2\,Amgbh)+(C^2n^2a-Amgh)=0$$

where a and b are constants depending on the initial circumstances of the motion

Solution:

We have equations of motion of the top as

$$-A\ddot{\phi}\sin\theta - 2A\dot{\phi}\,\dot{\theta}\cos\theta + Cn\dot{\theta} = 0 \qquad ...(1)$$

$$A\ddot{\theta} + Cn\,\dot{\phi}\sin\theta - A\dot{\phi}^2\sin\theta\cos\theta = Mgh\sin\theta \qquad ...(2)$$

$$A\dot{\phi}\sin^2\theta + Cn\cos\theta = D \qquad ...(3)$$

and $A(\dot{\theta}^2 + \dot{\phi}^2\sin^2\theta) + 2M\,gh\cos\theta = E$ ...(4)

Let the vertical component of the reaction at the vertex O be Y, thus for vertical motion of the top, we have

$$M\frac{d^2}{dt^2}(h\cos\theta) = Y - Mg$$

In case Y = M g, then $\frac{d^2}{dt^2}(\cos\theta) = 0$ ($\because$ h is constant)

or $\sin\theta\ddot{\theta} + \cos\theta\dot{\theta}^2 = 0.$

Now, putting for $\ddot{\theta}$ and $\dot{\theta}^2$ from (2) and (4)
and writing E = 2 Mgh b, we get

$$\sin\theta\,(A\dot{\phi}^2\sin\theta\cos\theta - Cn\dot{\phi}\sin\theta + Mgh\sin\theta)$$
$$+ \cos\theta\,(-A\dot{\phi}^2\sin^2\theta + 2M\,ghb + 2Mgh\,b\cos\theta) = 0$$

or $\sin\theta\,(-Cn\dot{\phi}\sin\theta + Mgh\sin\theta)$
$+ \cos\theta\,(2M\,ghb - 2M\,gh\,b\cos\theta) = 0$

or $2M\,gh\,(\sin^2\theta + 2b\cos\theta - 2\cos^2\theta) = Cn\dot{\phi}\sin^2\theta.$

In this put for $\dot{\phi}$ from (3) and putting D = Cna

We obtain $M\,gh\,(\sin^2\theta + 2b\cos\theta - 2\cos^2\theta)$

$$= \frac{Cn}{A}Cn\,(a - \cos\theta)$$

or $AM\,gh\,(1 + 2b\cos\theta - 3\cos^2\theta) = C^2n^2\,(a - \cos\theta)$

or $3AM\,gh\cos^2\theta - \cos\theta\,(C^2n^2 + 2AM\,gh\,b) + (C^2n^2a - AM\,gh) = 0$

Example 5:

Show that in order that it may be possible for a uniform cone, of height h and vertical angle 2α, to spin a top on a rough horizontal plane it is necessary that

$$n^2 > \frac{5g(4+\tan^2\alpha)\sin\alpha}{h\tan^4\alpha}$$

Solution:

The spinning is possible so long as the slant side just touches the horizontal plane. The motion then will be steady with the axis OC of the top making angle $\frac{1}{2}\pi - \alpha$ with the vertical OZ.

The condition for steady motion is

$C^2n^2 > 4A\ mgh \cos\alpha$ ...(1)

where A is M.I. about OA and C is M.I about OC (the axis on the top). In this case A = Moment of inertia about OA

= moment of inertia about a line through O $\perp$ to OC

$$= \frac{3m}{20}(a^2+4h^2) = \frac{3m}{20}(h^2\tan^2\alpha + 4h^2) \qquad \left(\because \tan\alpha = \frac{a}{h}\right)$$

$$= \frac{3mh^2}{10}(4+\tan^2\alpha)$$

C = moment of inertia about OC (the axis of the top)

= moment of inertia about the axis of the cone

$$= \frac{3ma^2}{10} = \frac{3mh^2}{10}\tan^2\alpha$$

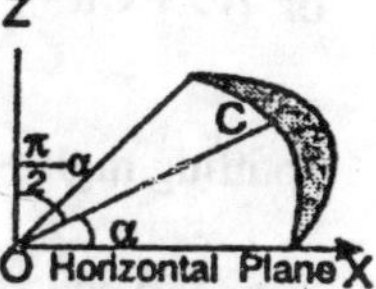

Fig. 2.4

The distance of the C.G. of the top from the vertex is $\frac{3h}{4}$ and the axis of the top is making an angle $\frac{1}{2}\pi - \alpha$ with the vertical.

Putting these values in the condition for steady motion, we have

$$\left(\frac{3mh^2\tan^2\alpha}{10}\right)^2 n^2 > 4\frac{3mh^2}{20}(4+\tan^2\alpha)mg\frac{3h}{4}\cos\left(\frac{1}{2}\pi - \alpha\right)$$

$$\text{or } n^2 > \frac{5g(4+\tan^2\alpha)\sin\alpha}{h\tan^4\alpha}$$

Example 6:

If initially the axis of the top is horizontal and it is set spinning with angular velocity ω *in* a horizontal plane, prove that the axis will start to rise if Cn ω> *mgh, and that when Cn* ω = *2m gh, the axis will rise to an angular distance.* $\cos^{-1}$(A ω / Cn), *provided that A*ω < *Cn, and will be there at an instantaneous rest.*

Solution:

We have equations of motion of the top as

$$A\ddot{\theta} + Cn\,\dot{\phi}\sin\theta - A\dot{\phi}^2 \sin\theta\cos\theta = mgh\sin\theta \quad ...(1)$$

$$A\,\dot{\phi}\sin^2\theta + Cn\cos\theta = D = A\omega \quad ...(2)$$

Initially $\theta = \frac{1}{2}\pi$ and $\dot{\phi} = \omega$, $\therefore D = A\omega$

Thus initially from (1) $A\ddot{\theta} = -(cn\,\omega - mgh)$

which is negative if Cn ω> mgh. In other words, the axis will start to rise if Cn ω> mgh.

Now, eliminating ϕ between (1) and (2) we get

$$A\ddot{\theta} + Cn\frac{A\omega - Cn\cos\theta}{A\sin^3\theta}\sin\theta - A\left(\frac{A\omega - Cn\cos\theta}{A\sin^2\theta}\right)^2 \sin\theta\cos\theta$$

$$= mgh\sin\theta$$

$$\text{or } A\ddot{\theta} + Cn\frac{A\omega - Cn\cos\theta}{A\sin^3\theta} - \frac{B\omega - Cn\cos\theta}{A\sin^2\theta}\cos\theta = \frac{Cn\omega\sin\theta}{2}$$

(putting $mgh = \frac{1}{2}Cn\,\omega$)

$$A\ddot{\theta} = \frac{A^2\omega^2 + C^2n^2}{A}\frac{\cos\theta}{\sin^3\theta} + Cn\,\omega\left\{\frac{1}{2}\sin\theta - \left(\frac{1}{\sin\theta} + \frac{2\cos\theta}{\sin^3\theta}\right)\right\}$$

Integrating it, $A\dot{\theta}^2 = -\dfrac{A^2\omega^2 + C^2n^2}{A\sin^2\theta} + Cn\,\omega\left(-\cos\theta + \dfrac{2\cos\theta}{\sin^2\theta}\right) + C'$

where C′ is constant.

But initially $\theta = \frac{1}{2}\pi, \dot{\theta} = 0, \quad \therefore C' = \dfrac{A^2\omega^2 + C^2n^2}{A}$

$$\therefore A\dot{\theta}^2 = -\frac{A^2\omega^2 + C^2n^2}{A\sin^2\theta} + Cn\omega\frac{(-\sin^2\theta\cos\theta + 2\cos\theta)}{\sin^2\theta} + \frac{A^2\omega^2 + C^2n^2}{A}$$

$$\text{or } A^2\dot{\theta}^2\sin^2\theta = -(A^2\omega^2 + C^2n^2)\cos^2\theta + Cn\,\omega A(-\sin^2\theta + 2)\cos\theta$$

$$= -(A^2\omega^2 + C^2n^2)\cos^2\theta + Cn\,\omega A(1 + \cos^2\theta)\cos\theta$$

$$= \cos\theta\,(A\omega - Cn\cos\theta)\,(Cn - A\omega\cos\theta)$$

For instantaneous res $\dot{\theta} = 0$

in which cos cosq $(A\,\omega - Cn\cos\theta)\,(Cn - A\,\omega\cos\theta) = 0$

i.e. when $\cos\theta = 0$ or $\theta = \frac{1}{2}\pi$ which is the initial positions.

and when $A\omega - Cn\cos\theta = 0$ or $\cos\theta = \frac{A\omega}{Cn}$

i.e. $\theta = \cos^{-1}\frac{A\omega}{Cn}$ provided $A\omega < Cn$

and when $Cn - A\omega\cos\theta$ or $\theta = \cos^{-1}\left(\frac{Cn}{A\omega}\right)$, which is impossible when $A\omega < Cn$.

Example 7:

AB, BC are two equal similar rods freely hinged at B and lie in a straight line on a smooth table. The end A is struck by a blow perpendicular to AB; show that resulting velocity of A is $3\frac{1}{2}$ times of B.

Solution:

Let P be the impulsive force applied at A. Just after the blow let μ_1, ω_1 and μ_2, ω_2 be the liner and angular velocities of the rods AB and BC respectively. When the blow is struck, there will be an impulsive action between the two rods at B. Let Q be the impulsive action at the joint B in opposite directions on two rods. Also let 2a be the length of each rod and m be the mass, then equations of motion for the rods AB and BC are

$$\left.\begin{aligned} &m(u_1 - 0) && \text{...(1)} \\ &m\cdot\frac{1}{3}a^2\omega_1 = (P - Q)a, && \text{...(2)} \end{aligned}\right\} \textit{for the rod AB}$$

$$\left.\begin{aligned} &\text{And } m\mu_2 = Q && \text{...(3)} \\ &\text{and } m\frac{1}{3}a^2\omega_2 = Qa && \text{...(4)} \end{aligned}\right\} \textit{for the rod BC.}$$

But the rods are connected at B so the velocity of B, as deduced from each rod must be equal,

$$\textit{i.e. } u_1 - a\omega_1 = -(u_2 + a\omega_2) \Rightarrow u_1 = \frac{5P}{4m}; a\omega_1 = \frac{9P}{4m} \qquad \text{...(5)}$$

$$\therefore \frac{\text{velocity of A}}{\text{velocity of B}} = \frac{u_1 + a\omega_2}{u_1 - a\omega_1} = \frac{\frac{5P}{4m} + \frac{9P}{4m}}{\frac{5P}{4m} - \frac{9P}{4m}} = -\frac{7}{2} = -3\frac{1}{2}$$

$\Rightarrow$ velocity of A = $3\frac{1}{2}$ times the velocity of B.

MOTION IN TWO DIMENSIONS

Introduction : *To obtain the equation of motion of a rigid body under impulsive forces.*

By 3.01, when forces are finite, the equations of motion are given by

$$M\frac{d^2x_G}{dt^2} = \Sigma X \quad i.e. \quad \frac{d}{dt}\left(M\frac{dx_G}{dt}\right) = \Sigma X \qquad ...(i)$$

$$M\frac{d^2y_G}{dt^2} = \Sigma Y \text{ i.e } \frac{d}{dt}\left(M\frac{dy_G}{dt}\right) = \Sigma Y \qquad ...(ii)$$

and $$Mk^2\,\ddot{\theta} = \Sigma(x'Y - y'X) \quad i.e. \quad \frac{d}{dt}(Mk^2\dot{\theta}) = \Sigma(x'Y - y'X) \qquad ...(iii)$$

where (x_G, y_G) are the co-ordinates of the centre of gravity.

When large forces act for a very short time then we say that the forces are impulsive.

Again when the forces are impulsive, let τ be the short time during which the impulsive forces act on the body.

Then integrating (i), we have $\left[M\frac{dx_G}{dt}\right]_0^\tau = \Sigma\left\{\int_0^\tau X dt\right\}$

$$i.e. \left[M\frac{dx_G}{dt}\right]_0^\tau = \Sigma X', \text{ where } X' = \int_0^\tau X dt \qquad ...(iv)$$

is the impulse acting at the point (x, y) parallel to x-axis.

Now let u_G and u'_G be the velocities, of the C.G., parallel to x-axis, just before and just after the application of the impulsive forces, then evaluating (iv), we get

$$M(u'_G - V_G) = \Sigma X' \qquad ...(v)$$

is the impulse acting at the point (x, y) parallel to x-axis.

Now let u_G and u'_G be the velocities, of the C.G., parallel to x-axis, just before and just after the application of the impulsive forces, then evaluating (iv), we get

$$M(u'_G - v_G) = \Sigma X' \qquad ...(v)$$

Integrating (ii), we have

$$\left[M\frac{dy}{dt}\right]_0^\tau = \Sigma\left\{\int_0^\tau Y\,dt\right\} = \Sigma Y',$$

where $$Y' = \int_0^\tau Y\,dt \qquad ...(vi)$$

i.e. $M(v' - u) = SY'$

where v_G, V'_G are the velocities of the centre of gravity just, before and after, the application of the impulsive forces.

Hence we conclude that change in the momentum of the mass M, supposed collected at the centre of gravity, in the direction is equal to the sum of the impulses in that direction.

Also $$\left[Mk^2\dot{\theta}\right]_0^\tau = \Sigma\left[x'\int_0^\tau Ydt - y'\int_0^\tau Xdt\right]$$

i.e. $$\left[Mk^2\dot{\theta}\right]_0^\tau = \Sigma(x'Y' - y'X') \quad \text{...(viii)}$$

Now let ω and ω′ be the angular velocities of the body just before and after the application of the impulsive forces, then ...(vii)

$$\Rightarrow \quad M k^2 (\omega' - \omega) = \Sigma (x'Y' - y'X') \quad \text{...(viii)}$$

This equation (viii) **states** that change in the moment of momentum about the centre of gravity is equal to the sum of the moments of the impulses of the forces about the centre of gravity.

WORK DONE BY AN IMPULSE

A body whose mass is M, is acted upon at a given point P by a blow of impulse X. If V and V_1 be the velocities of P in the direction of X just before and just after the action of X, show that the change in the kinetic energy of the body, that is the work done on it by the impulse, is

$$\frac{1}{2}(V + V_1)X.$$

Proof:

The section of the body through the direction of the impulse and through the centre of gravity G, of the body. Now take a line through G parallel to the direction of X as x-axis and another line through G, perpendicular Gx as y-axis.

Just before the impulse, let u and v be the velocities of G parallel to x-axis and y-axis respectively and ω the angular velocity about G. Similarly let u_1, v_1, ω_1 be the corresponding quantities, just after the action of the impulse.

Now consider a point $P \equiv (\lambda, y)$, where the impulse X is imparted, and let M be the mass of the body.

Hence equations of motion of the body are :

$$M(u_1 - u) = X \quad \text{...(1)}$$

$$M(v_1 - v) = 0 \quad \text{...(2)}$$

and $\quad Mk^2 (\omega_1 - \omega) = - y X. \quad$ ...(3)

Thus change in K.E. $= \frac{1}{2}M\left[u_1^2 + v_1^2 + k^2\omega_1^2\right] - \frac{1}{2}M\left(\omega_1^2 - \omega^2\right)$

$$= \frac{1}{2}M\left(u_1^2 - u^2\right) + \frac{1}{2}M\left(v_1^2 - v^2\right) + \frac{1}{2}M\left(\omega_1^2 - \omega^2\right)$$

$$= \frac{1}{2}M\left(u_1^2 - u^2\right) + \frac{1}{2}(u_1 + u)X - \frac{1}{2}yX(\omega_1 + \omega)$$

[using (1), (2) and (3)]

$$= \frac{1}{2}M\left(u_1^2 - u^2\right) + \frac{1}{2}X[(u_1 - y\omega_1) + (u - y\omega)] = \frac{1}{2}X(V_1 + V)$$

$\because$ V = velocity of the point P parallel to GX, before

$$\left[\begin{array}{l}\text{the impulse} = \text{velocity of G parallel GX} + \\ \text{velocity of P relative G} \Rightarrow V = u - y\omega \\ \text{Similarly, } V_1 = u_1 - y\omega_1\end{array}\right]$$

Theorem:

A rod, of length 2a, is held in a position inclined at an angle α to the vertical, and is that let fall on a smooth inelastic horizontal plane.

Show that the end which hits the plane will leave it immediately after the impact, if the height through which the rods falls is greater than,

$$\frac{1}{18}\ a \sec \alpha \text{ cose } c^2 \alpha\ (1 + 3 \sin^2 \alpha)^2.$$

Proof:

Let v be the vertical velocity of the rod AB just before the impact when the rod is inclined at an angle α to the vertical. Let R be the impulsive reaction of the plane and mg the weight of the rod.

Just after the impact of the end A, let V be the velocity of G and ω be its angular velocity. Just after the impact the inclination of the rod also remains α to the vertical.

Now change in momentum = impulse

$\Rightarrow$ m (V – v) = – R ...(i)

and change in moment of momentum about the centre of gravity G = moment of impulse R about G.

$$\Rightarrow \frac{m^2 a\omega}{3} = Ra \sin \alpha \qquad \text{...(ii)}$$

Also, since the end A does not rebound after impact (since the plane is inelastic), we have vertical velocity of the end A = 0.

$$\Rightarrow V - a\omega \sin \alpha = 0 \qquad \text{...(iii)}$$

Whence eliminating V and R between (i), (ii) and (iii), we get

$$\omega = \frac{3V \sin \alpha}{a\left(1 + 3\sin^2 \alpha\right)} \qquad \text{...(iv)}$$

Now assume that after impact, the end A remains in contact with the plane and AB moving about A. When the rod is inclined at θ to the vertical, let S be the normal reaction. Now vertical height of G above the plane is a cos θ motion is under finite forces S and mg.

$$\therefore S - mg = \frac{d^2}{dt^2}(a \cos \theta) \qquad \text{...(v)}$$

and $$m = \frac{a^2}{3}\ddot{\theta} \qquad \text{...(vi)}$$

$$\therefore m = \frac{a^2}{3}\ddot{\theta} - mg\ a \sin \theta = -\ ma^2 \sin \theta \left[\sin \theta \ddot{\theta} + \cos \theta \dot{\theta}^2\right]$$

[eliminating S between (v) and (vi)]

i.e. $$m\frac{a^2}{3}\ddot{\theta}\ (1 + 3 \sin^2 \theta) = mg\, a \sin \theta - ma^2 \sin \theta \cos \theta \dot{\theta}^2 \qquad \text{...(vii)}$$

Now eliminating $\ddot{\theta}$ between (vii) and (vi), we get

$Sa \sin \theta\ (1 + 3 \sin^2 \theta) = mg\ a \sin \theta \cos \theta\ \dot{\theta}^2$.

Initially, when $\theta = \alpha, \dot{\theta} = \omega$ and S = R

$\therefore Ra \sin \alpha\ (1 + 3 \sin^2 \alpha) = mg\alpha \sin \alpha - ma^2 \sin \alpha \cos \alpha\ \omega^2$

At this time, the end A will leave the plane, if R is negative, *i.e.* if $ma^2 \sin \alpha \cos a\omega^2 > mga \sin \alpha$

$$\Rightarrow \omega^2 > \frac{g}{a \cos \alpha} \Rightarrow \frac{9v^2 \sin^2 \alpha}{a^2\left(a + 3\sin^2 \alpha\right)^2} > \frac{g}{a \cos \alpha'}$$

$$\therefore \frac{v^2}{2g} > \frac{1}{18} a \sec \alpha \operatorname{cosec}^2 \alpha (1 + 3\sin^2 ga)^2,$$

⇒ height through which the rod falls is greater than

$\frac{1}{18} a \sec \alpha \operatorname{cosec}^2 \alpha\ (1 + 3 \sin^2 \alpha)^2$.

AN IMPERFECTLY ELASTIC SPHERE IMPINGING ON A FIXED PLANE

An imperfectly elastic uniform sphere, rotating with an angular velocity ω about an axis perpendicular to the plane of motion of its centre, impinges on a horizontal plane, find the resulting change in its motion.

First of all Assume that the Plane is Rough Enough to Prevent Any Sliding

Let u and v be the components of the linear velocities in the two assigned directions and ω the angular velocity just before impact while u′,v′ be the components and ω′ the angular velocity after the impact.

Let F be the impulsive friction and R the normal impulsive reaction, then the equation of motion are :

$$m(u' - u) = -F \qquad ...(1)$$

$$m(v' + v) = R \qquad ...(2)$$

and $$mk^2(\omega' - \omega) = Fa \qquad ...(3)$$

Since P, the point of contact is instantaneously reduced to rest, there being no sliding hence

$$u' - aw' = 0 \qquad ...(4)$$

Also by Newton's law

$$v' = ev \qquad ...(5)$$

where e is the coefficient of restitution. Thus, we obtain

$$u' = a\omega' = \frac{1}{7}(5u + 2a\omega) \qquad ...(6)$$

and $$F = \frac{2}{7}m(u - a\omega) \qquad ...(7)$$

Case (i) If u = a ω then F = 0, *i.e.* there is no frictional force,

Hence u = u′ and ω = ω′

which shows that u and w are unchanged. $\left(\because k^2 = \frac{2a^2}{5}\right)$

Case (ii) If u<aω, F is – ive, *i.e.* F, acts $(\rightarrow)$. Hence ω′<ω and u′>u.

Since u>a ω, the velocity of the point of contact P (= u – aω) is negative *i.e.* the direction is $(\leftarrow)$ and the angular velocity is decreased after impact.

Case (iii) If u> aω, F is + ive, *i.e.* F, acts $(\leftarrow)$. Hence w′>ω and u′ <u. Hence when the point of contact before impact is moving →, the angular velocity is increased, the horizontal velocity is diminished.

i.e. in this case the sign of ω is changed, so we have

$$u' = a\omega' = \frac{1}{7}(5u - 2a\omega), \qquad ...(8)$$

$$\text{and } F = \frac{2}{7}m(u + a\omega) \qquad ...(9)$$

Now there are further two cases.

(i) If $u = \frac{2}{5}a\omega$, then $u' = 0 = w'$ *i.e.* after the impact the sphere rebounds from the plane vertically with no spin.

(ii) If $u < \frac{2}{5}a\omega$, t then u¢ is + ive. and the sphere rebounds towards the direction from which it came. In both the above cases, vertical velocity after impact is $v' = ev$ and $R = m(1 + e)u$.

Case of Pure Rolling

In the case of pure rolling, we must have $F < \mu R$ in order that the point of contact may be instantaneous brought to rest

$$i.e. \ \frac{2}{7}(u - a\omega) < \mu(1 + e)v. \qquad ...(A)$$

But, if $\frac{2}{7}(u - a\omega) > \mu(1 + e)v$, the friction is not sufficient to bring the point of contact P to instantaneous rest, and hence in this case equation (4) will not hold good. Also instead of F, *we shall write the maximum frictional force* ⇒ , $(u' - u) = \mu R$...(A)

$$m(v' + v) = R \qquad ...(B)$$

$$\text{and} \quad mk^2(\omega' - \omega) = mRa \qquad ...(C)$$

$$\therefore u' = u - \mu v(1 + e), \ v' = ev \ \text{ and } \omega' = \omega + \frac{5\mu}{2a}v(1 + e) \qquad ...(D)$$

In case (iv) $F < \mu R$ so that the friction may be sufficient to bring the point of contact to rest.

$$\Rightarrow \frac{2}{7}(u + a\omega) < \mu v(1 + e).$$

$$\text{But if } \frac{2}{7}(u + a\omega) > \mu v(1 + e). \qquad ...(E)$$

The friction will be insufficient and then we have similar type of equations (A), (B), (C) with sign of ω changed. Solving these we get

$m' = u - \mu v(1 + e)$, $v' = ev$ and

$$\omega' = \frac{5\mu}{2a} v(1+e) - \omega.$$

Hence by virtue of (E), it will be possible for u to be less than μv $(1 + e)$, if ω be large enough. Hence if the ball is sufficiently large enough, under-cut u' can be negative *i.e.* the ball rebounds.

SOLVED EXAMPLES

Example 1:

Three equal rods, AB, BC, CD are freely jointed and placed in a straight line on a smooth table. The rod AB is struck at its end A by a blow which is perpendicular to the length; find the resulting motion and show that the velocity of the centre of AB is 19 times that of CD, and its angular velocity 11 times that of CD.

Solution:

Let P be the impulse of the blow applied at A and let (u_1, ω_1) (u_2, ω_2) (u_3, ω_3) be the velocities angular velocities of the rods AB, B C, CD respectively just after the blow.

Again let Q and R be the impulsive reactions at B and C respectively, then we have

$$mu_1 = P + Q \quad ...(1)$$

$$m\frac{a^2}{3}\omega_1 = (P - Q)a \quad ...(2) \quad \text{[for the rod AB]}$$

$$mu_1 = -R + Q \quad ...(3)$$

$$m\frac{a^2}{3}\omega_2 = (Q + R)a \quad ...(4) \quad \text{[for the rod BC]}$$

$$mu_3 = R \quad ...(5)$$

$$-m\frac{a^2}{3}\omega_3 = -Ra \quad \text{[for the rod CD]} \quad ...(6)$$

As the rods are connected at B and C, the velocity of B as considered from AB = the velocity of A as considered from BC.

$\Rightarrow$ velocity of G_1 + velocity of B relative to G_1

= velocity of G_2 + velocity of B relative to G_2.

$$\Rightarrow -u_1 + a\omega_1 = u_2 + a\omega_2 \quad ..(7)$$

Similarly for C, we have $a\omega_2 = u_2 = a\omega_3 + u_3$ ...(8)

Now from (7) and {(1) to (4)}, we easily obtain

$$3(P - Q)(-(P + Q) = 3(R + Q) + Q - R)$$

$\Rightarrow 2P = 8Q + 2R \Rightarrow P = 4Q + R$ ...(9)

Also from (8) and {(3) to (6)},

we get 3 (Q + R) – (– R + Q) = 3R + R ⇒ Q = – 4R

from (9) and (10), we get easily P = – 15R and Q = – 4R.

$$\therefore \frac{\text{velocity of } G_1}{\text{velocity of } G_3} = \frac{u_1}{u_3} = \frac{15R + 4R}{R} = 19$$

$$\text{and } \frac{\text{angular velocity of AB}}{\text{angular velocity of CD}} = \frac{\omega_1}{\omega_3} = \frac{3(15R + 4R)}{3R} = 11$$

Example 2:

Two equal uniform rods, AB and BC, are freely jointed at B and turn about a smooth joint at A. When the rods are in a straight line, ω being the angular velocity of AB and u the velocity of the centre of mass of BC, BC impinges on a fixed inelastic obstacle at point D, show that the rods are instantaneously brought to rest if $BC = 2a\,\dfrac{2u - a\omega}{3u + 2a\omega'}$ where 2a is the length of either rod.

Solution:

when the rods AB and BC are in a straight, line, ω is the angular velocity of AB and u the velocity of G_2 the centre of gravity of BC, and let ω_1 be the angular velocity of BC about G_2 before impinging on an inelastic obstacle at D, such that BC = x.

There will be an impulsive reaction between the two rods at B denoted by Q acting on opposite directions as marked. Bow the velocity of B as deduced from AB = the velocity of B as deduced from BC.

$\Rightarrow 2a\omega$ = velocity of G_2 + velocity of B relative to $G_2 = (u - a\omega_1)$

Take moments about A to remove the unknown reaction at A, we get

$$m \cdot \frac{4}{3} a^2 \omega = -Q \cdot 2a \Rightarrow m\frac{2a\omega}{3} = -Q \quad \text{...(1)}$$

For the rod BC, we get mu = – (P – Q) ...(2)

$$\text{and} \qquad m\frac{a^2}{3}\omega_1 = -\{P(x - a) + Qa\} \quad \text{...(3)}$$

$$\therefore (2)\text{and}(3) \Rightarrow m\left(u + \frac{a}{3}\omega_1\right) = -P - P\frac{(x - a)}{x} = -\frac{Px}{a} \quad \text{...(4)}$$

$$\text{Also (2) and (1), imply} - P = \left(mu + \frac{2ma\omega}{3}\right)$$

With this substitution in equation (4), we readily obtain

$$\frac{x}{a}\left(u+\frac{2a\omega}{3}\right)=\left(u+\frac{a}{3}\omega_1\right)=\left[u+\frac{(u-2a\omega)}{3}\right]$$

$$\Rightarrow \frac{x}{a}\left(\frac{3u+2a\omega}{3}\right)=\left(\frac{4u-2a\omega}{3}\right)=\frac{2(2u-a\omega)}{3}\Rightarrow x=\frac{2a(2u-a\omega)}{(3u+2aw)}$$

Example 3:

A disc of any form moving in its plane without rotation with velocity V at right angles to a fixed plane strikes the plane so that the distances of its centre of gravity from the point of impact and from the plane are r and p. Assuming the plane to be elastic and sufficiently rough to prevent sliding, show that the impulsive pressure and friction are respectively

$$\frac{m(1+e)V(p^2+k^2)}{r^2+k^2} \text{ and } \frac{m(1+e)Vp(r^2-p^2)^{1/2}}{r^2+k^2};$$

where k is the radius of gyration. Also show that loss of kinetic energy is

$$\frac{1}{2}\frac{m(1+e^2)(K^2+p^2)V^2}{(r^2+k^2)};$$

Solution:

Let the disc strike the horizontal plane at K. Before the impact, V is the vertical velocity of G. After the impact let (u, v, w) be the velocities and angular velocity of the disc. Angular velocity of K relative to G is r ω perp. to GK where GK = r.

Now equations of motion are,

$m\,[v-(-V)\,R$ ...(1)

$mu = F$ ...(2)

$mk^1\,\omega = -\,Fp + R\,r\sin\theta$

or $mk^2\,\omega = -\,Fp + R\sqrt{(r^2-p^2)}$ ...(3)

p being the perp. from G on the tangent at K.

Also since there is no sliding.

∴ tangential velocity of the point K = velocity of G + Velocity of K relative to G.

$= u - \frac{p}{r}(\omega r) = 0 \Rightarrow u - p\omega = 0$ ...(4)

Also Newton's rule (V = ev) $\Rightarrow v + \sqrt{(r^2-p^2)}\,\omega = eV$ ...(5)

Now eliminating u, ω from (4) with the help of (2) and (3), we readily obtain

$$\frac{F}{m}=p\left(-\frac{Fp}{mk^2}+\frac{R\sqrt{r^2-p^2}}{mk^2}\right)\Rightarrow\frac{F}{m}\left(1+\frac{p^2}{k^2}\right)=\frac{Rp\sqrt{r^2-p^2}}{mk^2}$$

$$\Rightarrow F\left(k^2+p^2\right)=Rp\sqrt{r^2-P^2} \qquad ...(6)$$

$$\text{Now } \frac{R}{m}-V+\sqrt{\left(r^2-p^2\right)}\left\{-\frac{Fp}{mk^2}+\frac{R\left(r^2-p^2\right)}{mk^2}\right\}=eV$$

$$\text{Now } \frac{R}{m}-V+\sqrt{\left(r^2-p^2\right)}\left\{-\frac{Fp}{mk^2}+\frac{R\sqrt{r^2-p^2}}{mk^2}\right\}=eV$$

[putting the values of v, ω in (5) from (1)].

$$\text{This gives, } \frac{R}{m}\left\{1+\frac{r^2-p^2}{k^2}\right\}-\frac{Rp\sqrt{\left(r^2-p^2\right)}}{mk^2}=V(1+e)$$

$$\Rightarrow\frac{R}{mk^2}\left[k^2+r^2-p^2\right]-\frac{Fp^2\left(r^2-p^2\right)}{\left(k^2+p^2\right)mk^2}=V(1+e)$$

$$\Rightarrow R=\frac{mV(1+e)\cdot\left(k^2+p^2\right)}{k^2+r^2}.$$

Second part

$$\therefore F=\frac{Rp\sqrt{\left(r^2-p^2\right)}}{k^2+p^2}=\frac{mV(1+e)\sqrt{\left(r^2-p^2\right)}}{k^2+r^2}p \qquad \text{[using (6)]}$$

$\therefore$ loss of K.E. $=\frac{1}{2}R$ (velocity of the point K in the direction of impulse before impact + the velocity after impact)

$$=\frac{1}{2}R\left[V-tV\right]=\frac{1}{2}(1-e)RV=E \text{ say}$$

[$\because$ velocity in the direction of F is zero, hence loss of K.E. in that direction is zero].

$$\Rightarrow E=\frac{1}{2}mv^2\left(1-e^2\right)\frac{k^2+p^2}{k^2+r^2} \qquad \text{[putting the value of R]}$$

Example 4:

Four freely jointed rods, of the same material and thickness, form a reactable of sides 2a and 2b and of mass M' When lying in this form on a horizontal plane, an inelastic particle of mass M moving with velocity V in a direction perp. to the rod of length 2a impinges on it at a distance c from its centre. Show that the K.E. lost in the impact is

$$\frac{1}{2}V^2 \div \left[\frac{1}{M}+\frac{1}{M'}\left(1+\frac{3a+3b}{a+3b}\frac{c^2}{a^2}\right)\right]$$

Solution:

Let AB be a rod of length 2b and mass m_2 and BC of length 2a and mass m_1. Let u be the linear velocity of G_1, the C.G. of BC, and w the angular velocity just after the action of the impulse (*i.e* when the particle of mass M strikes at E such that (G_1E = c). Let I be the impulse applied. Obviously the rods AB and CD will not rotate and remain parallel.

Now velocity of AB = velocity of B = velocity of G_1 + velocity of B rel. to G_1 = u – aω Velocity of CD = velocity of C = velocity of G_1 + velocity of C rel. to G_1 = u + aω and the velocity of the point E just after the blow

= Velocity of G_2 + velocity of E rel. to G_1 = u + cω.

(Since the a.v of BC is in opposite direction to the AD)

we also have

$$\frac{m_1}{2a}=\frac{m_2}{2b}=\frac{m_1+m_2}{2(a+b)}=\frac{M'}{4(a-b)}\left(\because m_1+m_2=\frac{M'}{2}\right).$$

Now equation of motion for the system (all the four rods) is

$$M'u = I \qquad ...(1)$$

and for the particle, of mass M, we have M (V – u – c ω) = I ...(2)

Taking moment of momentum about G, the centre for all the rods, we have

$$b+m_1\frac{a^2}{3}\omega - m_1ub + m_1\frac{a^2}{3}\omega - m_2(u-a\omega)a + m_2a(u+c\omega) = Ic$$

$$\Rightarrow 2\left(m_1\frac{a^2}{3}\omega + 2m_2a^2\omega\right) = Ic \Rightarrow \frac{2a^2\omega}{3}[m_1+3m_2] = Ic$$

$$\Rightarrow \frac{a^2\omega}{3}\left[\frac{M'a+3M'b}{(a+b)}\right] = cM(V-c\omega-u).$$

[putting the value of I and m_1, m_2]

$$\Rightarrow \frac{M'a^2\omega}{3}\cdot\frac{a+3b}{a+b} = cM(V-c\omega-u)$$

using (1) and (2), we get $M'u = M(V - c\omega - u)$ ...(3)

$$\Rightarrow (M + M')u = MV - Mc\omega$$

Now putting the value of in (3) from (4), we obtain

$$M'\frac{a^2}{3}\omega \cdot \frac{a+3b}{a+b} = cM\,(V - c\,\omega) - \frac{cM^2(V - c\omega -)}{M + M'}$$

$$= c\,M\,(V - c\,w)\,M + M' - M)\,/\,(M + M') = \frac{cMM'(V - c\omega)}{(M + M')}$$

$$\Rightarrow c\omega\left[\frac{M}{M + M'} + \frac{a^2}{3c^2}\frac{a+3b}{a+b}\right] = \frac{VM}{M + M'}$$

$$\Rightarrow c\omega = \frac{MVK}{M(1+K) + M'} \quad \text{where } K = \frac{3c^2}{a^2}\frac{a+b}{(a+3b)}$$

$$\therefore\ (M + M')\,u = M\left[v - \frac{MVK}{M(1+K) + M'}\right] = \frac{(M + M')MV}{M(1+K) + M'}$$

$$\Rightarrow u = \frac{MV}{M(1+K) + M'}$$

Now loss of K.E. = loss of the energy of the four rods + loss of energy of the particle.

$$\frac{1}{2}I\cdot\left[V + (u + c\omega)\right] - \frac{1}{2}I.(u + c\omega) = E \text{ say}$$

[∴ *Impulse on the particle and rod is equal and opposite*]

$$\therefore E = \frac{1}{2}I.\,V = \frac{1}{2}V.\,M[V - (u + c\omega)]$$

$$= \frac{1}{2}\frac{MM'V^2}{M(1+K) + M'} = \frac{v^2}{2\left[\frac{1}{M} + \frac{1}{M'}\left\{1 + \frac{3c^2}{a^2}\frac{(a+b)}{(a+3b)}\right\}\right]}$$

Example 5:

AB, BC, CD three equal uniform rods hinged freely at B and C are lying on a smooth horizontal table, so that ABC and BCD are at right angles on opposite sides of BC. A blow is given to A in the direction AC, prove that D begins to move in a direction $\tan^{-1}\left(\frac{7}{4}\right)$ with CD.

Solution:

Let P be the impulse applied at A in the direction of AC. *Before impulse* the system is at rest. *After impulse,* let the velocity of G_1, the centre of gravity of AB, be (u_1, v_1) and the angular velocity of this rod AB be ω_1. Similarly the angular velocities of the other rods BC and CD are ω_2 and w_3 respectively.

Hence, we obtain

velocity of B along AB = u_1 ...(1)

velocity if B perp. to AB = velocity of G_1 + velocity of B rela. to

$G_1 = v_1 + a\omega_1$ ...(2)

velocity of G_2 along AB = velocity of B + velocity of G_2 relative to

$B = u_1 - a\omega_2$ ...(3)

velocity of G_2 perp. to AB = the same as that of $G_1 = v_1 + a\omega_1$ ...(4)

velocity of C along AB = velocity of B + velocity of C relative to

$B = u_1 - 2a\omega_2$ ...(5)

velocity of C perp. to AB = the same as that of G_2

or $G_1 = v_1 + a\omega_1$ ... (6)

velocity of G_3 along AB = the same as that of C = $u_1 - 2a\omega_2$ ...(7)

velocity of G_3 perp. to AB = velocity of G_2 + velocity of G_3 relative to

$G_2 = v_1 + a\omega_1 + a\omega_3$ ...(8)

velocity of D along AB = the same as C = $u_1 - 2a\omega_2$ ...(9)

velocity of D perp, to AB = velocity of C + velocity of D relative to

$C = v_1 + a\omega_1 + 2a\omega_3 + a\omega_3$ ...(10)

Taking moments about C for the rod CD, we have

$$\frac{1}{3}a^2\omega_2 + a(v_1 + a\omega_1 + a\omega_3) = 0 \Rightarrow 3v_1 + 3a\omega_3 = 0 \quad ...(11)$$

Again taking moments about B for the rods BC and CD, we get

$$\frac{1}{3}a^2\omega_3 + a^2\omega_2 - 2a(u_1 - a\omega_2) = 0 \quad ...(12)$$

$$\Rightarrow \frac{a^2}{3}\omega_2 - 2a(u_1 - 2a\omega_2) - a(u_1 - a\omega_2) = 0 \quad \{\text{using (11)}\}$$

$$\Rightarrow 9u_1 - 16a\,\omega_2 = 0 \quad ...(13)$$

For all the rods, taking moments about A, we get

$$\frac{1}{3}a^2(\omega_1 + \omega_2 + \omega_3) - 2a(u_1 - 2a\omega_2) + 3a(v_1 + a\omega_1 + a\omega_3)$$

$$-(u_1 - a\omega_2) + 2a\,(v_1 + a\omega_1) + av_1 = 0 \quad ...(14)$$

$$\Rightarrow 15v_1 + 13a\omega_1 + 6a\omega_3 = 0 \quad ...(15)$$

Now resolving all the velocities perpendicular to AB, we have

$$\left(u_1 \cos 45^0 - v_1 \cos 45^0\right) + (u_1 - a\omega_2)\cos 45^0 - (v_1 + a\omega_1)\cos 45^0$$
$$+\left(u_1 - 2a\omega_2\right)\cos 45^0 - (V_1 + a\omega_1 + a\omega_3)\cos 45^0 = 0$$

or $3(u_1 - v_1) - 2a\omega_1 - 3a\omega_2 - aw_2 = 0$ ...(16)

If the direction of motion of D makes an angle θ with DC, then obtain

$$\tan\theta = \frac{v_1 + a\omega_1 + 2a\omega_2}{u_1 - 3a\omega_2} = \frac{3}{-\frac{2a\omega_2}{9}} = -3\left(\frac{\omega_3}{\omega_2}\right) \text{ [using (11) and (13)]}$$

From equation (11) and (15), we get

$$\frac{v_1}{-17} = \frac{a\omega_1}{21} = \frac{a\omega_2}{-3} \Rightarrow v_1 = \frac{17a\omega_3}{3}; a\omega_1 = -7a\omega_3$$

Putting these values in (16 and making use of (13), we have

$$\frac{16a\omega_2}{3} - 17a\omega_3 + 14a\omega_3 - 3a\omega_2 - a\omega_3 = 0$$

$$\Rightarrow \frac{7a\omega_2}{3} = 4aw_3 \Rightarrow \frac{3\omega_3}{\omega_2} = \frac{7}{4}$$

$$\therefore \tan\theta = -\frac{3\omega_3}{\omega_2} = -\frac{7}{4}$$

Example 6:

AB and Cd are two equal similar rods connected by a string BC; AB, BC and CD form three sides fo the square. The point A of the rod AB is struck by a blow in a direction perp. to the rod, show that the initial velocity of A is seven times that of D.

Solution:

Let u_1 be the velocity of G_1, the C.G. of AB and ω_1 the angular velocity of AB and u_2, ω_2 those of CD.

As a matter of fact, the initial motion of B must be perp. to Ab, so that the tension in the string at B must be along BC.

Let P be the impulse applied at A perp. to AB, then we have

$$mu_1 = P + T \quad ...(1)$$

$$m\frac{a^2}{3}\omega_1 = (P - T)a \quad ...(2)$$

$$mu_2 = T; \quad ...(3)$$

$$m\frac{a^2}{3}\omega_3 = T.a \quad ...(4)$$

As AB and CD are connected by a string, the velocity of B = the velocity of C

$\Rightarrow a_1\ \omega - u_1 = u_2 + a\omega_2$ ...(5)

Substituting the values of u_1, ω_1, u_2, ω_2,.

[From (1) to (4) in (5), we have 3 (P – T) – (P + T) = T + 3T ⇒ T = (P/4)

$$\therefore \frac{\text{initial velocity of A}}{\text{initial velocity of D}} = \frac{u_1 + a\omega_1}{a\omega_2 - u_2} = \frac{\frac{5T}{m} + \frac{9T}{m}}{\frac{3T}{m} - \frac{T}{m}} = \frac{7}{1}.$$

Example 7:

A light rod ABC has three particles each of mass m attached to it at A, B, C. The rod is struck by a blow P at right angles to it is a point, distant from A equal to BC. Prove that the K.E. set up is

$$\frac{1}{2}\frac{P^2(a^2 - ab + b^2)}{m(a^2 + ab + b^2)} \quad \textit{where } AB = a,\ BC = b.$$

Solution:

Let the three particles each of mass m be placed at A, B, C of a light rod ABC, and let the impulse P be applied at O such that AO = BC = b, where AB = a, BC = b.

Let u be the velocity of C and ω, the angular velocity of the rod just after the blow, then the velocity of B is u + bω, the velocity of A is u + (a + b) ω and the velocity of the point O at which the impulse is applied is u + aω. Since the system was at rest initially, the velocity of O just before the impact is zero.

Now equation the total momentum per. to rod, to the impulse, we have

$$mu + m(u + b\omega) + m\{u + (a + b)\omega\} = P \Rightarrow 3u + \omega(a + 2b) = \frac{P}{m}$$

Also taking moments about O, we easily obtain

$$\{u + (a + b)\}\,b - m(u + b\,\omega)(a - b) - mua = 0$$

$$\Rightarrow u(a - b) = b^2\omega.$$

$$\therefore \frac{u}{b^2} = \frac{\omega}{a - b} \Rightarrow \frac{3u + (a + 2ab)\omega}{3b^2 + (a + 2b)(a - b)} = \frac{(P/m)}{(a^2 + ab + b^2)}$$

$$\Rightarrow u = \frac{b^2}{a^2 + ab + b^2}\frac{P}{m} \text{ and } \omega = \frac{(a - b)}{(a^2 + ab + b^2)}\frac{P}{m}$$

$$\text{K.E. set up} = \frac{1}{2} P \text{ (velocity of the point O)} = \frac{1}{2} \frac{P^2\left(a^2+b^2-ab\right)}{m\left(a^2+b^2+ab\right)}$$

Aliter. $\text{K.E.} = \frac{1}{2} m \{u + (a + b)\omega\}^2 + (u + b\omega)^2 + u^2]$

$$= \frac{1}{2}\frac{P^2}{m}\left[\frac{a^2}{\left(a^2+ab+b^2\right)}+\frac{a^2b^2+b^4}{\left(a^2+b^2+ab\right)^2}\right]$$

but $u + (a + b)\omega = \dfrac{a^2}{a^2+ab+b^2}\dfrac{P}{m}$ and $u + b\omega = \dfrac{ab}{a^2+ab+b^2}\dfrac{P}{m}$

$$\therefore \text{K.E.} = \frac{1}{2}\frac{P^2}{m}\left[\frac{(a^2+b^2)^2-a^2b^2}{(a^2+b^2+ab)^2}\right] = \frac{1}{2}\frac{P^2}{m}\frac{(a^2+b^2-ab)}{(a^2+b^2+ab)}$$

Revision at a Glance

(i) If u and u¢ are the velocities of the C.G. parallel to x axis, just before and just after application of the impulsive forces, then we have

$M(u' - u) = \Sigma X'$, Similarly $M(v' - v) = \Sigma Y'$.

⇒ change in momentum of mass, supposed collected at the centre of gravity, in any direction is equal to the sum of the impulses in that direction.

(ii) If ω, ω' be the angular velocities of the body just before and just after the application of the impulsive forces, then we have

$Mk^2(\omega' - \omega) = S(x'Y' - y'X')$

⇒ change in moment of momentum about the centre gravity is equal to the sum of the moments of the impulses of the forces about the centre of gravity.

Example 8:

Two uniform rods AB and BC are freely joined at B and laid on a horizontal table. AB is struck by a horizontal blow of impulse P in a direction perpendicular to AB at a distance c form its centre; the length of AB, BC being 2a and 2b and their masses M′ find the motion immediately after the blow.

Solution:

Let u_1, u_2 be the velocity of G_1 and G_2, the centres of gravity of the rods aB and BC respectively, and w_1, w_2 be the angular velocities of the rods just after blow. Let D be a point in AB where the impulse P is imparted, and $DG_1 = c$.

Before the impulse, the rods are at rest. There will be an impulsive action at B between the two rods AB and BC when the blow is struck. Let this action Q in opposite directions on the two rods, then for the motion of AB, we have

$$M\,(u_1 - 0) = P - Q \qquad ...(1)$$

and $M\dfrac{a^2}{3}\omega_1 = Pc - Qa \qquad ...(2)$

and for the motion of BC, we have

$$M'\,(u_2 - 0) = Q...(3)$$

and $M'\dfrac{a^2}{3}\omega_2 = -Qb \qquad ...(4)$

Now as the rods are connected at B, the velocity of the point of the rods AB is the same as that of the some point B of rod BC.

$\therefore\ u_1 + aw_1 = u_2 - bw_2 \qquad ...(5)$

substituting the values of u_1, w_1; u_2, w_2 from (1), (2), (3), (4) in (5), we have

$$\frac{P-Q}{M} + 3\frac{(Pc-Qa)}{aM} = \frac{Q}{M'} - \frac{3Q}{M'}\left(1+\frac{3c}{a}\right)$$

$$\therefore\ u_1 = \frac{P}{M}\left[1 - \frac{1}{4}\frac{M'}{M+M'}\left(1+\frac{3c}{a}\right)\right] \text{ and}$$

$$\omega_1 = \frac{3P}{Ma}\left[\frac{c}{a} - \frac{1}{4}\frac{M}{M+M'}\left(1+\frac{3c}{a}\right)\right]$$

$$u_1 = \frac{1}{4}\frac{P}{M'+M'}\left(1+\frac{3c}{a}\right) \text{ and}$$

$$\omega_1 = -\frac{3}{4}\frac{P}{b(M+M')}\left(1+\frac{3c}{a}\right)$$

Hence the four quantities which determine the motion have been obtained

Example 9:

Four equal uniform rods, AB BC, and DE are freely joined at B, C and D and lie on a smooth table in the form of a square. The rod AB is struck by a blow at A at right angles to AB from the inside of the square; show that the initial velocity of A is 79 times that of E.

Solution:

Let the impulse applied at A be P from inside, so that u_1, u_2, u_3, u_4 are the velocities of G_1, G_2, G_3 and G_4 in the direction of blow,. Further let w_1

and w_2 be the angular velocities of AB and CD respectively. The angular velocities of BC and DE are zero, because the impulsive reactions upon these two rods are along the rods themselves.

Then we have :

$$\left.\begin{aligned} mu_1 &= P + X_1 \quad \text{...(1)} \\ \text{and}\; m\frac{a^2}{3}\omega_1 &= Pa - X_1 a \quad \text{...(2)} \end{aligned}\right] \quad \text{(for the rod AB)}$$

where AB = 2a and X_1 is the impulsive action at B.

$mu_2 = X_2 - X_1$ (for the rod BC)

Where X_2 is the impulsive action at C.

$$\left.\begin{aligned} mu_3 &= (X_2 + X_3) \quad \text{...(4)} \\ \text{and}\; m\frac{a^2}{3}\omega_3 &= X_1 a - X_3 a \quad \text{...(5)} \end{aligned}\right]$$

where X_3 is the impulsive action at D. $mu_4 = X_3$ (for the rod DE) ...(6)

Now the velocity of the point B as deduced from AB must be equal to the velocity as deduced from BC.

$\therefore\; u_1 - aw_1 = u_2$ ...(7)

Similarly; for the point C, $u_2 = u_3 - a\omega_3$. ...(8)

and for the poind D, $u_3 + a\omega_3 = u_4$. ...(9)

whence substituting the values of u_1, ω_1 and u_2 in (7), we readily obtain

$P + X_1 - 3(P - X_1) = X_2 - X_1$ *i.e.* $5X_2 = 2P$ ...(10)

Also substituting the value of u_1, u_3 and ω_3 and u_4 in (9), we obtain

$X_2 - X_1 = -(X_2 + X_3) = X_3$ *i.e.* $2X_2 - 0$ ...(11)

Finally substituting the values of u_3, ω_3 and u_4 in (9), we obtain

$-(X_2 - X_3) + 3(X_2 - X_3) = X_3$ *i.e.* $2X_2 - 5X_3 = 0$ ...(12)

Solving (11) and (12), we get

$$X_2 = \frac{5}{21}X_1$$

and $$X_3 = \frac{2}{21}X_1 \quad \therefore (10) \Rightarrow 5x_1 - \frac{5}{21}x_1$$

$$= 2P \text{ i.e. } X_1 = \frac{21P}{50}$$

Hence $$X_2 = \frac{P}{10} \text{ and } X_3 = \frac{P}{25}$$

Putting these values in (1), (2) and (6), we get

$$mu_1 = P + \frac{21P}{50}$$

i.e. $u_1 = \frac{71P}{50m}$ and $a\omega_1 = \frac{3}{m}\left(P - \frac{21P}{50}\right)$

i.e. $a\omega_1 = \frac{87P}{50m}$ and $mu_4 = \frac{P}{25}$ *i.e.* $u_4 = \frac{P}{25m}$

$$\Rightarrow \frac{\text{velocity of A}}{\text{velocity of E}} = \frac{u_1 + a\omega_1}{u_4} = \frac{\left(\frac{71P}{50m}\right) + \left(\frac{87P}{50m}\right)}{\left(\frac{P}{25m}\right)} = \frac{79}{1}.$$

Example 10:

Two rods AB and BC; of length 2a and 2b and of masses proportional to their lengths, are freely joined at B are lying in a straight line. A blow is communicated to the end A; show that the resulting kinetic energy when the system is free is to the energy when C is fixed as

$$(4a + 3b)(3a + 4b) : 12(a + b)^2.$$

Solution:

Case I. When the system is free. Let the mass of the unit length be m, then length of the rod AB = 2a ⇒ mass of AB = 2ma; length of the rod BC =2B ⇒ mass of BC = 2mb; Further let G_1 be the C.G. of the rod AB and G_2 that of BC.

Let P be the impulse applied at A at right angles to Ab, then there will be an impulsive action between the two rods at B. Let the impulse be Q, in opposite directions on the two rods AB and BC respectively.

Just after the impulse, let u_1 be the velocity of the centre of gravity of AB and ω_1 its angular velocity; u_2 and ω_2 similar quantities for BC. Since the rods AB, BC are started from rest, the equations of motion of the rod AB are:

$$2mau_1 = P + Q \text{ (motion of } G_1) \quad ...(1)$$

$$\text{and } 2ma\frac{a^2}{3}\omega_1 = (P - Q)a \text{ [taking moment about } G_1] \quad ...(2)$$

Similarly for the motion of BC, $2mbu_2 = Q$ (motion of G_2) ...(3)

$$\text{and } 2mb\frac{b^2}{3}\omega_2 = Qb \text{ [taking a moment about } G_2] \quad ...(4)$$

The rods are connected at B, so the velocity of the point B of the rod AB

= velocity of the point B referred to BC

i.e. $$u_1 - a\omega_1 - u_2 - b\omega_2 \qquad ...(5)$$

Substituting the values for ω_1, u_1; u_2, ω_2 in (5), we get

$$\frac{3(P-Q)}{2a} - \frac{P+Q}{2a} = \frac{Q}{2b} + \frac{3Q}{2b} \Rightarrow Q = \frac{pb}{2(a+b)}$$

$\therefore$ velocity of the point A at which the below has been given

$$= u_1 + a\,\omega_1 = \frac{P+Q}{2am} + \frac{3(P-Q)}{2am} + \frac{P(4a+3b)}{2am(a+b)}$$

Now substituting the value of Q in (1), (2), (3), and (4), we get

$$u_1 = \frac{1}{2ma}\left\{P + \frac{bP}{2(a+b)}\right\} - \frac{(2a+3b)P}{4ma(a+b)},$$

$$a\omega_1 = \frac{3}{2ma}\left\{P - \frac{bP}{(a+b)}\right\} = \frac{3(b+2a)P}{4ma(a+b)},$$

$$u_2 = \frac{1}{2mb}\left\{\frac{bP}{2(a+b)}\right\} = \frac{P}{4ma(a+b)},$$

$$\text{and } b\omega_2 = \frac{3}{2mb}\left\{\frac{bP}{2(a+b)}\right\} = \frac{3P}{4m(a+b)},$$

So in this case total kinetic energy,

= K.E. of the rod AB + K.E. of the rod BC.

$$= \frac{1}{2}\cdot 2ma\left[u_1{}^2 + \frac{a^2\omega_1^2}{3}\right] + \frac{1}{2}\cdot 2mb\left[u^2 + \frac{a^2\omega_1^2}{3}\right]$$

$$= ma\left[\left\{\frac{2a+3b^2P^2}{16m^2a^2(a+b)^2}\right\} + \left\{\frac{3(b+2a)^2P^2}{16m^2a^2(a+b)^2}\right\}\right]$$

$$+ mb\left[\left\{\frac{P^2}{16m^2a^2(a+b)^2}\right\} + \left\{\frac{3P^2}{16m^2(a+b)^2}\right\}\right]$$

$$= ma\left[\frac{(2a+3b)^2P^2}{16m^2a^2(a+b)^2} + \frac{3(b+2a)^2P^2}{16m^2a^2(a+b)^2}\right]$$

$$+ mb\left[\frac{P^2}{16m^2(a+b)^2} + \frac{3P^2}{16m^2(a+b)^2}\right]$$

$$= \frac{P^2(4a+3b)(a+b)}{4ma(a+b)^2} = \frac{(4a+3b)P^2}{4ma(a+b)} = E_1 \text{ say.}$$

Case II. When C is kept fixed.

In this case, for the motion of AB, we get

$$2mau_1 = P + Q. \quad \text{...(1)}$$

and $2ma\frac{a^2}{3}\omega_1 = (P - Q)a$

For the motion of BC, we also have

$$2mb\,\frac{4b^2}{3}\omega_2 = 2bQ$$

[taking moments about C]. (2)

Now velocity of B referred to AB = velocity of B referred to B(

$$\Rightarrow -u_1 + a\omega_1 = 2b\,\omega_2 \quad \text{4)}$$

From (1) and (2), we get $u_1 - a\omega_1 = (-2P + 4Q).\frac{1}{2ma}$

Substituting from this and from (3) in (4) we readily get

$$(-2P + 4Q)\frac{1}{2ma} = -3\frac{Q}{2mb} \text{ or } Q = \frac{(2bP)}{(3a+4b)}$$

Substituting this value of Q in (1), (2) and (3), we get

$$u_1 = \frac{1}{2ma}\left(P + \frac{2bP}{3a+4b}\right) = \frac{(3a+6b)P}{2ma(3a+4b)},$$

and $a\omega_1 = \frac{3}{2ma}\left(P - \frac{2bP}{3a+4b}\right) = \frac{3}{2ma}\cdot\frac{3a+2b\cdot P}{(3a+4b)}.$

Also $b\omega_2 = \frac{3}{2ma}\left(\frac{bP}{3a+4b}\right)$

$\therefore$ Total K. E. of AB + K.E. of BC.

$$= \frac{1}{2}\cdot 2ma\left(u_1^{\,2} + \frac{1}{3}a^2\omega_1^{\,2}\right) + \frac{1}{2}\cdot 2mb\left(\frac{4b_2\omega_2^2}{3}\right)$$

$$= ma\left[\frac{1}{4m^2a^2}\left(\frac{3a+6b}{3a+4b}\right)^2 P^2 + \frac{1}{3}\frac{9}{4m^2a^2}\left(\frac{3a+2b}{3a+4b}\right)P^2\right]$$

$$+ mb\left[\frac{4}{3}\cdot\frac{9}{4m^2b^2}\frac{b^2P^2}{(3a+4b}\right]$$

$$= 12b\frac{(3a^2+7ab+4b^2)}{4mab(3a+4b^2)}P^2 = \frac{3(a+b)}{ma(3a+4b)}P^2 = E_2 \text{ Say}$$

$$\Rightarrow \frac{E_1}{E_2} = \left\{\frac{4a+3b)P^2}{4ma(a+b)}\right\} / \left\{\frac{3(a+b)P^2}{ma(3a+4b)}\right\}$$

or $\frac{E_1}{E_2}$ = {4a + 3b}/{12(a+b)^2.

Example 11:

AB, BC are two equal similar rods freely hinged at B and lie in a straight line on a smooth table. The end A is struck by a blow perpendicular to AB; show that resulting velocity of A is $3\frac{1}{2}$ times of B.

Solution:

Let P be the impulsive force applied at A. Just after the blow let μ_1, ω_1 and μ_2, ω_2 be the liner and angular velocities of the rods AB and BC respectively. When the blow is struck, there will be an impulsive action between the two rods at B. Let Q be the impulsive action at the joint B in opposite directions on two rods. Also let 2a be the length of each rod and m be the mass, then equations of motion for the rods AB and BC are

$$\left.\begin{aligned} &m(u_1-0) && ...(1)\\ &m\cdot\frac{1}{3}a^2\omega_1=(P-Q)a, && ...(2)\end{aligned}\right\} \text{for the rod AB}$$

$$\left.\begin{aligned} &\text{And } m\mu_2=Q && ...(3)\\ &\text{and } m\frac{1}{3}a^2\omega_2=Qa && ...(4)\end{aligned}\right\} \text{for the rod BC.}$$

But the rods are connected at B so the velocity of B, as deduced from each rod must be equal,

i.e. $u_1 - a\omega_1 = -(u_2 + a\omega_2) \Rightarrow u_1 = \frac{5P}{4m}; a\omega_1 = \frac{9P}{4m}$ ...(5)

$$\therefore \frac{\text{velocity of A}}{\text{velocity of B}} = \frac{u_1+a\omega_2}{u_1-a\omega_1} = \frac{\frac{5P}{4m}+\frac{9P}{4m}}{\frac{5P}{4m}-\frac{9P}{4m}} = -\frac{7}{2} = -3\frac{1}{2}$$

$\Rightarrow$ velocity of A = $3\frac{1}{2}$ times the velocity of B.

Example 12:

A rectangular lamina, whose sides are of lengths 2a and 2b, is at rest when one corner is ought and suddenly made to move with prescribed speed V in the plane of the lamina; show that the greatest angular velocity which can thus be imparted to the lamina is

$$\frac{3V}{4\sqrt{(a^2+b^2)}}.$$

Solution:

The corner A is suddenly made to move with prescribed velocity V, in the plane of the lamina, such that V makes an angle θ (say) with BA. Just after the impulse, let μ, v, be the velocities of the centre of gravity, G, parallel and perpendicular to AB, and let ω, be the angular velocity of the lamina.

Now $DG = \sqrt{(a^2+b^2)}$;

So $\cos\beta = \frac{b}{\sqrt{a^2+b^2}}$,

∴ equations of motion are $mu = X$ ...(1)

$mv = Y$ ...(2)

and $m\frac{a^2+b^2}{3}\omega = Xb + Ya$ ...(3)

Now velocity of A parallel BA = velocity of G parallel to BA + velocity of A parallel to BA relative to G.

$$\Rightarrow V\cos\theta = u + \sqrt{(a^2+b^2)}\,\omega\cos\beta = u + \sqrt{a^2+b^2}\,\omega\frac{b}{\sqrt{(a^2+b^2)}}$$

$$\Rightarrow V\cos\theta = v + a\omega \quad ...(4)$$

and velocity of A perpendicular to AB = velocity of G perpendicular to AB + velocity of A perpendicular to AB relative to G.

$$\Rightarrow V\sin\theta = v + \sqrt{a^2+b^2}\,\omega\sin\beta = v + \sqrt{a^2+b^2}\,\omega\frac{b}{\sqrt{a^2+b^2}}$$

$$\Rightarrow V\sin\theta = v + a\omega$$

Substituting the values of X and Y [using (1) and (2)] in (3), we have

$$\frac{a^2+b^2}{3}\omega = ab + a = [(V\cos\theta - b\omega)b + V\sin\theta - a\omega)]$$

[using (4), (5)]

$$\Rightarrow \frac{4(a^2+b^2)}{3}\omega = V(b\cos\theta + a\sin\theta) \quad ...(6)$$

Differentiating (6), with respect to " θ", we get

$$\frac{4}{3}\left(a^2+b^2\right)\frac{d\omega}{d\theta} = V\ (-\ b \sin\theta + a\cos\theta)$$

For ω to be maximum, we must have $\frac{d\omega}{d\theta} = 0$,

i.e. $-\ b \sin \theta + a \cos \theta = 0, \Rightarrow \frac{\cos\theta}{b} = \frac{\sin\theta}{a} = \frac{1}{\sqrt{(a^2+b^2)}}$ ...(7)

∴ (6) and (7) give $\frac{4}{3}\left(a^2+b^2\right) = V\left[\frac{b^2}{\sqrt{(a^2+b^2)}} + \frac{a^2}{\sqrt{a^2+b^2}}\right]$

or $\omega = \frac{3V}{4\sqrt{(a^2+b^2)}}$

Example 13:

Two equal uniform rods. AB and BC are freely joined at B and turn about a smooth joint at A. When the rods, are in a straight line, ω being angular velocity of AB and u the velocity of the centre of mass BC; BC impinges on a fixed inelastic obstacle at a point D; show that the rods are instantaneously brought to rest if BD = 2 a $\frac{2u - a\omega}{2u + 2a\omega}$ *where 2a is the length of the either rod.*

Solution:

Let ω_1 be the angular velocity of BC before the impulse P is given at D. Here BD = x say so that $G_1D = x - a$.

Obviously there will be an impulsive action between the two rods at B and let it be X, in opposite directions on the two rods at B and let it be X, in opposite directions on the two rods. Now, further if the rods are instantaneously brought to rest, then the equation of motion of rod AB is

$$m\cdot\frac{4}{3}a^2 w = X.\ 2a$$

(taking moments about B) ...(1)

Also equations of motion of BC are mu = P − X ...(2)

$$m\cdot\frac{1}{3}a^2\omega = P\ (x-a) + Xa.\ [\because G_1\ C = x - a] \quad ...(3)$$

But the rods are connected at B so the motion of B as deduced from each rod must be the same.

$\Rightarrow 2a\omega$ = vel. of G_1+vel. rel. to $G_2 = u - a\omega_1$.

Putting the values of P and ω_1 from (2) and (4) in (3), we obtain

$$m\cdot\frac{1}{3}a(u-2a\omega) = (mu + X)(x - a) + Xa = mu\,(x - a) + Xx.$$

$$\Rightarrow m\frac{1}{3}a(u-2a\omega) = mu\,(x-a) + m\cdot\frac{2}{3}a\omega\cdot x \text{ [putting for X from (1)]}$$

$$\Rightarrow \frac{1}{3}a(u-2a\omega+3u) = \frac{1}{3}x(3u+2\omega a) \Rightarrow x = BD = 2a\ \frac{2u-a\omega}{3u+2a\omega}\cdot$$

Example 14:

Three particles of equal masses are attached to the ends A and C and the middle point B of a light rod ABC and the system is at rest on a smooth table. The particle C is struck a blow at right angles to the rod. Show that the energy communicated to the system when A is fixed to the energy communicated when the system is free as 24 : 25.

Solution:

Let P be the impulse of the blow imparted at B and mass of each particle at A, B, C be m where AC = 2a.

Ist Case. Let A be not fixed. *i.e. system is free.*

The C.G. of the three particles is at B and the system is at rest before the action of the impulse. Let u be the velocity of the point B. When total mass 3m is supposed to be placed at B, let ω be the angular velocity of the rod, after the action of the impulse, then the equations of motion are 3mu = p.

[motion of C.G. *i.e.* B] ...(1)

$3mk^2\,\omega$ = Pa. [taking moments about B] ...(2)

and $3mk^2 = ma^2 + ma^2$

so that $k^2 = \dfrac{2a^2}{3}$

Now, K. E. $= \dfrac{1}{2}3mu^2 + \dfrac{1}{2}.3mk^2\omega 2.$

$$= \frac{5}{2}m\cdot\frac{4P^2}{2m5^2} = \frac{2P}{5m} = \frac{(K\cdot E)_2}{(K\cdot E)_1} = \frac{24}{5}.$$

Example 15:

An inelastic sphere of radius a rolls down a flight of perfectly rough steps, show that if the velocity of the centre on the first step exceeds $\sqrt{(ga)}$

its velocity will be the same on every step, the step being such that, in its flight, the sphere never impinges on an edge.

Solution:

Let E be the edge of the first step and let v be its velocity at E. Now the sphere has a tendency to turn about the edge E and let θ be the angle through which it turns in time t.

Now equations of motion of the sphere are given

by $ma\dot{\theta}^2 = ma\cos\theta - R$ ...(2)

(taking moments about E)

$$(2) \Rightarrow a^2\dot{\theta}^2 = -\frac{10ga}{7}\cos\theta + c$$

when $\theta = o, a\dot{\theta} = v, \Rightarrow c = v^2 + \frac{10ga}{7}$

$$\therefore a^2\dot{\theta}^2 = \frac{10ga}{7}(1-\cos\theta) + v^2 \text{ or } a\dot{\theta}^2 = \frac{10g}{7}(1-\cos\theta) + \frac{v^2}{a}]$$

$$\therefore (1) \text{ gives } \frac{10g}{7}(1-\cos\theta) + \frac{v^2}{a} = g\cos\theta - \frac{R}{m}$$

$$\text{or } R = m\left[g\cos\theta - \frac{10g}{7}(1-\cos\theta) + \frac{v^2}{a}\right] \qquad \therefore (R)_{\theta=0} = m\left(g - \frac{v^2}{a}\right)$$

obviously, $(R)_{\theta=0}$ will not remain positive, if

$v^2 a > g$ *i.e.* if $v > \sqrt{(ga)}$

which implies that the sphere leaves the step at once if the velocity $v > \sqrt{(ga)}$. After travelling the distance on the first step, the sphere strikes the second step say at the point K. But the step is inelastic so the sphere will not rebound and will roll on the second step with the velocity v.

When it has rolled a distance x on the second step, let S be the force of friction, sufficient for pure rolling, then equations of motion are given by

$m\ddot{x} = S$ ...(3) and $m\frac{2a^2}{5}\ddot{\theta} = -Sa$ ...(4)

But the motion is of pure rolling, so we have

$\dot{x} = a\dot{\theta} \Rightarrow \ddot{x} = a\ddot{\theta}$ ...(5)

from above, we have

$\ddot{x} = 0 \Rightarrow \dot{x} = \text{cons tan t} = v. = 0 \Rightarrow x = x = \text{cons tan t} = v.$

which implies that the sphere rolls on the second step with the uniform velocity v. Hence velocity at every step is the same.

Example 16:

Three equal uniform rods AB, BC, CD are freely jointed and placed in a straight line on a smooth table. The rod AB is struck at its end A by a by a blow which is perpendicular to its length, find the resulting motion and show that the velocity of the centre of AB is 19 times that of CD and its angular velocity 11 times that of CD.

Solution:

Let each rod be of length 2a and mass m and P be the impulse of the blow at A. Hence there will be impulsive action at B and C in opposite directions, which also taken as X and Y respectively.

Just, before the blow, the three rods are at rest and after the blow let

$u_1, \omega_1; u_2, \omega_2; u_3, \omega_3$ be the velocities of C.G.'s and the angular velocities of the rods AB, BC and CA respectively. Then we have

For, AB, $mu_1 = P - X,\ m\frac{a^2}{3}\omega_1 = pa + Xa \cdot$ ...(A)

For, BC, $mu_2 = X - Y,\ m\frac{a^2}{3}\omega 3 = Xa + Ya \cdot$ ...(B)

For, CD, $mu_3 = Y,\ m\ \frac{a^2}{3}\omega_3 = Y\ a.$ ...(C)

Now, velocity of B should be the same as deduced from motion of AB and BC and similarly velocity of C should be the same as deduced from the motion of BC and CD respectively.

For B $u_1 - a\omega_1 = u_2 + a\omega_2$ ...(1)

For C $u_2 - a\omega_2 = u_3 + a\omega_3$ ...(2)

$\Rightarrow u_1 - a\omega_1 = \frac{P - X}{m} - \frac{3(P + X}{m} = \frac{-2P - 4X}{m}$

From (B), we have $u_2 + a\omega_2 = \frac{X - Y}{m} + \frac{3(X + Y)}{m} = \frac{4X + 2Y}{m}$

$\therefore$ (1) $\Rightarrow 2P - 4X = +\ 2\ Y$

or $4X + Y = -P.$ ...(3)

Again from (B), we obtain $u_2 - a\omega_2 = \frac{X - Y}{m} + \frac{3(X + Y)}{m} = \frac{-2X - 4Y}{m}$

and $u_3 + a\omega_3 = \frac{Y}{m} + \frac{3Y}{m} = \frac{4Y}{m}.$ [using C]

$\Rightarrow -\ 2X - 4Y = 4Y$ or $X + 4Y = 0.$ [using (2)] ...(4)

Solving (3) and (4), we get $X = -\dfrac{4P}{15}$ and $Y = \dfrac{P}{15}$

$$\Rightarrow u_1 = \frac{1}{m}\left(P + \frac{4P}{15}\right) = \frac{19P}{15m}, \omega_1 = \frac{3}{ma}\left(P - \frac{4P}{15}\right) = \frac{11P}{5ma}$$

$$u_2 = \frac{1}{m}\left(-\frac{4P}{15} - \frac{P}{15}\right) = -\frac{P}{3m}, \omega_2 = \frac{3}{ma}\left(-\frac{4P}{15} - \frac{P}{15}\right) = \frac{-5P}{5ma}$$

$$u_3 = \frac{1}{15m}, \omega_3 = \frac{3}{ma}\left(\frac{P}{15}\right) = \frac{P}{5ma}$$

$$\Rightarrow u_1 : u_3 = \frac{19P}{15m} : \frac{P}{15m} = 19 : 1 \text{ i.e. } u_1 = 19u_3$$

i.e. velocity of centre of AB is 19 times that of CD.

Further, $\omega_1 : \omega_2 = \dfrac{11P}{5ma} : \dfrac{P}{5ma} = 11 : 1$ *i.e.* $\omega_1 = 11\omega_3$

i.e. the angular velocity of AB is 11 times that of CD.

Example 17:

Two uniform rods, AB and BC, of the same material are smoothly joined to B and placed in a horizontal line; the rod BC is struck at G by a blow at right angles to it, find the position of G that the angular velocities of AB and BC may be equal in magnitude.

Solution:

Let AB = 2a and BC = 2b and let m be mass of each rod per unit length

Also let G_1 be the centre of gravity of the rod BC and G_2 that of the rod AB. Let P be impulse applied at a point G of the rod BC such that $GG_1 = x$

After the application of the blow let u_1 be the velocity of G_1 the centre of gravity of BC, and ω_1 its angular velocity, u_2 and ω_2 similar quantities for the rod AB, in the direction as shown in the above figure.

When the blow is struck, let the impulsive action at B between the two rods be Q, in opposite directions on the two rods.

Initially the rods BC and AB were at rest

$\therefore m_2bu_1 = P - Q$(motion of G_1) ...(1)

$m\ 2b\dfrac{b^2}{3}\omega_1 = Px + Qb$, (motion about G_2) ...(2)

$m \cdot 2au_2 = Q$; (motion about G_2) ...(3)

and m $2a\frac{a^2}{3}\omega_2 + Qa$; (motion about G_2) ...(4)

Further the rods are connected at B, so the velocity of B, form each rod, must be the same *i.e.*

$u_1 - b\omega_1 = u_2 + a\omega_2$ ...(5)

Now we have two cases:

Case (i) If $\omega_1 = \omega_2$ (*equal in magnitude and same in direction*)

Equations (3) and (4) $\Rightarrow u_2 = \frac{a\omega_2}{3} = \frac{a\omega_1}{3}$ ...(6)

and equations (5) $\Rightarrow u_1 - b\omega_1 = \frac{a\omega_1}{3} + a\omega_1$, *i.e.* $u_1 = \left(\frac{4a+3b}{3}\right)\omega_1$

Also (2), Þ $xP = 2m\frac{b^2}{3}\omega_1 - Qb = = \frac{2mb^3}{3}\omega_1 - 2mabu_2$ [using (3)].

$= 2mb\frac{4a+3b}{3}\omega_1 + \frac{2ma^2\omega_1}{3}$ {after substituting for u_1 and u_2}

$= \frac{2m}{3}(a^2 + 4ab + 3b^2)\omega_1 = \frac{2m}{3}(a+b)(a+3b)\omega_1$

$\Rightarrow x = \frac{2m(b^2 - a^2}{3}\cdot\frac{3}{2m(a+b)(a+3b)} = \frac{b-a}{a+3b}$.

Case (ii)

If $\omega_1 = -\omega_2$ (magnitude equal but opposite in direction)

In this case (3) (4) $\Rightarrow u_2 = \frac{a\omega_1}{3} = -\frac{a\omega_2}{3}$

and (5), $\Rightarrow u_1 - b\omega_1 = u_2 + aw_2 = -\frac{aw_1}{3} - 0w_1, \Rightarrow u_1 = \frac{3b-4a}{2}\omega_1$.

$\therefore xP = \frac{2mb^3}{3}\omega_1 - Qb = \frac{2mb^3}{3}\omega_1 - 2mabu_2$ [using (2)]

$= \frac{2mb^3}{3}\omega_1 + \frac{2ma^2b}{3}\omega_1\left(\therefore u_2 = \frac{a\omega_1}{3}\right) = \frac{2mb}{3}(b^2 - a^2)\omega_1,$

Now $P = 2mbu_1 + Q$ {from (1) }

$= \frac{2mb(3b-4a)}{3}\omega_1 - \frac{2ma^2}{3}\omega_1$ [substituting for u_1 and u_2]

$= \frac{2m}{3}(3b^2 - 4ab - a^2)\omega_1$.

$$\Rightarrow x = \frac{2mb(b^2+a^2)}{3}\frac{3}{2m(3b^2-4ab-a^2)} = \frac{b(b^2+a^2)}{3b^2-4ab-a^2}.$$

Example 18:

Two uniform rods. AB, AC are freely joined at A and laid on a smooth horizontal table so that the angle BAC is a right angle. The rod AB is struck by a blow P at B in a direction perpendicular to AB, show that the initial velocity of A is $\frac{2P}{4m'+m'}$ *where, m, m′ are the masses of AB, AC respectively.*

Solution:

The initial motion of A is to be perpendicular to AB, hence the action at A (say X) must be along AC.

Let u_1 be the linear velocity of G_1 and ω_1 the angular velocity of AB. Then since impulse on AC is along CA, the rod AC will only move in the direction CA say with linear velocity u_2. Now for equation of motion, we have

$$\left.\begin{array}{ll} mu_1 = P + X & \text{...(1)} \\ m\frac{1}{3}a^3\omega_1 = (P-X)a, & \text{...(2)} \end{array}\right\} \text{motion of AB}$$

$m' u_2 = X$ motion of Ac. ...(3)

But the rods are connected at A, so the motion of A as deduced form the motion of AB and AC must be the same

$$\Rightarrow u_1 = a\omega_1 = -u_2 \qquad \text{...(4)}$$

Now putting the values of u_1, ω_1 and u_2 [form (1), (2), (3)] in (4) we have

$$\frac{(P+X)}{m} - \frac{3(P-X)}{m} = -\frac{X}{m'} \Rightarrow X = \frac{2Pm'}{4m'+m}$$

Whence substitution in (3) provides us

$$u_2 = \frac{X}{m'} = \frac{2P}{4m'+m} \text{ i.e. velocity of the rod AC} = \frac{2P}{4m'+m}$$

$$\text{or velocity of A} = \frac{2P}{4m'+m}$$

Example 19:

AB, BC and CD are three equal uniform rods lying in a straight line on a smooth plane, and they are freely jointed at B and C. A blow is applied at the centre of BC in a direction perpendicular to BC. If ω be the initial *angular velocity of AB or CD, and θ the angle they make with BC any time, show that the angular velocity is* $\dfrac{\omega}{\sqrt{(a+\sin^2\theta)}}$

Solution:

Let P be the impulse of the blow applied at G_2, the centre of BC, and X the impulsive action at B or C.

Just after the impulse, let U be the velocity of the centre of BC; and V be the velocity of centre of AB and CD, the angular velocities being ω.

Now, we have;$mU = P = 2X$ ...(1) for the rod BC

$$mV = X \qquad ...(2)$$

and $$\left.m\frac{a^2}{3}\omega = Xa\right\}$$ for the rod AB or CD

Also, AB and BC are connected at B, so the velocity of B as deduced from BC and AB, must be the same *i.e.* $U = V + a\omega$ ...(4)

$$\therefore (2) \text{ and } (3) \Rightarrow V = \frac{a\omega}{3} \qquad ...(5)$$

$$\text{and } U = \frac{4a\omega}{3} \qquad ...(6)$$

After the action of the impulse, the rods are set in motion and move in the horizontal plane under finite forces. The rod BC retains is horizontal position where as AB, and DC turn about B and C.

At any time t, let AB or DC make an angle θ with BC and further let u be the velocity of BC. Now co-ordinates of G_1 relative to BC (with B as origin) are $x = a\cos\theta$, $y = a \text{ sing } \theta$

$$\Rightarrow \dot{X} = -a\sin\theta\dot{\theta},\ \dot{y} = a\sin\dot{\theta}.$$

$\Rightarrow$ actual velocity of G_1 along CB and the right angles to CB is given by

$$\left(-a\sin\theta\dot{\theta}\right) \text{ and } \left(u - a\cos\theta\dot{\theta}\right).$$

Now K. E. of the system

$$= \frac{1}{2}mu^2 + \frac{1}{2}2m\left[u - a\dot{\theta}\cos\theta\right]^2 + a^2\dot{\theta}^2\sin^2\theta + \frac{a^2}{3}\dot{\theta}^2$$

$$= \frac{1}{2}m\left[3u^2 - 4au\dot{\theta}\cos\theta + \frac{8a^2}{3}\dot{\theta}^2\right]$$

When $\theta = 0$, $u = U$; and $\theta = w$

$$\therefore \text{Initial K. E. of the system} = \frac{1}{2}m\left[3U^2 - 4aU\omega + \frac{8a^2}{3}\omega^2\right].$$

Now there is no displacement, in the points of application of (reactions and weights), at right angles to the horizontal plane, so no work is done by these forces, and thus implying that there should be no change in the K. E. of system. *i.e.*

$$= \frac{1}{2}m\left[3U^2 - 4bu\dot{\theta}\cos\theta + \frac{8a^2}{3}\dot{\theta}^2\right]$$

$$= \frac{1}{2}m\left(3U^2 - 4aU\omega + \frac{8a^2}{5}\omega^2\right)$$

or $$3u^2 - 4au\dot{\theta}\cos\theta + \frac{8a^2}{3}\dot{\theta}^2 = \left(8a^2\omega^2/3\right) \quad ...(7)$$

[substituting the value of U]

Again after the action of the impulse, the motion is under finite forces hence there is no force on the system in the horizontal plane. The horizontal momentum of the system remains constant viz;

$$mu + 2m\left(u - a\theta\cos\dot{\theta}\right) = mU + 2m\left(U - a\omega\right)$$

or $3u - 2a\dot{\theta}\cos\theta = 3U - 2a\omega$

or $3u - 2a\dot{\theta}\cos\theta = 2a\omega$ [putting the value of U] ...(8)

$\therefore$ (7) and (8) $\Rightarrow \dot{\theta} = \dfrac{\omega}{\sqrt{\left(1+\sin^2\theta\right)}}$ (eliminating u)

Example 20:

A uniform flat rod, of length 2a, rests on a rough horizontal plane with its weight uniformly distributed. A horizontal force P large enough to produce motion is applied suddenly at the end perpendicular to the length of the rod. Show that initially point, where x is given by the positive root of the equation

$$x^3 - \left(\frac{1}{3} - \frac{2P}{\mu W}\right)a^2x - \frac{2}{3}\frac{P}{\mu W}a^3 = 0,$$

W being the weight of the rod and μ the coefficient of friction.

Solution:

Let the impulse P be given at the end A and let O′ be the point about which the rod begins to turn where GO′ = x. Just after the application of the impulse, let ω be the angular velocity of the rod. Hence velocity of the centre of gravity G just after the impulse is x ω as shown in the figure. Due to the impulse P, there is an impulsive friction at each point of the rod.

Now consider an element δy of the rod to the right and also to the left of the point O′, where O′ Q = y.

Friction on each of these elements $=\mu\frac{W}{2a}\delta y$

Now taking moments about the point O', we have

$$*\,M\left(\frac{a^2}{3}+x^2\right)\omega = P(a+x) - \int_0^{a+x}\mu\frac{W}{2a}y\,dy - \int_0^{a-x}\mu\frac{W}{2a}y\,dy.$$

[The moments of impulsive frictions are negative because they tend to decrease ω].

$$= P(a+x) - \frac{\mu W}{2a}\left[\frac{y^2}{2}\right]_0^{a-x}$$

i.e. $M\left(\frac{a^2}{3}+x^2\right)\omega = P\,(a+x) - \frac{\mu W}{2a}\left(a^2+x^2\right).$

Also moment of centre of gravity G, gives

Change in angular moments about O′ is equal to the sum of the moments of the impulses about O′

$$Mx\omega = P - \int_0^{a+x}\frac{\mu W}{2a}dy + \int_0^{a-x}\frac{\mu W}{2a}dy.$$

[The friction on the right hand of O is opposite to P, while on the left is in direction of P].

$$\Rightarrow Mx\omega = P - \frac{\mu W}{2a}(a+x) + \frac{\mu W}{2a}(a-x) \Rightarrow Mx\omega = P - \frac{\mu W}{2a}x \qquad ...(2)$$

Whence eliminating ω between (1) and (2), we readily obtain

$$\left(\frac{a^2}{3}+x^2\right)\left(\frac{P}{x}-\frac{\mu W}{2a}\right) = P(a+x) - \frac{\mu W}{2a}\left(a^2+x^2\right)$$

$$\Rightarrow x^3 - \left(\frac{1}{3}-\frac{2P}{\mu W}\right)a^2x - \frac{2}{3}\frac{P}{\mu W}a^3 = 0.$$

Example 21:

A lamina in the form of an equilateral triangle ABC lies on a smooth horizontal plane. Suddenly it receives a blow at A in a direction parallel to BC, which causes A to move with velocity V. Determine the instantaneous velocity of B and C and describe the subsequent motion of the lamina.

Solution:

As the impulse is parallel to BC, the velocity of G_1, the centre of gravity of the triangular lamina, AVC must also be parallel to BC. Let this velocity be u, and ω be the angular velocity Δ of AVC

Equations of motion of the C.G. of the lamina are : mu = P and ...(1)

$$*\frac{m}{3}\left(\frac{a^2}{3}+\frac{a^2}{3}+\frac{a^2}{3}\right)\omega = P\frac{2}{3}a\sqrt{3} \quad ...(2)$$

(taking moments about G) $\left(\because GD \text{ etc.} = a/\sqrt{3}\right)$.

$\therefore$ Velocity of the point A = (velocity of G + velocity of A relative to G)

or $V = u + \frac{2}{3}a\sqrt{3}\omega$. Now (1) and (2)

$\Rightarrow a\omega = 2\sqrt{3}\cdot u\cdot$

$\Rightarrow V = u + 4u = 5u$

i.e. $u = \frac{1}{5}V$ and $a\omega = \frac{2\sqrt{3}}{5}V$.

* Triangle ABC is kinetically equivalent to three particles, each one third of the mass of the triangle, placed at the middle points of the sides.

$\therefore$ velocity of B = velocity of G + velocity of B relative to G

$= u + \frac{2}{3}a\sqrt{3}\omega$

$\Rightarrow$ velocity of B parallel to BC

= (velocity of B parallel to BC) + velocity of B relative to G parallel to BC),

$= u - \frac{2}{3}a\sqrt{3}\omega\cos 60^0 = -a\omega = -\frac{2\sqrt{3}}{5}V.$

Finally, proceeding in the same manner, the velocities of C are

$-\frac{V}{5}$ and $\frac{2\sqrt{3}}{5}V$ along and perpendicular to BC.

Example 22:

A square plate, of side 2a, is falling with velocity u, a diagonal being vertical, when an inelastic string attached to the middle point of an upper edge becomes tight in vertical position. Show that the impulsive tension of the string is 4/7 Mu, where M is the mass of the plate.

Solution:

When the string becomes tight, a jerk experienced by the string resulting an impulsive tension in the string say, T.

Just after the impulse let u′ be the vertical velocity of G, and ω be the angular velocity of the square, while just before the jerk, the velocity of G is u and there no angular velocity. It is to note that there will be no velocity in the horizontal direction, as there is no horizontal impulse.

Equations of motion of the square plate ABCD are:

$$M(u' - u) = -T \text{...(1) and } M\frac{2a^2}{3}\omega = T\frac{a}{\sqrt{2}} \quad \text{...(2)}$$

Also, the velocity of K relative to G is aω, at right angles to GK. Hence its resolved part is aω cos 45° *i.e.* $a\omega\frac{1}{\sqrt{2}}$ in vertical upward direction. But just after the impulse, the point K is reduced to rest.

$$\Rightarrow \text{vertical velocity of the point K} = 0 \Rightarrow u' - \frac{a\omega}{\sqrt{2}} = 0. \quad \text{...(3)}$$

$$\therefore \left\{u - \left(\frac{T}{m}\right)\right\} - \left(\frac{3T}{4M}\right) = \textit{i.e. } T = \frac{4}{7}Mu.$$

Example 23:

A light string is wound round the circumference of a uniform reel of radius a and radius of gyration k about its axis. The free end of the string being tied to a fixed point, the reel is lifted up and let fall so that, at the moment when the sting becomes tight, the velocity of the centre of reel is u and the string is vertical. Find the change in the motion and show that the impulsive tension is $mu\left(\frac{k^2}{a^2+k^2}\right)$

Solution:

When the string becomes tight, a jerk is experienced by the string resulting an impulsive tension in the string, say T.

Just after the jerk let v be the velocity of the centre of gravity G and ω the angular velocity, while just before the jerk the velocity of G is u and there is no angular velocity.

Equations of motion of the reel are,

$$m(v - u) = -T \quad \text{...(1)}$$

$$\text{and } mk^2\omega = Ta \quad \text{...(2)}$$

Just after the impulse, the velocity of the point contact K is zero

$$\Rightarrow v - a\omega = 0 \quad \text{...(3)}$$

$$\therefore \left(u - \frac{1}{m}T\right) - \frac{Ta^2}{mk^2} = 0 \Rightarrow T = mu\left(\frac{k^2}{a^2+k^2}\right)$$

Example 24:

A uniform inelastic rod falls without rotation, being inclined at an angle β to the horizon and hits a smooth fixed peg at a distance form its upper end equal to one third of its length. Show that the lower end begins to descend vertically.

Solution:

Let AB be the rod which strikes the fixed smooth peg at C; the inclination of the rod, say, β at that time. Let S be the impulse at the peg C perpendicular to the rod. Just before the impact, the rod was falling without rotation under gravity. Hence it must have then only the vertical velocity V. Just after impact, let u, v, be the horizontal and vertical velocities of the C.G. of the rod AB and let ω its angular velocity.

Now equations of motion of the rod AB are as follows:

$$\left.\begin{aligned} mu &= S\sin\beta \quad (1) \\ m(v - V) &= -S\cos\beta, \quad (2) \end{aligned}\right\} \text{motion of C.G.}$$

and $\quad m\dfrac{a^2}{3}\omega = S\cdot\dfrac{a}{3}$ ...(3) (taking moments about C.G.)

Substituting the value of S from (3) in (1) and (2), we readily get

u = – aω sin β, v = v – aω cos β.

Now velocity of the end A relative to G = aω(perpendicular to AB)

and horizontal velocity at A = horizontal velocity of G + horizontal velocity of A relative to G

u + aω sin β = – aω sin β + aω sin β (substituting value of u)

and vertical velocity of A = vertical velocity of G

+ vertical velocity of A relative of G.

= v + aω cos β = (V – aω cos β) + aω cos β = V.(substituting for v)

implies that after the impact the lower end A begins to descend vertically.

Example 25:

Four equal rods, each of mass m and length 2a are freely joined at their ends so as to form a rhombus. The rhombus falls with a diagonal vertical, and is moving with velocity V when it hits a fixed horizontal inelastic plane. Find the motion of the rods immediately after the impact, and show that their angular velocities are equal to

$$\frac{3V\sin\alpha}{2a\left(1+3\sin^2\alpha\right)},$$ *where α is the angle each rod makes with the vertical.*

Show also that the impact destroys a fraction $\left(\dfrac{3\sin\alpha}{1+3\sin^2\alpha}\right)$ *of the kinetic energy just before the impact.*

Solution:

Let PQRS be the rhombus formed of four equal rods each of length 2a and mass m, fall with the diagonal RP vertical. By symmetry, the motion of the rod RS is the same as the motion of RQ while the motion of the rod PS is the same that of PQ. Hence we need only to consider the motion of PQ and QR alone.

Just after impact at P with the horizontal plane, the rod PQ turns about P, say with angular velocity ω_1, while the rod QR turns about Q, say with angular velocity ω_2, with the direction as shown in the figure.

Due to symmetry, the impulsive action at R will be only horizontal, let it be equal to H. Further let X_1, Y_1 be the horizontal and vertical impulse at Q in opposite directions on the rods PQ, QR respectively. As after impact, R moves in vertical direction, so horizontal velocity of the point R relative to Q = 0 ⇒ horizontal velocity of Q + horizontal velocity of R relative to Q = 0

$$\Rightarrow 2a\,\omega_1 \cos\alpha + 2a\,\omega_2 \cos a = 0$$

$$\Rightarrow \omega_2 = -\,\omega_2,$$

Now we have horizontal velocity of $G_1 = a\omega_1 \cos a$, and vertical velocity of $G_1 = a\,\omega_1 \sin\alpha$.

⇒ horizontal velocity of G_2 = horizontal velocity of Q + horizontal velocity of G_2 relative to Q.

$$= 2\,a\,\omega_1 \cos\alpha + a\,\omega_2 \cos\alpha = a\omega_1 \cos a \qquad (\therefore\ \omega_2 = -\,\omega_1)$$

and vertical velocity of $G_2 = 2a\,\omega_1 \sin\alpha - a\omega_2 \sin\alpha = 3a\,\omega_1 \sin\alpha$.

Now considering the combined motion of PQ and QR and taking moments about P, we get

$$\left\{m\frac{4a^2}{3}\omega_1 + m\left(\frac{a^2}{3}\omega 1 + a\omega_1 \cos\alpha.3a\cos\alpha + 3a\omega_1 \sin\alpha.a\sin\alpha\right)\right\}$$

$$-\,2m\,Va\sin\alpha = 4a\cos\alpha\,H$$

$$\Rightarrow 2\omega_1 = \frac{V\sin\alpha}{a} + \frac{2H\cos\alpha}{ma} \qquad ...(3)$$

∴ (2) and (3) give,

$$\omega_1\left(\frac{4}{3} + 4\sin^2\alpha\right) = -\frac{V\sin\alpha}{a} \Rightarrow \omega_1 = \frac{3V\sin\alpha}{2a\left(1+3\sin^2\alpha\right)}$$

Now K.E. just before the impulse $= \frac{1}{2}4mV^2 = 2mV^2 = E_1$ (say)

and K.E. just after the impulse = 2 [K.E. of PQ + K.E. of QR] = E_2 (say)

$$\text{or } E_2 = 2\left[\frac{1}{2}m\frac{4a^2}{3}\omega_1^2 + \frac{1}{2}m\left(\frac{a^2}{3}\omega_1^2 + a^2\omega_1^2\cos^2\alpha + 9a^2\omega_1^2\sin^2\alpha\right)\right]$$

$$= \frac{8}{3}ma^2\left(1+3\sin^2\alpha\right)\omega_1^2 (\because \omega_2 = -\omega_1)$$

$$= \frac{3\sin^2\alpha}{1+3\sin^2\alpha}2m\ V^2 = \frac{3\sin^2\alpha E_1}{1+\sin^2\alpha}$$

Example 26:

An equilateral triangle, formed by uniform rods freely hinged at their ends, is falling freely with one side horizontal and upper-mass. If the middle point of this side be suddenly stopped, show that the impulsive actions at the upper and lower hinges are in the ration $\sqrt{(13)}:1$.

Solution:

The middle point O of the rod QR is suddenly stopped, so the impulse is imparted at O. Hence an impulsive action between the two rods at Q is generated. A similar impulse is generated at R as there is symmetry about O. The action at P will be horizontal due to symmetry. Let it be X in opposite directions on the two rods PQ and PR.

Just before the blow there was only vertical velocity for every rod. As the system has been stopped, there are no linear velocities and no angualr velocities for any rod after the blow. Now considering the motion of the rod PQ, or (PR), we get

$X_1 - X = 0$ ...(1)

$\because$ there is no horizontal velocity of G before and after the impulse]

Taking moments about G, we get X_1 LQ – Y_1 GL + X_1 LM = 0

$\Rightarrow x_1 a \sin 60° - y_1 a \cos 60°$

$+ X a \sin 60° + X a \sin 60° = 0$

$$\Rightarrow X_1\frac{a\sqrt{3}}{2} + X\frac{a\sqrt{3}}{2} - Y_1\frac{a}{2} = 0 \quad ...(2)$$

[$\because$ *there is no angular velocity of PQ before and after the impulse]*

These give $X_1 = X$

and $Y_1 = 2\sqrt{3X}.$

$$\Rightarrow \frac{\text{reaction at Q}}{\text{reaction at P}} = \frac{\sqrt{(X_1^2 + Y_1^2)}}{X} = \frac{\sqrt{\sqrt{(X^2 + 12X^2)}}}{X} = \frac{\sqrt{(13)}}{1}.$$

Example 27:

A square lamina ABCD rest on a smooth horizontal plane. If the corner A is made tq move with velocity u along the BA produced, then determine the initial angular velocity of the lamina.

Solution:

For a square let us choose b = a. The corner A is made to move with velocity u along BA therefore V = u and $\theta = \pi$. Hence angular velocity u along BA is obtained by putting V = u, $\theta = \pi$.

$$\therefore \frac{4}{3}(a^2 + a^2)\ w = u\ (a \cos \pi + a\ \text{sing}\ \pi) \text{ or } \frac{8}{3}a^2\omega = -\frac{3u}{8a}.$$

Above relation gives the required angular velocity.

Example 28:

A sphere of mass m falls with velocity V on a perfectly rough inclined plane of mass M and angle a which rests on a smooth horizontal plane. Show that the vertical velocity of the centre of the sphere immediately after the impact is $\frac{5(M+m)V\sin^2\alpha}{7M+2m+5m\sin^2\alpha}$, *the bodies being all supposed perfectly inelastic.*

Solution:

Just before the impact velocity of the sphere is V in vertical direction $(\downarrow)$ there being no angular velocity then. Just after the impact let u and v be the velocities and ω the angular velocity of the sphere as shown in the figure.

Just after the impact, the inclined plane also begins to move in the horizontal direction. Now equations of motion are:

$$\left.\begin{aligned} m(-u) &= R\sin\alpha - S\cos\alpha; \quad &(1)\\ m(v - V) &= -R\cos\alpha - S\sin\alpha \quad &(2)\end{aligned}\right\}$$

(motion of the C.G. of the sphere

and $\quad m\frac{2a^2}{5}\omega = Sa \qquad ...(3)$

Also the motion of the inclined plane is given by

$MV' = R \sin \alpha - S \cos \alpha.$ ...(4)

Now horizontal velocity of the point K of the sphere

= horizontal velocity of the point K of the inclined plane.

$\therefore u + a\,\omega \cos \alpha = V'$

and vertical velocity of the point K of the sphere

= vertical velocity of the point K of the inclined plane.

$\therefore v - a\,\omega \sin \alpha = 0 \Rightarrow v = a\omega \sin \alpha.$

From (1) and (4) it is easy to see that $MV' = -mu$, *i.e.* $V' = -\frac{mu}{M}$

$$\Rightarrow u + a\omega \cos a = -\frac{mu}{M} \Rightarrow u = -\frac{Ma\omega\cos\alpha}{M+m}.$$

Now multiplying (2) by sin a and (1) by cos a, and then adding these to (3), we obtain $-mu \cos \alpha + m(v - V)\sin \alpha + m\frac{2a\omega}{5} = 0.$

$$\Rightarrow \frac{Ma\omega\cos^2\alpha}{M+m} + (v - V)\sin\mu + \frac{2a\omega}{5} = 0\left(\because v = -\frac{Ma\omega\cos^2\alpha}{M+m}\right)$$

$$\Rightarrow \left[\frac{Ma\omega\cos^2\alpha}{M+m} + \frac{2}{5}\right]\frac{v}{\sin\alpha} + (v - V)\sin\alpha = 0[\because v = a\omega\sin\alpha]$$

$$\Rightarrow [5M\cos^2\alpha + 2(M+m) + (M+m)\sin^2\alpha]v$$

$$= 5(M+m)V\sin^2\alpha$$

$$\Rightarrow [7M + 2M + 5m\sin^2]\alpha$$

$$\Rightarrow v = \frac{5(M+m)V\sin^2\alpha}{7M + 2m\ 5m\sin^2\alpha}\cdot$$

Example 29:

Of two inelastic circular discs with milled edged. Each of mass m and radius a, one is rotating with angular velocity ω round its centre O, which is fixed on a smooth plane, and the other is moving with spin in the plane with velocity v directed towards O. Find the motion immediately afterwards, and show that the energy lost by the impact is

$$\frac{1}{2}m\left(v^2 + \frac{a^2\omega^2}{5}\right).$$

Solution:

The disc P is rotating about its centre O with angular velocity ω (say) while disc Q is moving with linear velocity v towards O as shown in the figure.

Further let F be the impulsive friction at the point of contact, K. But the discs are inelastic, so they will not rebound, and hence after the impact, the velocity of the disc Q will be along O_1O.

Further let the velocity of Q be u, along the common tangent. Also let ω_1 and ω_2 be angular velocities of P and Q after the impact, then equations of motion are:

$$\frac{ma^2}{2}(\omega_1 - \omega) = -Fa \qquad \text{(for the disc P)} \quad ...(1)$$

$$mu = F \quad ...(2)$$

and $$\frac{ma^2}{2}\omega^2 = Fa \qquad \text{[for the disc P]} \quad ...(3)$$

But the discs P and Q touch each other at K, so the velocity of the point of contact K as deduced from discs must be equal,

i.e. $a\omega_1 = u + a\omega_2$ ...(4)

Now putting the value of u, ω_1 and ω_2 from (2), (1) and (3) in (4), we easily obtain

$$-\frac{2F}{m} + a\omega = \frac{F}{m} + \frac{2F}{m} \quad \textit{i.e.} \quad F = \frac{ma\omega}{5}.$$

$$\therefore a\omega_1 = -\frac{2a\omega}{5} + a\omega = \frac{3a\omega}{5}:$$

and $u = \frac{a\omega}{5}$: Also $a\omega_2 = \frac{2a\omega}{5}$.

$\therefore$ Total K.E. after the impact = K.E. of the disc P + K.E. of the disc Q

$$= \frac{1}{2}m\frac{a^2}{2}\omega_1^2 + \frac{1}{2}m\left(u^2 + \frac{a^2}{2}w_2^2\right)$$

$$= 2m\left[\frac{9a^2\omega^2}{50} + \frac{a^2\omega^2}{50} + \frac{4a^2\omega^2}{50}\right] = \frac{3a^2m\omega^2}{20} = E_2 \text{ (say)}$$

But K.E. before the impact

$$= \frac{1}{2}m\frac{a^2}{2}\omega^2 + \frac{1}{2}mv^2 = E_1 \text{ (say)}$$

$$= \frac{1}{2}m\frac{a^2}{2}\omega^2 + \frac{1}{2}mv^2 - \frac{3ma^2\omega^2}{20} = \frac{1}{2}m\left(v^2 + \frac{a^2\omega^2}{5}\right)$$

Example 30:

If a hollow lawn tennis ball of elasticity e has on striking the ground supposed perfectly rough, a vertical velocity v and angular velocity ω about a horizontal axis, find its angular velocity after impact and that the range of the rebound will be $\frac{4a\omega}{5g}ev$.

Solution:

Just before the impact, v is vertical velocity and ω the angular velocity while, just after impact let u′, v′ be the horizontal and vertical velocities and ω′ the angular velocity ( ), then equations of motion are

$$mu' = -F \qquad ...(1)$$

and $$m(v' + v) = R \qquad ...(2)$$

and $$m\frac{2}{3}a^2(\omega' - \omega) = Fa \qquad ...(3)$$

The point of contact P is reduced to rest instantaneously, there being no sliding,

$\Rightarrow u' - a\omega' = 0$ also $v' = ev$.

Now eliminating from (1), (3) we get

$$\frac{2}{3}a(\omega' - \omega) = -u'$$

or $$\frac{2}{3}(u' - a\omega) = -u' \Rightarrow \frac{5}{3}u' = \frac{2}{3}a\omega$$

$$\text{or } u' = \frac{2}{5}a\omega \qquad ...(4)$$

$$\therefore \text{ range after rebound} = \frac{2(\text{horizontal velo.})(\text{vert.velo.})}{g}$$

$$= \frac{2u'v'}{g} = \frac{2\frac{2}{5}a.\omega.ev}{g} = \frac{4a\omega}{5g}ev.$$

Example 31:

An imperfectly elastic sphere descending vertically comes in contact with a fixed rough point, the impact taking place at a point distant α from the lowest point, and the coefficient of elasticity being e. Find the motion, and show that the sphere will start moving horizontally after the impact if

$$\alpha = \tan^{-1}\sqrt{\left(\frac{7e}{5}\right)}$$

Solution:

Before the impact the sphere is descending vertically say with velocity V; implies that it has then no horizontal velocity and no angular velocity. Just after the impact let u_1 and v_1 be the velocities of the sphere along and perpendicular to PG and ω its angular velocity as marked in the above figure.

Then the equations of motion are :

$$m(v_1 - V\sin\alpha) = -F \quad ...(1)$$

$$m(v_1 + V\cos\alpha) = R \quad ...(2)$$

$$\text{and } m\frac{2a^2}{5}\omega = Fa. \quad ...(3)$$

After impact there is no sliding velocity *i.e.* velocity of the point P along tangent at P is zero.

$\therefore v_1 - a\omega = 0 \Rightarrow v_1 = a\omega$

Also $u_1 = eV\cos\alpha$ (by Newton's Law)

Form (1) and (3), we get $(v_1 - V\sin a) = -\frac{2a}{5}\omega$

$$\Rightarrow v_1 - V\sin\alpha = -\frac{2}{5}v_1 \Rightarrow v_1 = \frac{5}{7}V\sin\alpha.$$

$$\therefore v_1 = a\omega = \frac{5}{7}V\sin\alpha.$$

The sphere will start moving horizontally after impact if the vertical velocity of sphere = 0 *i.e.* if $u_1\cos\alpha - v_1\sin\alpha = 0$.

$$\text{or } \tan\alpha\frac{u_1}{v_1} \text{ or } \tan\alpha\frac{eV\cos\alpha}{\frac{5V}{7}\sin\alpha}$$

$$\text{or } \tan^2\alpha = \frac{7}{5}e \Rightarrow \alpha = \tan 1\sqrt{\left(\frac{7e}{5}\right)}$$

Example 32:

A rough imperfectly elastic ball is dropped vertically and when its velocity is V, a man suddenly moves his racket forward in its own plane with velocity U, and thus subjects the ball to [illegible] e cut in a downward direction making an angle α with the horizon. Show that, on striking the rough found. the ball will not proceed beyond the point of impact, provide

$$(U - v\sin\alpha)(1 - \cos\alpha) > (1+e)\left(1+\frac{a^2}{k}\right)V\sin\alpha\cos\alpha.$$

Solution:

Let P be a point on the ball such that it is hit by the man. Obviously the plane of the racket is tangential to the ball. Since the man moves the racket in its own plane with velocity U, the velocity of the point of contact P will also be U along the tangent at P.

Just before the impact the velocity of the ball is given to be V, there being no horizontal velocity and no angular velocity.

Just after the impact, let u,v be the horizontal and vertical velocities and ω the angular velocity as marked in the figure. *The we have for the motion of ball.*

Just before the impact, the moment of momentum about P

$= mV\ a \sin\alpha.$ $\left[\because \text{moment of momentum} = mk^2\dot{\theta} + mv\,p\right]$

After impact, moment of momentum about P

$= mk^2\omega - mua\cos\alpha + mv\,a\sin\alpha$

$\therefore$ Change in moment of momentum

$= (mk^2\omega - mua\cos\alpha + mv\,a\sin\alpha) - mV\,a\sin\alpha$

But the impulse is applied at P, hence moment of the impulse at P is zero Now

$mk^2\omega - mua\cos\alpha + mv\,a\sin\alpha - mV\,a\sin\alpha = 0$

($\therefore$ Change in moment of momentum = moment of the impulse).

But velocity of the point P of the racket = velocity of the point of the ball

$\Rightarrow U = u\cos\alpha - v\sin\alpha + a\omega$ ...(2)

Again multiplying (1) by cos α and (3) by sin α and adding, we get

Also by Newton's experimental law, we have

$(mk^2\omega_1 - mu_1 a) - (mk^2\omega - mua) = 0$ ...(4)

($\because$ change in moment of momentum = moment of the impulse) Also, the point of contact has no horizontal velocity so we get $u_1 + a\omega_1 = 0$ ...(5)

(4) and (5) $\Rightarrow u_1\left(1+\frac{k^2}{a^2}\right) = u - \frac{k^2}{a}\omega$ ...(6)

From (6), it is clear that u_1 will be negative if $u < \frac{k^2}{a}\omega$.

Thus we can say that the ball will not proceed beyond the point of contact, if

$$u < \frac{k^2}{a}\omega, \text{ or } \frac{Uk^2\cos\alpha + V\sin\alpha\cos\alpha\{a^2 + e(k^2+a^2)\}}{a^2+k^2}$$

$$< \frac{k^2 a(U - V\sin\alpha)}{a(a^2+k^2)}$$

if $k^2 (U - V \sin\alpha) > Uk^2 \cos\alpha + V \sin\alpha \cos\alpha \{a^2 + e(k^2 + a^2)\}$

$= Uk^2 \cos\alpha - Vk^2 \sin\alpha \cos\alpha$

$+ Vk^2 \sin\alpha \cos\alpha + V \sin\alpha \cos\alpha \{a^2 + e(k^2 + a^2)\}$

$= k^2 (U - V \sin\alpha) \cos\alpha + V \sin\alpha \cos\alpha \{(a^2 + k^2) + e(k^2 + a^2)\}$

$= k^2 (U - V \sin\alpha) \cos\alpha + (1 + e)(k^2 + a^2) V \sin\alpha \cos\alpha.$

Example 33:

A tennis ball of hallow spherical space is given by underground cut, and hits the ground at the other side of the net at a distance c from it. If u and v its horizontal and vertical velocities and ω its angular velocity when it hits the perfect rough ground, show that the ball will return back towards the net if $2a\omega > 3u$.

Further show that it will rebound over the net if $c < \dfrac{2ev(2a\omega - 3u)}{5g}$

will touch the net over head if $k < \dfrac{5c}{2} \cdot \dfrac{2ev(2a\omega - 3u) - 5gc}{(2a\omega - 3u)^2}$, *where e is the coefficient of restitution and h is the height of the net.*

Solution:

After the impact let u_1 and v_1 be the velocities of the centre of gravity G of the ball and ω_1 its angular velocity.

Let F be the impulsive friction and R the impulsive normal reactions of motion if the ball are

$m(u_1 + u) = F$ ...(1) $m(v_1 + v) = R$ ...(2)

and $m\frac{2}{3}a^2(\omega_1 - \omega) = -Fa$ ...(3)

where $ev = v_1$,

Just after the impact there is no horizontal velocity of the point of contact,

so $u_1 - a\omega_1 = 0$ ...(4)

From (1) and (3), we obtain

$$u_1 + u + \frac{2}{3}a(\omega_1 \ \omega) = 0$$

$$\Rightarrow 5u_1 = 2a\omega - 3u \Rightarrow u_1 = \frac{2a\omega - 3u}{5}$$

Hence the ball will return back towards the net if u_1 is positive when $2a\omega - 3u > 0$ or when $2a\omega > 3u$.

Second part. After rebouding from the ground, the ball moves in parabolic path. Now considering the horizontal motion of the ball, we have $t = \frac{c}{u_1}$

Now t, must be less than the time of reaching the ground.

$$\therefore \frac{5c}{2a\omega - 2u} < \frac{2ev}{g}$$

$$\text{or } c < \frac{2ev(2a\omega - 3u)}{5g}.$$

Third part. Let the vertical height to which the ball rises be h then have

$$h' = v_1 t - \frac{1}{2}gt^2 = ev - \frac{1}{2}gt^2 \qquad (\because v_1 = ev).$$

$$= \frac{5}{2}e\frac{2ev(2a\omega - 3u) - 5gc}{(2a\omega - 3u)^2}$$

Example 34:

Three particles of equal masses are attached to the ends, A and C, and the middle point B of light rod ABC, and the system is at rest on a smooth table. The particle C is struck by a blow at right angles to the rod: show that the energy communicated when the system is free as 24 : 25.

Solution:

Let A, B, C be the three points of a rod, where the three particles, each of mass m are placed. Now let the end A be free, and an impulse P be applied at C, such that the rod begins to rotate about the point B. Then, if the velocity of mass at is u_1, the velocities of the masses A and C are u_1 $u_1 + a\omega_1$ respectively.

Case I. *When the end A is free*

We have

$mu_1 + m(u_1 - a\omega_1) + (u_1 + a\omega_1)$

$$= P \Rightarrow u_1 = \frac{P}{3m} \qquad ...(1)$$

Taking moments about C, we have

$$mu_1 + m(u_1 - a\omega_1)\,2a = 0 \Rightarrow 3u - 2a\omega_1 = 0. \qquad ...(2)$$

$$\Rightarrow a\omega_1 = \frac{P}{2m}[\text{using}(1)].$$

Velocity of the mass at C = $u_1 + aw_1 = \frac{P}{3m} + \frac{P}{2m} = \frac{5P}{6m}$

and the K.E. communicated to the rod $= \frac{1}{2}$ impulse at C × (velocity of C)

$$= \frac{1}{2} P \cdot \frac{5P}{6m} = \frac{1}{12} \frac{5P^2}{m} = E_1 \text{ (Say).}$$

Case II. *When A is fixed*

In this case the rod will begin to rotate about A, with an angular velocity ω and an impulsive thrust (= X say) will be generated at A.

Now the moment about A gives

$$m(2a)^2 \omega + ma^2\omega = p.$$

$$2a \Rightarrow m5a\omega = 2P \Rightarrow a\omega = \frac{2P}{5m}.$$

∴ Velocity communicated to C = 2aω

(∵ C describes a circle, about A, of radius 2a)

hence its velocity perpendicular to AC = $2a\omega = \frac{4P}{5m}$.

Hence the kinetic energy communicated in this case becomes

$$E_2 = \frac{1}{2} P \text{ (Velocity of C)}$$

$$= \frac{1}{2} P \frac{4P}{5m} = \frac{2P^2}{5m} = E_2 \text{ (say).}$$

$$\Rightarrow \frac{E_1}{E_2} = \frac{(5p^2/12m)}{(2P^2/5m)} = \frac{25}{24} \Rightarrow \frac{E_2}{E_1} = \frac{24}{25}.$$

Example 35:

Three equal uniform rods AB, BC, CD are freely jointed and placed in a straight line on a smooth table. The rod AB is struck at its end A by a by a blow which is perpendicular to its length, find the resulting motion and show that the velocity of the centre of AB is 19 times that of CD and its angular velocity 11 times that of CD.

Solution:

Let each rod be of length 2a and mass m and P be the impulse of the blow at A. Hence there will be impulsive action at B and C in opposite directions, which also taken as X and Y respectively.

Just, before the blow, the three rods are at rest and after the blow let $u_1, \omega_1; u_2, \omega_2; u_3, \omega_3$ be the velocities of C.G.'s and the angular velocities of the rods AB, BC and CA respectively. Then we have

For, AB, $mu_1 = P - X,\ m\frac{a^2}{3}\omega_1 = pa + Xa \cdot$ ...(A)

For, BC, $mu_2 = X - Y,\ m\frac{a^2}{3}\omega 3 = Xa + Ya \cdot$ ...(B)

For, CD, $mu_3 = Y,\ m\ \frac{a^2}{3}\omega_3 = Y\ a.$ ...(C)

Now, velocity of B should be the same as deduced from motion of AB and BC and similarly velocity of C should be the same as deduced from the motion of BC and CD respectively.

For B $u_1 - a\omega_1 = u_2 + a\omega_2$ ...(1)

For C $u_2 - a\omega_2 = u_3 + a\omega_3$ ...(2)

$\Rightarrow u_1 - a\omega_1 = \frac{P - X}{m} - \frac{3(P + X}{m} = \frac{-2P - 4X}{m}$

From (B), we have $u_2 + a\omega_2 = \frac{X - Y}{m} + \frac{3(X + Y)}{m} = \frac{4X + 2Y}{m}$

$\therefore \quad (1) \Rightarrow 2P - 4X = + 2Y$

or $\qquad 4X + Y = -P.$ ...(3)

Again from (B), we obtain $u_2 - a\omega_2 = \frac{X - Y}{m} + \frac{3(X + Y)}{m} = \frac{-2X - 4Y}{m}$

and $u_3 + a\omega_3 = \frac{Y}{m} + \frac{3Y}{m} = \frac{4Y}{m}.$ [using C]

$\Rightarrow -2X - 4Y = 4Y$ or $X + 4Y = 0.$ [using (2)] ...(4)

Solving (3) and (4), we get $X = -\frac{4P}{15}$ and $Y = \frac{P}{15}$

$$\Rightarrow u_1 = \frac{1}{m}\left(P + \frac{4P}{15}\right) = \frac{19P}{15m}, \omega_1 = \frac{3}{ma}\left(P - \frac{4P}{15}\right) = \frac{11P}{5ma}$$

$$u_2 = \frac{1}{m}\left(-\frac{4P}{15} - \frac{P}{15}\right) = -\frac{P}{3m}, \omega_2 = \frac{3}{ma}\left(-\frac{4P}{15} - \frac{P}{15}\right) = \frac{-5P}{5ma}$$

$$u_3 = \frac{1}{15m}, \omega_3 = \frac{3}{ma}\left(\frac{P}{15}\right) = \frac{P}{5ma}$$

$$\Rightarrow u_1 : u_3 = \frac{19P}{15m} : \frac{P}{15m} = 19 : 1 \text{ i.e. } u_1 = 19u_3$$

i.e. velocity of centre of AB is 19 times that of CD.

Further, $\omega_1 : \omega_2 = \dfrac{11P}{5ma} : \dfrac{P}{5ma} = 11 : 1$ *i.e.* $\omega_1 = 11\omega_3$

i.e. the angular velocity of AB is 11 times that of CD.

EXERCISES

1. Prove that a top can be set spinning steadily with its axis of the figure horizontal; by an impulsive couple about an axis making with the vertical and angle

$$\tan^{-1}\left(\frac{C^2n^2}{Amgh}\right)$$

2. A top is a right cone of height 1 and vertical [angle, 90° and move about its vertex under gravity. Initially it started rotating with angular velocity $5\sqrt{(3g/l)}$, the axis being instantaneously at rest and inclined as 60° to the upward vertical. Show that in the subsequent motion the angle between the axis and vertical oscillations between 60°. and 120°.

3. A ring of wire of radius c rests on the top of smooth fixed sphere of radius a and is set rotating about the vertical diameter of the sphere. If the ring is slightly displaced, prove that the motion is unstable if the angular velocity is less than

$$\left[2g\frac{2a^2 - c^2}{c^4}\sqrt{\{(a^2 - c^2)\}}\right]^{1/2}$$

4. A top is processing steadily with one end of its axis fixed and its axis horizontal. If a small weight W be suddenly attached to the other end of its axis without impulse, show that an oscillatory motion is set up in which the maximum dip of the axis below the horizontal is approximately.

   $2W\ a/(A^2\ \Omega + C^2n^2)$,

   Where Ω is the initial angular velocity of precession and a the length of the axis.

5. A square lamina, ABCD rests on a smooth horizontal plane. If the corner A is made to move with velocity u along the line produced then determine the initial angular velocity of the lamina [– 3u/8a].

6. A billard ball is at rest on a horizontal table and is struck by a horizontal table and is struck by a horizontal blow, in a vertical plane passing through the centre of the ball; if the initial motion is one of pure rolling, find the height of the point struck above the table.

7. Two equal uniform rods AB and AC, are freely hinged at A and rest in a straight line on a smooth table. A blow is struck at B perpendicular to the rods; show that the kinetic energy generated is 7/4 times what it would be if the rods were rigidly fastened together at A.

8. Three uniform rods, AB, BC, CD are hinged freely at their ends B and C, so to form three sides of a square and are laid on a smooth table; the end is struck by a horizontal blow P at right angles to AB. Show that the initial velocity of A is nineteen times of D and that the impulsive action at B and C are respectively (5/12) P and (1/12) P.

9. Two equal uniform rods, AB and AC, are freely jointed at A, and placed on a smooth table so as to be at right angles. The rod AC is struck by a blow at C in a direction perpendicular to itself, show that the resulting velocities of the middle points of AB and AC are in the ratio 2 : 1.

10. When the axis of a symmetrical top is stationary and the spin is large and equal to u, a blow J is applied perpendicular to the axis at a distance c from the fixed point. Prove that the maximum angular deviation of the axis is approximately

    $2\tan^{-1}(Jc/Cn)$

    C being the moment of inertia of the top about its axis of symmetry.

11. A symmetrical top is set in motion on a rough horizontal plane with an angular motion about its figure, the axis being inclined at angle i to the vertical. Show that between the great approach to end recess from the vertical, the centre of gravity describes an are

    $$h\tan^{-1}\left(\frac{\sin i}{p-\cos i}\right),$$

    where p and h have the usual meanings.

12. A top of vertex O, is set in motion so that the angular momentum Cn is equal to that about the vertical drawn upward through O. The inclination of the axis to the vertical was initially i, and every point on the axis was moving horizontally. Determine if the axis will become vertical in a finite time, and if it does, show that the velocity of the centre of gyration P at that instant is equal to

    $$2\sqrt{(gl)}\tan\frac{1}{4}i\left\{\sqrt{\left(p-\cos^2\frac{1}{4}i\right)}\right\} \text{ where } 4A^2 gp = C^2 n^2 l \text{ and } OP = l.$$

3

LAGRANGE'S EQUATIONS OF MOTION SMALL OSCILLATIONS : NORMAL CO-ORDINATES

GENERALISED CO-ORDINATES

Suppose that a particle or a system of N-particles moves subject to possible constraints, as for example a particle moving along a circular wire or a rigid body moving along an inclined plane, then there will be necessarily a minimum number of independent co-ordinates then needed to specify the motion. These co-ordinates may be distances, angles or quantities relating to them.

LAGRANGE'S EQUATIONS WITH IMPULSIVE FORCES

When the forces are finite,

$$\frac{d}{dt}\left(\frac{\partial T}{\partial \dot{q}_\alpha}\right)-\frac{\partial T}{\partial q_\alpha}=\phi_\alpha \text{ where } \phi_\alpha=\sum_v V_v\cdot\frac{\partial r_v}{\partial q_\alpha}$$

Integrating both sides of (1) w.r.t. "t" form t = 0 to t = τ, we get

$$\left[\left(\frac{\partial T}{\partial \dot{q}_\alpha}\right)\right]_{t=0}^{t=\tau}-\int_0^\tau\frac{\partial T}{\partial q_\alpha}dt=\int_{t=0}^{\tau}\phi_\alpha dt=\sum_v\left\{\left(\int_{t=0}^{\tau}F_v dt\right).\frac{\partial r_v}{\partial q_\alpha}\right\} \quad ...(2)$$

Taking the limit as $\tau\to 0$, we get

$$\lim_{\tau\to 0}\left\{\left(\frac{\partial T}{\partial \dot{q}_\alpha}\right)_{t=\tau}-\left(\frac{\partial T}{\partial \dot{q}_\alpha}\right)_{t=0}\right\}-\lim_{\tau\to 0}\int_0^\tau\frac{\partial T}{\partial q_\alpha}dt$$

$$=\sum_v\left\{\left(\lim_{\tau\to 0}\int_0^\tau F_v dt\right)\cdot\frac{\partial r_v}{\partial q_\alpha}\right\}$$

$$\Rightarrow\left(\frac{\partial T}{\partial \dot{q}_\alpha}\right)_1-\left(\frac{\partial T}{\partial \dot{q}_\alpha}\right)_0=\Sigma^{*}l_v\cdot\frac{\partial r_v}{\partial q_\alpha}=**P_\alpha\,(\text{say}) \qquad ...(3)$$

where subscripts 0 and 1 denote respectively quantities before and after the application of the impulsive force.

These equations are known as Lagrange's equations under impulsive forces.

LAGRANGE'S EQUATION

Let F be the net external force acting on the Vth particle of a system, then bt Newton's second law applied to Vth particle, we have

$$m_v\ddot{r}_v = F_v$$

$$\Rightarrow m_v\ddot{r}_v\bullet\frac{\partial r_v}{\partial q_\alpha}=F_v\bullet\frac{\partial r_v}{\partial q_\alpha} \qquad ...(8)$$

$$\Rightarrow \Sigma_{v=1}^{N} m_v\ddot{r}_v\bullet\frac{\partial r_v}{\partial q\alpha}=\Sigma_v^N F_v\bullet\frac{\partial r_v}{\partial q\alpha}$$

$$\Rightarrow\frac{d}{dt}\left(\Sigma_{v=1}^{N}m_v\dot{r}_v\bullet\frac{\partial r_v}{\partial q_\alpha}\right)-\Sigma_{V=1}^{N}m_v\dot{r}_v\bullet\frac{d}{dt}\left(\frac{\partial r_v}{\partial q\alpha}\right)=\Sigma_{v=1}^{N}F_v\bullet\frac{\partial r_v}{\partial q_\alpha}$$

$$\text{But } r_v=r_v(q_1,q_2,....,q_n;t) \qquad ...(10)$$

$$\therefore \dot{r}_v=\frac{\partial r_v}{\partial q_1}\dot{q}_1+\frac{\partial r_v}{\partial q_2}\dot{q}_2+...+\frac{\partial r_v}{\partial q_n}\dot{q}_n+\frac{\partial r_v}{\partial q\alpha} \qquad ...(11)$$

$$\Rightarrow\frac{\partial \dot{r}_v}{\partial \dot{q}\alpha}=\frac{\partial r_v}{\partial q\alpha} \qquad \text{[Cancellation law of the dots]} \qquad ...(12)$$

$$\text{Also, }\frac{\partial \dot{r}_v}{\partial q\alpha}(\dot{r}_v)=\frac{\partial}{\partial q\alpha}\left(\frac{\partial r_v}{\partial q_1}\dot{q}_1+\frac{\partial r_v}{\partial q_2}\dot{q}_2+...+\frac{\partial r_v}{\partial q_n}q_{\dot{n}}+\frac{\partial r_v}{\partial t}\right)$$

$$=\frac{\partial^2 r_v}{\partial q_\alpha\partial q_1}\dot{q}_1+\frac{\partial^2 r_v}{\partial q_\alpha\partial q_1}\dot{q}_2+...+\frac{\partial^2 r_v}{\partial q_\alpha\partial q_n}\dot{q}_n+\frac{\partial}{\partial q_\alpha}\left(\frac{\partial r_v}{\partial t}\right)$$

$$=\frac{\partial}{\partial q_1}\left(\frac{\partial r_v}{\partial q_\alpha}\right)\dot{q}_1+\frac{\partial}{\partial q_2}\left(\frac{\partial r_v}{\partial q_\alpha}\right)\dot{q}_2+...+\frac{\partial}{\partial q_\alpha}\left(\frac{\partial r_v}{\partial q_n}\right)\dot{q}_n+\frac{\partial}{\partial t}\left(\frac{\partial r_v}{\partial q_\alpha}\right)$$

$$\text{or }=\frac{\partial}{\partial q_\alpha}\left(\frac{\partial r_v}{\partial t}\right)=\frac{d}{dt}\left(\frac{\partial r_v}{\partial q_\alpha}\right)\Rightarrow\frac{d}{dt}\left(\frac{\partial}{\partial q_\alpha}\right)=\frac{\partial}{\partial q\alpha}\left(\frac{d}{dt}\right) \qquad ...(13)$$

[interchange law of the order of operators]

$$\text{Now }\frac{d}{dt}\left\{\Sigma_{v=1}^{N}m_v\dot{r}_v\bullet\frac{\partial r_v}{\partial q_\alpha}\right\}-\Sigma_{v=1}^{N}m_v\dot{r}_v\bullet\frac{\partial \dot{r}_v}{\partial q_\alpha}=\Sigma_{v=1}^{N}F_v\bullet\frac{\partial r_v}{\partial q_\alpha} \qquad ...(14)$$

and $T = \frac{1}{2}\sum_v m_v \dot{r}_v^2 = \frac{1}{2}\sum_v m_v (\dot{v}_v \cdot \dot{r}_v)$ ...(15)

$$\Rightarrow \frac{\partial T}{\partial q_\alpha} = \sum_v m_v \dot{r}_v \cdot \frac{\partial \dot{r}_v}{\partial q_\alpha} \quad ...(16)$$

and $\Rightarrow \frac{\partial T}{\partial \dot{q}_\alpha} = \sum_v m_v \dot{r}_v \cdot \frac{\partial \dot{r}_v}{\partial \dot{q}_\alpha} = \sum m_v \dot{r}_v \cdot \frac{\partial v_v}{\partial q_\alpha}$ [using (12)] ...(17)

$\therefore (14) \Rightarrow \frac{d}{dt}\left(\frac{\partial T}{\partial \dot{q}_\alpha}\right) - \frac{\partial T}{\partial q_\alpha} = \phi_\alpha = \frac{\partial W}{\partial q_\alpha}$ using (7) ...(18)

Note. The quantity $p_\alpha = \frac{\partial T}{\partial \dot{q}_\alpha}$ is called the generalised momentum associated with the general co-ordinates q_α.

LAGRANGIAN FUNCTION

If the forces are derivable from a potential function V, then

$$\phi_\alpha = \frac{\partial W}{\partial q_\alpha} = -\frac{\partial V}{\partial q_\alpha},$$

since the potential, or potential energy is a function of q's only (and possibly the name t) then, we have

$$\frac{d}{dt}\left(\frac{\partial T}{\partial \dot{q}_\alpha}\right) - \frac{\partial T}{\partial q_\alpha} = -\frac{\partial V}{\partial q_\alpha} \Rightarrow \frac{d}{dt}\left[\frac{\partial}{\partial \dot{q}_\alpha}(T - V)\right] - \left(\frac{\partial T}{\partial q_\alpha} - \frac{\partial V}{\partial q_\alpha}\right) = 0$$

$\Rightarrow \frac{d}{dt}\left(\frac{\partial L}{\partial \dot{q}_\alpha}\right) - \frac{\partial L}{\partial q_\alpha} = 0$, where $L = T - V$ ...(19)

The function L defined by L = T – V is said to be Lagrangian function.

DEGREES OF FREEDOM

The number of independent co-ordinates required to specify the position of a system of one or more particles is called the number of degrees of freedom of the system.

Example 1:

A particle moving freely in space require 3 co-ordinates, e.g. (x, y, z), to specify its position. Thus the number of degrees of freedom is 3.

Example 2:

A system containing of N-particles moving freely in space require 3N co-ordinates to specify the position. The number of degrees of freedom is 3N.

A rigid body which can move freely in space has 6 degrees of freedom i.e. 6. co-ordinates are required to specify the position.

Let 3 non-collinear points of a rigid body be fixed in space, then the rigid body also fixed in space. Let these points have co-ordinates (x_1,y_1,z_1); (x_2,y_2,z_2); (x_3,y_3,z_3) respectively, a total of 9. Since the body is rigid, we must have

$$(x_1-x_2)^2+(y_1-y_2)^2+(z_1-z_2)^2 = \text{constant.}$$

$$(x_2-x_3)^2+(y_2-y_3)^2+(z_2-z_3)^2 = \text{constant.}$$

$$(x_3-x_1)^2+(y_3-y_1)^2+(z_3-z_1)^2 = \text{constant.}$$

Hence 3 co-ordinates can be expressed in terms of the remaining six. Thus six independent co- ordinates are needed to describe the motion *i.e.* there exit six degrees of freedom.

TRANSFORMATION EQUATION

Let $rv = x_v i + y_v j + z_v k$ be the position vector of v-th particle with respect to xyz co-ordinates system. The relationships of th generalised co-ordinates $q_1, q_2, \ldots, q_n$ the position co-ordinates are given by the transformation equations.

$$\left.\begin{aligned} x_v &= x_v(q_1,q_2,\ldots,q_n;t) \\ y_v &= y_v(q_1,q_2,\ldots,q_n;t) \\ z_v &= z_v(q_1,q_2,\ldots,q_n;t) \end{aligned}\right\} \quad \ldots(1)$$

where t denotes the time. In vector (1) can be written as

$$r_v = r_v(q_1,q_2,\ldots,q_n;t) \ldots(2)$$

where the functions in (1) or (2) are continuous and have continuous derivatives.

CLASSIFICATION OF MECHANICAL SYSTEMS

(a) Scleronomic System

The mechanical system in which t, the time, does not enter explicity in equations (1) or (2) is called a scleronomic system.

(b) Rheonomic System

The mechanical system in which the moving constraints are involved and the time t does enter explicity is called a Rheonomic system.

(c) Holonomic System and Non Holonomic System

Let $q_1, q_2; \ldots, q_n$ denote the generalised co-ordinates describing a system and let t denote the time. If all the constraints of the system can be expressed as equations having the form $(q_1,q_1,\ldots q_n;t)=0$ or their equivalent, then the system is said to be Holonomic otherwise it is be Non- Holonomic system.

(d) Conservation and Non-conservative System

If the forces acting on the system are derivable from a potential function [or potential energy] V, then the system is called conservative, otherwise it is non-conservative.

KINETIC ENERGY AND GENERALISED VELOCITIES

The K.E of the system is $T=\frac{1}{2}\Sigma_{v=1}^{n} mv\,\dot{r}_v$ ...(3)

The K.E of the system can be written as a quadratic form in the generalised co-ordinates q_α If the system is independent of time explicitly *i.e.* scleronomic then the quadratic form has only terms of the type $q_{\alpha\beta}\, q_\alpha\, q_\beta$ In case the system is Rhenomic, linear terms in q_α are also present.

GENERALISED FORCES

If W is the total work done on a system of particles by forces Fv acting on the v-th particle, then $dW=\Sigma_{\alpha=1}^{n}\phi_\alpha dq_\alpha$ where $\phi_\alpha=\Sigma_{v=1}^{N} F_v\bullet\frac{\partial r_v}{\partial q_\alpha}$ is called the *generalised force* associated with generalised co-ordinator q_α

Suppose that a system undergoes increments $dq_1, dq_2, \ldots dq_n$; then the v-th particle undergoes a displacement.

$$dr_v=\Sigma_{\alpha=1}^{n}\frac{\partial r_v}{\partial q_\alpha}dq_\alpha \quad \text{...(4)}$$

$\therefore$ Total work done is given by

$$dW=\Sigma_{v=1}^{N} F\bullet dr_v=\Sigma_{v=1}^{N}\left\{\Sigma_{\alpha=1}^{n} F_v\bullet\frac{\partial r_v}{\partial q_\alpha}\right\}dq_\alpha \quad \text{...(5)}$$

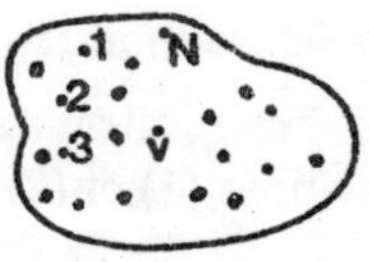

Now, let $\phi_\alpha=\Sigma_{v=1}^{N}\left(\Sigma_{v=1}^{N} F_v\bullet\frac{\partial r_v}{\partial q_\alpha}\right)$

Now, let $\phi_\alpha=\Sigma_{v=1}^{N} F_v\bullet\frac{\partial r_v}{\partial q_\alpha}$

Fig. 3.1

then (5) $dW=\Sigma_{\alpha=1}^{N}\left(\Sigma_{v=1}^{N} F_v\bullet\frac{\partial r_v}{\partial q_\alpha}\right)d_{\alpha\alpha}=\Sigma_{\alpha=1}^{n}\phi_\alpha d_{\alpha\alpha}$ ...(6)

We have $dW=\Sigma_{\alpha=1}^{N}\frac{\partial W}{\partial q_\alpha},\therefore\frac{\partial W}{\partial q_\alpha}=\phi_\alpha$ ...(7)

Note:

(i) varies from (1) to n, the number of degrees of freedom.

(ii) varies from 1 to N, the number of particles in the system.

GENERALISED MOMENTUM

We defined $p_\alpha = \frac{\partial T}{\partial \dot{q}_\alpha}$ *to be the generalised momentum associated with generalised co-ordinates* q_α *or the conjugate momentum.*

In case the system is conservative, we have

$$T = L + V \Rightarrow (\partial T / \partial \dot{q}_\alpha) = (\partial L / \partial \dot{q}_{\dot{\alpha}}) + (\partial V / \partial \dot{q}_\alpha) = (\partial L / \partial \dot{q}_\alpha)$$

because V, the P.E. of the system does not depend upon $\dot{q}_\alpha$

$$\therefore P_\alpha = (\partial L / \partial q_\alpha).$$

ILLUSTRATIVE EXAMPLES

Example 1:

(i) *Set up the Lagrangian for a simple pendulum, and*

(ii) *Obtain an equation describing its motion.*

Solution:

(i) Choose as generalised coordinates, the angle θ made by the string OB of the pendulum and the vertical OA. Let l be the length of OA, then K.E. is given by

$$T = \frac{1}{2} mv^2 = \frac{1}{2} m(l\dot{\theta})^2 = \frac{1}{2} ml^2\dot{\theta}^2$$

where m is the mass of the bob.

The potential energy of mass m is given by

$$V = mg\,(OA - OC) = mg\,(l - l\cos\theta)$$
$$= mgl\,(1 - \cos\theta)$$

$$\therefore L = T - V = \frac{1}{2} ml^2\dot{\theta}^2 - mgl(1 - \cos\theta)$$

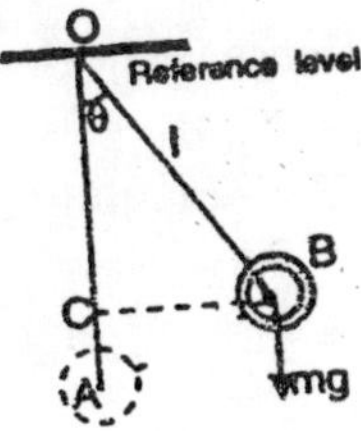

Fig. 3.2

(ii) Hence Lagrange's θ equation gives

$$\frac{d}{dt}\left(\frac{\partial L}{\partial \dot{\theta}}\right) - \frac{\partial L}{\partial \theta} = 0 \Rightarrow \frac{d}{dt}(ml^2\dot{\theta}) - (-mgl\sin\theta) = 0$$

$$\frac{d}{dt}\left(\frac{\partial L}{\partial \dot{\theta}}\right) - \frac{\partial L}{\partial \theta} = 0 \Rightarrow l\ddot{\theta} = -g\sin\theta \Rightarrow \ddot{\theta} = -\frac{g}{l}\sin\theta,$$

which is the required equation of motion.

KINETIC ENERGY AS A QUADRATIC FUNCTION OF VELOCITIES

If at time t, the position of the vth particle (mass m), of a holonomic system is defined by r_v then K.E. is given by

$$T=\frac{1}{2}\Sigma_{v=1}^{N}m_v\dot{r}_v^2,$$

where $r_v = r_v(q_1,.....q_n;t)$ ...(1)

So that $\dot{r}_v = \dot{q}_1\frac{\partial r_v}{\partial q_1}+\dot{q}_2\frac{\partial r_v}{\partial q_2}+...+\dot{q}_n\frac{\partial r_v}{\partial q_n}+\frac{\partial r_v}{dt}$

$$\Rightarrow T=\frac{1}{2}\Sigma_{v=1}^{N}m_v\left(\dot{q}_1\frac{\partial r_v}{\partial q_1}+\dot{q}_2\frac{\partial r_v}{\partial q_2}+...+\dot{q}_n\frac{\partial r_v}{\partial q_n}+\frac{\partial r_v}{\partial t}\right)^2$$

$$=\frac{1}{2}[(a_{11}\dot{q}_1^2+a_{22}\dot{q}_2^2+....+a_{nn}\dot{q}_n^2+2a_{12}\dot{q}_1\dot{q}_2+2a_{1n}\dot{q}_1\dot{q}_n+...)$$

$$+2(a_1\dot{q}_1+a_2\dot{q}_2+.+a_n\dot{q}_n)+a] \quad ...(2)$$

where $5a_{rs}=\Sigma_{v=1}^{N}m_v(\partial r_v/\partial q_r).(\partial r_v/\partial q_s)(s\geq r)$

$$a_{rr}=\Sigma_{v=1}^{N}m_v(\partial r_v/\partial q_r)^2, a=\Sigma_{v=1}^{N}m_v(\partial r_v/\partial t)^2, =\Sigma_{v=1}^{N}m_v\left(\frac{\partial r_v}{\partial q_r}\right).\left(\frac{\partial r_1}{\partial t}\right)$$

From (2), we see that T is a quadratic function of the of the generalised velocities.

The case t is not explicity involved, is of considerable importance.

Hence we have $\frac{\partial r_v}{\partial t}=0$ and therefore (2) implies that

$$T=\frac{1}{2}(a_{11}\dot{q}_1^2+a_{22}\dot{q}_2^2+...+a_{nn}\dot{q}_n^2+2a_{12}\dot{q}_1\dot{q}_2+...) \quad ...(3)$$

$$=\frac{1}{2}\Sigma_{s=1}^{n}\Sigma_{r=1}^{n}a_{rs}\dot{q}_r\dot{q}_s \text{ where } a_{rs}=a_{sr}. \quad ...(4)$$

Now using Euler's theorem for homogenecus functions, we get

$$\dot{q}_1\frac{\partial T}{\partial \dot{q}_1}+\dot{q}_2\frac{\partial T}{\partial \dot{q}_2}+...+\dot{q}_n\frac{\partial T}{\partial \dot{q}_n}=2T$$

$$\Rightarrow 2T=\Sigma_{\alpha=1}^{n}\dot{q}_\alpha\frac{\partial T}{\partial \dot{q}_\alpha}p_\alpha\dot{q}_\alpha$$

i.e. $2T=p_1\dot{q}_1+p_2\dot{q}_2+...+p_n\dot{q}_n$

TO DEDUCE THE PRINCIPLE OF ENERGY FROM THE LAGRANGE'S EQUATIONS (CONSERVATIVE FIELD)

Lagrange's equations are:

$$\frac{d}{dt}\left(\frac{\partial T}{\partial \dot{q}_\alpha}\right)-\frac{\partial T}{\partial q_\alpha}=-\frac{\partial V}{\partial q_\alpha}; \qquad (\alpha = 1, 2, \ldots n) \qquad \ldots(1)$$

Also by 7.11 equation we know that

$$T=\frac{1}{2}(a_{11}\dot{q}_1^{\,2}+a_{22}\dot{q}^2+\ldots+a_m\dot{q}_n^{\,2}+2a_{12}\dot{q}_1\dot{q}_2+\ldots)$$

that is, T can be expressed as a quadratic expression in generalised velocities. Hence applying Euler's theorem. We get

$$\Sigma_{\alpha=1}^{n}\dot{q}_\alpha\frac{\partial T}{\partial \dot{q}_\alpha}=2T \qquad \ldots(2)$$

$$\text{Also } \frac{dT}{dt}=\Sigma_{\alpha=1}^{n}\frac{\partial T}{\partial q_\alpha}\dot{q}_\alpha+\Sigma_{\alpha=1}^{n}\frac{\partial T}{\partial \dot{q}_\alpha}\ddot{q}_\alpha \qquad \ldots(3)$$

Now multiplying the n equations of (1) by $\dot{q}_1, \dot{q}_2, \ldots \dot{q}_n$, respectively and then adding. we get

$$\left\{\dot{q}_1\frac{d}{dt}\left[\frac{\partial T}{\partial \dot{q}_1}\right]+\ldots+\dot{q}_n\frac{d}{dt}\left[\frac{\partial T}{\partial \dot{q}_1}\right]\right\}-\left\{\dot{q}_1\frac{\partial T}{\partial q_1}+\ldots+\dot{q}_n\frac{\partial T}{\partial \dot{q}_n}\right\}$$

$$=-\left\{\dot{q}_1\frac{\partial V}{\partial q_1}+\ldots+\dot{q}_n\frac{\partial V}{\partial q_n}\right\}$$

$$\Rightarrow\frac{d}{dt}\left\{\Sigma_{\alpha=1}^{n}\dot{q}_\alpha\frac{\partial T}{\partial \dot{q}_\alpha}\right\}-\left(\Sigma_{\alpha=1}^{n}\ddot{q}_\alpha\frac{\partial T}{\partial \dot{q}_\alpha}\right)-\left\{\Sigma_{\alpha=1}^{n}\dot{q}_n\frac{\partial T}{\partial q_\alpha}\right\}$$

$$=-\left(\Sigma_{\alpha=1}^{n}\dot{q}_\alpha\frac{\partial V}{\partial q_n}\right)$$

$$\Rightarrow\frac{d}{dt}(2T)-\frac{dT}{dt}=-\frac{dV}{dt}\Rightarrow\frac{dT}{dt}+\frac{dV}{dt}=0\Rightarrow\frac{d}{dt}(T+V)=0\Rightarrow T+V=\text{constant.}$$

SMALL OSCILLATIONS

To explain how Lagrange's equations are used in case of small oscillations. (when there exist three generalised co-ordinates),

In order to investigate the theory of small oscillations by the use of Lagrange's equation about the position of equilibrium, the generalised co-ordinates q_1, q_2, q_3 must be chosen in such a way that they vanish in the position of equilibrium.

But the system makes small oscillations about the position of equilibrium, so q_1, q_2, q_3 and their differentials $\dot{q}_2$, $\dot{q}_2$, $\dot{q}_3$ will remain small during the whole motion. Hence we shall reject all the powers of small quantities except the lowest one.

Now, let T be kinetic energy, and W the work-function of the system; then wc have

$$T = A_{11}\dot{q}_1^{\ 2} + A_{22}\dot{q}_2^{\ 2} + A_{33}\dot{q}_3^{\ 2} + 2A_{12}\dot{q}_2\dot{q}_1 + 2A_{23}\dot{q}_2\dot{q}_3 + 2A_{13}\dot{q}_1\dot{q}_3 \quad ...(1)$$

$$\dot{W} = C + B_1q_1 + B_2\,q_2 + B_3q_3 + B_{11}q_1^{\ 2} + B22\,q_2^{\ 2} + q_3^{\ 2} \quad ..(2)$$

Now assume that q_1, q_2, q_3 can be expressed in terms of X, Y, Z by the equations of the form

$$q_1 = \lambda_1X + \lambda_2Y + \lambda_3Z; q_2 = \mu_1X + \mu_2Y + \mu_3Z; \quad q_3 = v_1X + v_2Y + v_3Z;$$

and further assume $\lambda_1, \lambda_2, \lambda 3, \mu_1, \mu_2, \mu_3, v_1, v_2, v_3$ in such a way that if we put value of q_1, q_2, q_3 in (1) and (2), then T does not involve $\dot{Y}\dot{Z}, \dot{Z}\dot{X}, \dot{X}\dot{Y}$ and W does not involve YZ, ZX, XY. Then X,T, Z, are called the *normal or Principal Co-ordinates.*

Thus equation (1) and (2) $\Rightarrow$

$$T = A'_{11}\dot{X}^2 + A'_{22}\dot{Y}_{22}\dot{Y}^2 + A'_{33}\dot{Z}^2$$

$$W = C' + B_1X + B'_2Y + B'_3Z + B'_{11}X^2 + B_{22}Y^2 + B'_{33}Z^2$$

Now, using Lagrange's equations,

viz. $\dfrac{d}{dt}\left(\dfrac{dT}{d\dot{X}}\right) - \left(\dfrac{dT}{dX}\right) = \left(\dfrac{dW}{dX}\right)$ etc., we obtain

$$2A'_{11}\ddot{X} = B'_1 + 2B'_{11}X; \;\; 2A'_{22}\ddot{Y} = B'_2 + 2B'_{22}Y; \;\; 2A'_{33}\ddot{Z} = B'_3 + 2B'_{33}Z$$

which can be put in the forms

$$\ddot{X} = -\omega^2{}_1X, \ddot{Y} = -\omega^2{}_3Y, \ddot{Z} = -\omega^2{}_3Z \text{ etc.}$$

which represents simple Harmonic Motions, Or in other words they give small oscillations about the position equilibrium.

SOLVED EXAMPLES

Example 1:

Three equal uniform rods AB, BC, CD, each of mass m and length 2a, are at rest in a straight line smoothly jointed at B and C. A blow I is given to the middle rod at a distance c from the centre O in a direction perpendicular to it, show that the initial velocity of O is $\dfrac{2I}{3T'}$ *and that the initial angular velocities of the rods are*

$$\frac{(5a+9c)I}{10ma^2}, \frac{6cI}{5ma^2} \text{ and } \frac{(5a-9c)I}{10ma^2}$$

Solution:

Just after the blow let $\dot{y}$ be the linear velocity of O, and let θ, φ, ψ be the inclination of BC, CD and AB to their initial positions. Now let T be K.E. of the system, then we have

$$T = \frac{1}{2}\left(\frac{a^2}{3}\dot{\theta}^2 + \dot{y}^2\right) + \frac{1}{2}m\left\{\frac{a^2}{3}\dot{\psi}^2 + (\dot{y} - a\dot{\theta} + a\dot{\psi})^2\right\}$$

$$+\frac{1}{2}m\left\{\frac{a^2}{3}\dot{\phi}^2 + (\dot{y} - a\dot{\theta} + a\dot{\phi})^2\right\}$$

$$= \frac{1}{2}m\left[3\dot{y}^2 + \frac{7a^2}{3}\dot{\theta}^2 + \frac{4a^2}{3}\dot{\psi}^2 + \frac{4}{3}a^2\dot{\phi}^2 + 2a\dot{y}\dot{\psi} + 2a\dot{y}\dot{\phi} + 2a\dot{\theta}\dot{\phi} - 2a\dot{\theta}\dot{\psi}\right]$$

Also just before the action of the impulse, we have T = 0

∴ Lagrange's equation for blows gives

$$\left(\frac{\partial T}{\partial \dot{y}}\right)_2 - \left(\frac{\partial T}{\partial \dot{y}}\right)_1 = I \Rightarrow 3m\dot{y} + ma\dot{\phi} + ma\dot{\psi} = I$$

$$\Rightarrow 3\dot{y} + a\dot{\theta} + a\dot{\psi} = \frac{1}{m}.$$

Similarly Lagrange's θ, φ, ψ equations give

$$\frac{7}{3}a\dot{\theta} + a\dot{\phi} - a\dot{\psi} = \frac{Ic}{ma'}\dot{y} + \frac{4}{3}a\dot{\phi} + a\dot{\theta} = 0, \dot{y} - a\dot{\theta} + \frac{4}{3}a\dot{\psi} = 0$$

Last two equations $\Rightarrow 3\dot{y} + 2a\dot{\phi} + 2a\dot{\psi} = 0 3\dot{y} = \frac{2I}{m'}$ or $\dot{y} = \frac{2I}{3m}$

Also $2a\dot{\theta} = \frac{4a}{3}(\dot{\psi} - \dot{\phi})$, i.e. $\frac{3}{2}a\dot{\theta} + a\dot{\phi} - \dot{\psi} = 0$

$$\therefore \frac{5a}{6}\dot{\theta} = \frac{Ic}{ma} \text{ i.e. } \dot{\theta} = \frac{6Ic}{5ma^2}$$

Substituting now the values of $\dot{y}$ and $\dot{\theta}$ in the equation

$\dot{y} + \frac{4}{3}a\dot{\phi} + a\dot{\theta} = 0$ we get

$$\frac{2I}{3m} + \frac{4}{3}a\dot{\phi} + \frac{6Ic}{5ma} = 0 \text{ or } \dot{\phi} = \frac{(5a-9c}{10ma^2}.$$

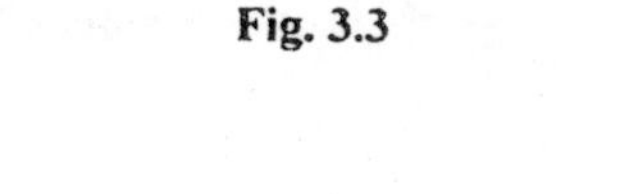

Also substituting values of $\dot{y}$ and $\dot{\theta}$ in

equation $\dot{y} - a\dot{\theta} + \frac{4}{3}a\dot{\psi} = 0,$

Fig. 3.3

we get $\frac{I}{3m} - \frac{6Ic}{5ma} + \frac{4}{3}a\dot{\psi} = 0$ or $\dot{\psi} = \frac{(5a - 9c)I}{10ma^2}$.

Example 2:

Six equal uniform rods form a regular hexagon, loosely jointed at the angular points, and rest on a smooth table; a blow is given perpendicular to one of them at its middle point, find the resulting motion and show that the opposite rod begins to move with one tenth of the velocity of the rod that is struck.

Solution:

The impulse is given at the middle point of AB in the direction as shown in the figure so the ensuing motion of BC, AF and CD, EF will be symmertrical.

Therefore they have after impulse same angular velocity say ω.

Also the rods AB and DE will begin to move at right angles to themselves. Now let $\dot{x}$ and $\dot{y}$ be their velocities just after the action of impulse.

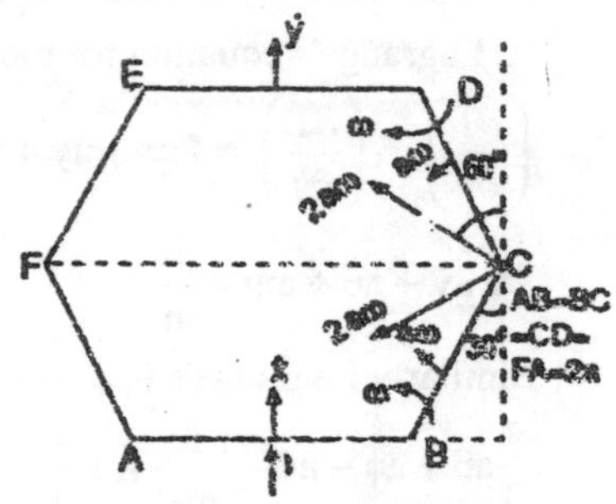

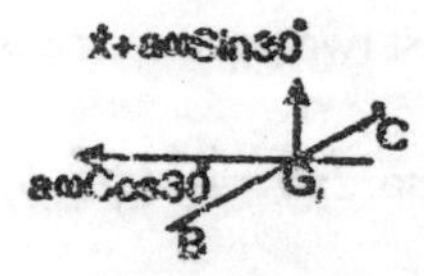

Fig. 3.4

∴ Velocity of C in the direction of $\dot{x}$

= velocity of B + velocity of C relative to B

$= \dot{x} + 2a\omega\sin 30^\circ = \dot{x} + a\omega$ ...(1)

and velocity of C in the same direction (with respect to the rod CD)

= velocity of D + velocity of C relative to D,

$= \dot{y} - 2a\omega\sin 30^\circ = \dot{y} - a\omega$ ...(2)

∴ (1) and (2) ⇒ $\dot{x} + a\omega = \dot{y} - a\omega \Rightarrow a\omega = \frac{1}{2}(\dot{y} - \dot{x})$

Now actual velocity of the C.G of the rod BC is $a\omega\cos 30^\circ$ parallel to AB and $\dot{x} + a\omega\sin 30^\circ$ at right angles to AB

∴ (velocity)^2 of $G_1 = (a\omega\cos 30^\circ)^2 + (\dot{x} + a\omega\sin 30^\circ)^2$

Thus K.E. of BC

$= \frac{1}{2}m[\frac{1}{3}a^2\omega^2 + \{(a\omega\cos 30)^2 + (\dot{x} + a\omega\sin 30)^2\}]$

$$=\frac{1}{2}m(\frac{4}{3}a^2\omega^2+\dot{x}^2+a\omega\dot{x})=\frac{1}{12}m[5\dot{x}^2+2\dot{y}^2-\dot{x}\dot{y}]=T_1\text{say}$$

$$[\because a\omega=\frac{1}{2}(\dot{y}-\dot{x})]$$

Also Kinetic energy of CD

$$=\frac{1}{2}m[\frac{1}{3}a^2\omega^2+\{(a\omega\cos 30)^2+(\dot{y}-a\omega\sin 30)^2\}]$$

$$=\frac{1}{2}m(\frac{4}{3}a^2\omega^2+\dot{y}^2-a\omega\dot{y}]=\frac{1}{12}m[2\dot{x}^2+5\dot{y}^2-\dot{x}\dot{y}]=T_2\text{say}$$

$\therefore$ Total kinetic energy T is given by $T=2T_1+2T_2+T_3+T_4$

where T_3 and T_4 are K.E.'s of AB and DE respectively.

$$\therefore T=\frac{1}{2}m\dot{x}^2+\frac{1}{2}m\dot{y}^2+2.(m/12)[5\dot{x}^2+2\dot{y}^2-\dot{x}\dot{y}]$$

$$+2.(m/12)[5\dot{y}^2+2\dot{x}^2-\dot{x}\dot{y}]$$

or $T=\frac{1}{3}m(5\dot{x}^2+5\dot{y}^2-\dot{x}\dot{y})$ $\quad\therefore$ Lagrange's x-equation is

$$\left(\frac{\partial T}{\partial \dot{x}}\right)_2-\left(\frac{\partial T}{\partial \dot{x}}\right)_1=I\Rightarrow\frac{1}{3}m(10\dot{x}-\dot{y})=I$$

Lagrange's y-equation gives $\frac{1}{3}m(10\dot{y}-\dot{x})=0$

Solving (1) and (2), we get $\dot{x}=\frac{10}{33}\frac{I}{m}$ and $\dot{y}=\frac{I}{33m}$

Also $\dot{y}=(x/10)$ and $a\omega=\frac{1}{2}(\dot{y}-\dot{x})\Rightarrow\omega=-\frac{3I}{22m}a$

Example 3:

Use Lagrange's equations to find the differential equation for a compound pendulum which oscillates in a vertical plane about a fixed horizontal axis.

Solution:

Let the plane of oscillation be represented by xy-plane, where B is its intersection with the axis of rotation and G is the centre of gravity. Let the mass of the pendulum be M and let its moment of inertia about the axis of rotation be MK^2. Then potential energy relative to the horizontal plane through N is V = -Mgh cos.

$$T=\frac{1}{2}Mk^2\dot{\theta}^2\;\therefore\;L=T-V=\frac{1}{2}Mk^2\dot{\theta}^2+Mgh\cos\theta \qquad ...(1)$$

$$\Rightarrow \frac{\partial L}{\partial \dot{\theta}} = Mk^2\dot{\theta} \text{ and } \frac{\partial L}{\partial \theta} = -Mgh\sin\theta \qquad ...(2)$$

Now Lagrange's θ equation gives

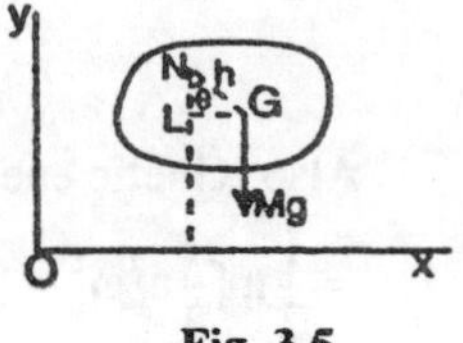

Fig. 3.5

$$\frac{d}{dt}\left(\frac{\partial L}{\partial \dot{\theta}}\right) - \frac{\partial L}{\partial \theta} = 0 \Rightarrow \frac{d}{dt}(Mk^2\dot{\theta}) + Mgh\sin\theta = 0$$

i.e. $Mk^2\ddot{\theta} + Mgh\sin\theta = 0 \Rightarrow \ddot{\theta} = -\frac{gh}{k^2}\sin\theta$

When θ is small, we have $D^2\theta = -\frac{gh}{k^2}\theta \quad (\because \sin\theta = \theta)$

or $\left(D^2 + \frac{gh}{k^2}\right)\theta = 0.$

This is the differential equation of the pendulum.

Example 4:

A particle of mass m moves in a conservative force field. Find a the Lagrangian function, (b) the equations of motion in cylindrical co-ordinates (ρ, ϕ, z).

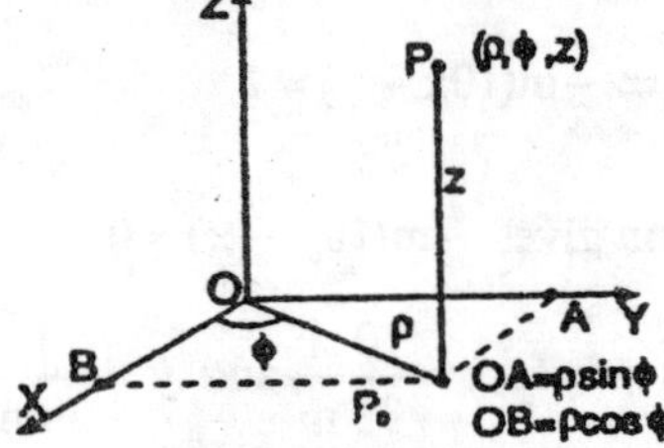

Fig. 3.6

Solution:

We have $OP = OP_0 + P_0P = OA + Ap_0 + P_0P = \vec{\rho}$ (say)

$\therefore \vec{\rho} = \rho\sin\phi j + \rho\cos\phi i + zk$ where i, j, k

are the unit vector along OX , OY and OZ respectively.

Hence the unit vector along the direction of ρ increasing is

given by $\vec{\rho_1} = \frac{\partial \vec{\rho}}{\partial \rho} / \left|\frac{\partial \vec{\rho}}{\partial \rho}\right| = \sin\phi j + \cos\phi i$

Similarly $\vec{\phi_1} = \frac{\partial \vec{\rho}}{\partial \phi} / \left|\frac{\partial \vec{\rho}}{\partial \phi}\right|$

$$= \frac{\rho\cos\phi j - \rho\sin\phi i}{\rho} = -\sin\phi i + \cos\phi j$$

Now $v = \frac{d\vec{\rho}}{dt} = \frac{d}{dt}(\rho\sin\phi j + \rho\cos\phi i + zk)$

$$= \rho\cos\phi\dot{\phi} j + \dot{\rho}\sin\phi j - \rho\sin\phi\dot{\phi} i + \dot{\rho}\cos\phi i + k\dot{z}$$

$$= \dot{\rho}\cos\phi i + \dot{\rho}\sin\phi j + \rho\dot{\phi}(\cos\phi j - \sin\phi i) + z\dot{k}$$

$$= \rho\vec{\rho}_1 + \rho\dot{\phi}\vec{\phi} + \dot{z}k$$

$$\therefore T = \frac{1}{2}m\{\dot{\rho}^2 + \rho^2\dot{\phi}^2 + \dot{z}^2\} \text{ and } V = V(\rho, \phi, z)$$

(a) Hence the Lagrangian function is

$$L = T - V = \frac{1}{2}m\left[\dot{\rho}^2 + \rho^2\dot{\phi}^2 + \dot{z}^2\right] - V(\rho, \phi, z)$$

(b) Lagrange's equations are

$$\frac{d}{dt}\left(\frac{\partial L}{\partial \dot{\rho}}\right) - \frac{\partial L}{\partial \rho} = 0 \textit{ i.e. } \frac{d}{dt}(m\dot{\rho}) - \left(m\rho\phi^2 \frac{\partial V}{\partial \rho}\right) = 0$$

$$\textit{i.e. } m(\ddot{\rho} - \rho\dot{\phi}^2) = -\frac{\partial V}{\partial \rho} \qquad ...(1)$$

$$\frac{d}{dt}\left(\frac{\partial L}{\partial \dot{\phi}}\right) - \frac{\partial L}{\partial \phi} = 0 \textit{ i.e. } \frac{d}{dt}(m\rho^2\dot{\phi}) + \frac{\partial V}{\partial \phi} = 0,$$

$$\text{or } \frac{d}{dt}(\rho^2\dot{\phi}) = -\frac{\partial V}{\partial \phi} \qquad ...(2)$$

$$\text{and } \frac{d}{dt}\left(\frac{\partial L}{\partial \dot{z}}\right) - \frac{\partial L}{\partial z} = 0 \; \frac{d}{dt}(m\dot{z}) + \frac{\partial V}{\partial z} = 0 \text{ or } m\ddot{z} = -\frac{\partial V}{\partial z} \qquad ...(3)$$

Example 5:

A particle Q moves on a smooth horizontal circular wire of radius, a which is free to rotate about a vertical axis through a point 0, distance c from the centre C. If the $\angle QCA = \theta$, show that

$$a\ddot{\theta} + \dot{\omega}(a - c\cos\theta) = c\omega^2\sin\theta.$$

where ω is the angular velocity of the wire.

Solution:

Let $0Q = r$, and $\angle AOQ = \alpha$

$$\Rightarrow r^2 = a^2 + c^2 - 2ac\cos\theta \qquad ...(1)$$

$r\cos(\alpha-\theta)=a-c\cos\theta.$ ...(2)

The particle Q m oves on circle of radius a, *so its velocity along the tangent QT will be $a\theta$ but Q revolves about O with angular velocity ω, which causes a velocity aw at the right angles to 0Q.*

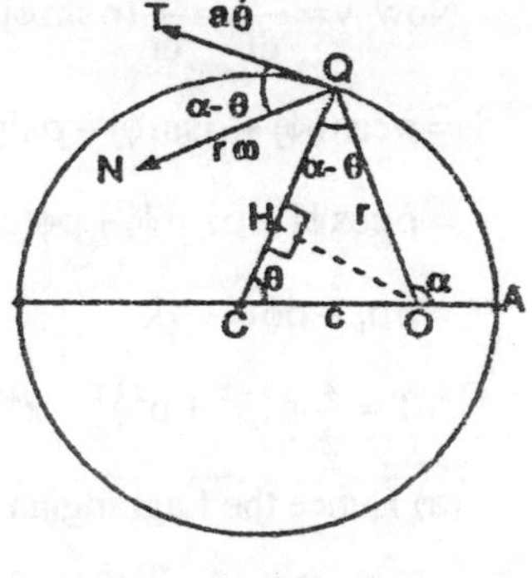

Fig. 3.7

$\Rightarrow v\frac{1}{2}=$ (velocity)^2 of the particle at Q

$=a^2\dot{\theta}^2+r^2\omega^2+2ar\dot{\theta}\cos(\alpha-\theta)\omega$

$\angle AOQ=\alpha, \angle CQO=\alpha-\theta$

Now $T=\frac{1}{2}mV_q^{\ 2}=\frac{1}{2}[a^2\dot{\theta}^2+r^2\omega^2$

$+2a\,r\,\omega\theta\cos(\alpha-\theta)]$

$\left[\begin{array}{l}\angle NQT=\alpha-\theta, OQ=r\\ HQ=a-c\cos\theta\end{array}\right.$

Note: *If r is the position vector of the particle at any time t, then $\partial r/\partial r$ is the vector tangent to the curve q = constant *i.e.* a vector in the direction of r (increasing r). A unit vector in this direction is thus given by

$$r_1=\frac{\partial r}{\partial r}\Big/\left|\frac{\partial r}{\partial r}\right|$$

Similarly, $\partial r/\partial\theta$ is the vector tangent to the curve r = constant, A unit vector in this direction is given by $\vec{\theta}_1=\frac{\partial r}{\partial\theta}\Big/\left|\frac{\partial r}{\partial\theta}\right|.$

$=\frac{1}{2}m[a^2\dot{\theta}^2+(a^2+c^2$

$=r\cos(\alpha-\theta)]$

$-2ac\cos\theta)\omega^2+2a\omega\dot{\theta}(a-c\cos\theta)$ and work function = 0

($\because$ weight does no work)

$\therefore$ Lagrange's θ equation

$$\Rightarrow\frac{d}{dt}\left(\frac{\partial T}{\partial\dot{\theta}}\right)-\frac{\partial T}{\partial\theta}=0.$$

$$\Rightarrow\frac{d}{dt}[a^2\dot{\theta}+a\omega(a-c\cos\theta)]-ac\,\omega^2\sin\theta-ac\,\omega\dot{\theta}\sin\theta=0$$

$$\Rightarrow a^2\ddot{\theta}+a\dot{\omega}(a-c\cos\theta)]+a\omega c\dot{\theta}\sin\theta-ac\,\omega^2\sin\theta-ac\,\omega\dot{\theta}\sin\theta=0$$

$$\Rightarrow a\ddot{\theta}+\dot{\omega}(a-c\cos\theta)=c\,\omega^2\sin\theta$$

Example 6:

A uniform rod, of mass 3m and length 2l, has its middle point fixed and a mass m attached at one extremity. The rod when in horizontal position is set rotating about a vertical axis through its centre with on angular velocity equal to $\sqrt{\left(\frac{2ng}{l}\right)}$ show that the heavy end of the rod will fall till the inclination of the rod to the vertical is $\cos^{-1}[\sqrt{(n^2+1)}-n$ and will the rise again.

Solution:

The mass is attached at L. On the rod ML. Take a point p such that OP $-\xi$, the element PQ $-d\xi$. Further at any time t, let the plane through it and the vertical have turned through an angle ϕ from its initial position and let the rod be inclined at an angle θ to the vertical. Taking O, the mid point of the rod, as the origin and OX, OY (a line perpendicular to the plane of the paper) and OZ as axes of reference then co-ordinates of the point P on the rod are:

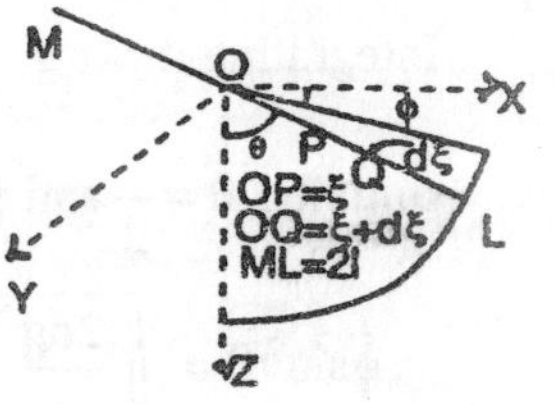

Fig. 3.8

$$x = \xi \sin\theta\cos\phi, y = \zeta \sin\theta \sin\phi, z = \xi\cos\theta$$

$$\therefore \dot{x} = \xi\cos\theta\cos\dot{\theta}, -\sin\phi\dot{\phi}\theta.$$

$$\dot{y} = \xi\cos\theta\sin\phi\theta, + \xi\sin\theta\dot{\theta}. \text{ Thus,}$$

$$v_p^2 = (\text{velocity})^2 \text{ of } P = \dot{x}^2 + \dot{y}^2 + \dot{z}^2 = \xi^2(\dot{\theta}^2 + \dot{\phi}^2\sin^2\theta).$$

$$\therefore v_L^2 = l^2(\dot{\theta}^2 + \dot{\phi}^2\sin^2\theta) = (\text{velocity})^2 \text{ of mass m},$$

Now mass of the element $PQ = \frac{3m}{2l}d\xi = dm, \text{say}.$

$\therefore$ Its kinetic energy

$$= \frac{1}{2}dm.v_p^2 = \frac{1}{2}\cdot\frac{3m}{2l}d\xi(\dot{\theta}^2 + \dot{\phi}^2\sin^2\theta)\xi^2$$

$$= \frac{3m}{4l}(\dot{\theta}^2 + \dot{\phi}^2\sin^2\theta)\xi^2 d\xi$$

and K.E. of the rod $= \frac{3m}{4l}(\dot{\theta}^2 + \dot{\phi}^2\sin^2\theta)\int_{-l}^{l}\xi^2 d\xi$

$$= \frac{1}{2}m(\dot{\theta}^2 + \dot{\phi}^2\sin^2\theta)l^2.$$

Again, (velocity)^2 of the particle $m = l^2(\dot{\theta}^2 + \dot{\phi}^2\sin^2\theta).$

$\therefore$ Kinetic energy of the particle of mass $m = \frac{1}{2}ml^2(\dot{\theta}^2 + \dot{\phi}^2 \sin^2\theta)$.

$\therefore$ Total K.E. = T = K.E. of the rod + K.E. of the particle

$$= \frac{1}{2}ml^2(\dot{\theta}^2 + \dot{\phi}^2 \sin^2\theta) + \frac{1}{2}ml^2(\dot{\theta}^2 + \dot{\phi}^2 \sin^2\theta)$$

i.e. $T = ml^2(\dot{\theta}^2 + \dot{\phi}^2 \sin^2\theta)$

Also the work function is given by $W = mgl\cos\theta + C$.

Lagrange's ϕ-equation is $\frac{d}{dt}\left(\frac{\partial T}{\partial \dot{\phi}}\right) - \frac{\partial T}{\partial \phi} = \frac{\partial W}{\partial \phi}$

which gives $\frac{d}{dt}(2ml^2\dot{\phi}\sin^2\theta) = 0$.

Integrating it, we get $\dot{\phi}\sin^2\theta = K$ (constant).

Initially, $\theta = \frac{\pi}{2}$ and $\dot{\phi} = \sqrt{\left(\frac{2ng}{l}\right)}$. $\therefore K = \sqrt{\left(\frac{2ng}{l}\right)}$.

$$\therefore \dot{\phi}\sin^2\theta = \sqrt{\left(\frac{2ng}{l}\right)}. \quad \text{...(1)}$$

and Lagrange's θ-equation is $\frac{d}{dt}\left(\frac{\partial T}{\partial \dot{\theta}}\right) - \frac{\partial T}{\partial \theta} = \frac{\partial W}{\partial \theta}$

i.e. $\frac{d}{dt}(2ml^2\dot{\theta}) - 2ml^2\dot{\phi}^2\sin\theta\cos\theta = mgl\sin\theta$

$$\text{or } 2l\ddot{\theta} - 2l\dot{\phi}^2\sin\theta\cos\theta = -g\sin\theta. \quad \text{...(2)}$$

Substituting value of $\dot{\phi}$ from (1) in (2), we have

$$2l\ddot{\theta} - 4ng\cot\theta\,\mathrm{cosec}^2\theta = -g\sin\theta. \quad \text{...(3)}$$

Integration provides us $2l\dot{\theta}^2 + 4ng\cot^2\theta = 2g\cos\theta + k$.

Initially $\theta = \frac{\pi}{2}, \dot{\theta} = 0, \therefore k = 0$.

$$\therefore 2l\dot{\theta}^2 + 4ng\cot^2\theta = 2g\cos\theta. \quad \text{...(4)}$$

The rod will fall till $\dot{\theta} = 0$.

i.e. $4ng\cot^2\theta = 2g\cos\theta$ or $2n\cos^2\theta - \cos\theta\sin^2\theta = 0$.

$\therefore$ either $\cos\theta = 0 \Rightarrow \theta = \frac{\pi}{2}$ which gives initial position.

as $2n\cos\theta - \sin^2\theta = 0 \Rightarrow \cos^2\theta + 2n\cos\theta - 1 = 0.$

Solving it, $\cos\theta = \dfrac{-2n \pm \sqrt{(4n^2+4)}}{2} = \left\{-n + \sqrt{(n^2+1)}\right\}$

[the other value being inadmissible because θ can not be obtuse]

or $\theta = \cos^{-1}[-n + \sqrt{(n^2+1)}]$. This proves the required result. If we substitute this value of θ in equation (2′), then we find that θ comes out to be positive. Hence at that time the rod begins to rise.

Example 7:

A bear, of mass M, slides on a smooth fixed wire, whose inclination to the vertical is α, and has hinged to it a rod, of mass m and length 2l, which can move freely in the vertical plane through the wire. If the system starts from rest with the rod hanged vertically, show that

$$\{4M + m(1 + 3\cos^2\theta\}l\dot{\theta}^2 = 6(M+m)\,g\sin\alpha(\sin\theta - \sin\alpha)$$

where θ is the angle between the rod and the lower part of the wire.

Solution:

Let OL be the fixed wire. At any time t. Let the bead of mass M be at A where OA = x, also let θ be the angle which the rod AB makes with the lower part of the fixed wire.

Take O as origin and the fixed wire OL as x axis and a line though O and prep to OL as y axis; the co-ordinates of G, the C.G. of the rod AB, are

$$\{x + l\cos\theta, l\sin\theta\}$$

i.e. $x_G = x + l\cos\theta)$ and $y_G = l\sin\theta$.

$$\dot{x}_G = (\dot{x} - l\sin\theta\dot{\theta});\ \dot{y}_G = l\cos\theta\dot{\theta}$$

$\therefore$ (velocity)^2 of $G = v_G^2 = \dot{y}_G^2 + \dot{y}_G^2 = (\dot{x} - l\sin\theta\dot{\theta})^2 + (l\cos\theta\dot{\theta})^2$.

Now let T be the kinetic energy and W the work function of the work function of the system Then we easily get

Total energy = T = K.E. of the bead + K.E, of the rod

$$= \frac{1}{2}M\dot{x}^2 + \frac{1}{2}m\left[\frac{l^2}{3}\dot{\theta}^2 + (\dot{x} - l\sin\theta\dot{\theta})^2 + (l\cos\theta\dot{\theta}^2\right]$$

$$= \frac{1}{2}(M+m)\dot{x}^2 - ml\dot{x}\dot{\theta}\sin\theta + \frac{2}{3}ml^2\dot{\theta}^2.$$

Also, the work function is given by

$W = M g x \cos\alpha + mg\ \{x \cos\alpha + l\cos(\theta - \alpha)\}$

$= (M + m)\ gx \cos\alpha + mgl \cos\cos(\theta - \alpha)$

$\therefore$ Lagrange's x-equation gives, $\dfrac{d}{dt}\left(\dfrac{\partial T}{\partial \dot{x}}\right) - \dfrac{\partial T}{\partial x} = \dfrac{\partial W}{\partial x}$

i.e $\dfrac{d}{dt}[M + m)\,\dot{x} - ml\theta\sin\theta] = (M + m)g\cos\alpha$

or $(M + m)\ddot{x} - ml\ddot{\theta}\sin\theta - ml\dot{\theta}^2\cos\theta = (M + m)go\cos\alpha.$ ...(i)

Again Lagrange's θ – equation gives

$$\frac{d}{dt}\left(\frac{\partial T}{\partial \dot{\theta}}\right) + \frac{\partial T}{\partial \theta} = \frac{\partial W}{\partial \theta}$$

i.e. $\dfrac{d}{dt}[-ml\dot{x}\sin\theta + \dfrac{4}{3}ml^2\dot{\theta}] + ml\dot{x}\dot{\theta}\cos\theta = -mgl\sin(\theta - \alpha),$

or $-\ddot{x}ml\sin\theta - \dot{x}\dot{\theta}ml\cos\theta + \dfrac{4}{3}ml^2\ddot{\theta} + \dot{x}\dot{\theta}ml\cos\theta = -mgl\sin(\theta - \alpha).$

or $-\ddot{x}\sin\theta + \dfrac{4}{3}l\ddot{\theta} = -g\sin(\theta - \alpha)$ ...(ii)

Eliminating $\ddot{x}$ between (i) and (ii), we get

$\ddot{\theta}[-ml\sin^2\theta + \dfrac{4}{3}(M + m)l] - ml\dot{\theta}^2\sin\theta\cos\theta$

$= (M + m)\ g\ [\cos a \sin\theta - \sin(\theta - a)]$

or $l\ddot{\theta}[3M + m + 3m\cos^2\theta] - 3ml\dot{\theta}^2\sin\theta\cos\theta$

$= 3\ (M + m)\ g \cos\theta \sin\alpha.$

Whence on integrating, we get

$l\dot{\theta}^2[4M + m + 3m\cos^2\theta] = 6\ (M + m)\ g \sin a \sin\theta + C$ ...(iii)

When $\theta = a, \dot{\theta} = 0,$

$\therefore C = -6(M + m)g\sin^2\alpha.$

Putting the value of C in (iii), we get

$l\dot{\theta}^2(4M + m + 3m\cos^2\theta) = 6\ (M + m)g\sin\alpha\ (\sin\theta - \sin\alpha).$

Example 8:

A uniform rod, of length 2a, which has one end attached to a fixed point by a light inextensible string, of length $\dfrac{5}{12}$a, performing small oscillations in a vertical plane about its position of equilibrium. Find the position at any time, and show that the period of its principal oscillations are $2\pi\sqrt{\left(\frac{5a}{3g}\right)}$ and $\pi\sqrt{\left(\frac{a}{3g}\right)}$.

Solution:

Figure is self explanatory at any time t, let the string and the rod be inclined at θ and ϕ to the vertical OY.

Co-ordinates of G are given by

$$x_G = \frac{5}{12} a \sin\theta + a \sin\phi,$$

$$y_G = \frac{5}{12} a \cos\theta + a \cos\phi,$$

$$\dot{x}_G = \frac{5a}{12} a \cos\theta\dot{\theta} + a \cos\phi\dot{\phi},$$

$$\dot{y}_G = -\left(\frac{5a}{12}\sin\theta\dot{\theta} + a\sin\phi\dot{\phi}\right)$$

$$\therefore \dot{x}_G{}^2 + \dot{y}_G{}^2 = (\text{velocity})^2 \text{of } G$$

$$= \frac{25a^2}{144}\dot{\theta}^2 + a^2\dot{\phi}^2 + \frac{5a^2}{6}\dot{\theta}\dot{\phi}\cos(\theta+\phi) = \frac{25a^2}{144}\dot{\theta}^2 + a^2\dot{\phi}^2 + \frac{5}{6}a^2\dot{\theta}\dot{\phi}$$

[$\because \theta$ and ϕ are small so $\cos(\theta+\phi) = 1$]

Again let T, be the kinetic energy and W, the work function of the system, then we easily get

$$T = \frac{1}{2}m\left[\frac{a^2}{3}\dot{\phi}^2 + \left(\frac{25}{144}a^2\dot{\theta}^2 + a^2\dot{\phi}^2 + \frac{5}{6}a^2\dot{\theta}\dot{\phi}\right)\right]$$

$$= \frac{ma^2}{288}[25\dot{\theta}^2 + 192\dot{\phi}^2 + 120\dot{\theta}\dot{\phi}]$$

$$\text{and } W = mg\left[\frac{5}{12}a\cos\theta + a\cos\phi\right]$$

$\therefore$ Lagrange's θ-equation gives

$$\frac{d}{dt}\left(\frac{\partial T}{\partial \dot{\theta}}\right) - \frac{\partial T}{\partial \theta} = \frac{\partial W}{\partial \theta} \Rightarrow \frac{d}{dt}\left\{\frac{ma^2}{144}(25\dot{\theta} + 60\dot{\phi})\right\} = -\frac{5mga}{12}\theta$$

{$\sin\theta = \theta$ is small}

$$\Rightarrow 5\ddot{\theta} + 12\ddot{\phi} = -\frac{12g}{a}\theta. \qquad ...(1)$$

and Lagrange's ϕ- equation gives

$$\frac{d}{dt}\left\{\frac{ma^2}{144}(192\dot{\phi}+60\dot{\theta}\right\}=-mga\phi \Rightarrow 5\ddot{\theta}+16\ddot{\phi}=-12\frac{g}{a} \quad ...(2)$$

Equations (1) and (2) $\Rightarrow (5D^2 + 12c)\,\theta + 12D^2\theta = 0$ ...(3)

and $5D^2\theta + (6D^2 + 12c)\,\phi = 0$ where $(g/a) = c$. ...(4)

Now eliminating f between these two equations, we get

$[(5D^2 + 12c)(16D^2 + 12c) - 60D^4]\,\theta = 0.$ ...(5)

Let $\theta = A\cos(pt + B)$ $\therefore D\theta = -pA\sin(pt + B)$,

$D^2\theta = -p^2A\cos(pt + B) = -p^2\,\theta$ and $D^4\theta = p^4\theta$.

Substituting these values in (5), we get

$$(5p^4 - 63c^2 - 36c^2)\,\theta = 0 \Rightarrow (5p^4 - 63cp^2 + 36c^2) = 0 \qquad (\because \theta \neq 0)$$

$$\Rightarrow (5p^2 - 3c)(p^2 - 12c) = 0 \Rightarrow \left(5p^2 - \frac{3g}{a}\right)\left(p^2 - \frac{12g}{a}\right) = 0$$

$$\therefore p_1^2 = \frac{3g}{5a} \text{ and } p_2^2 = \frac{12g}{a}$$

The periods of oscillations are $\frac{2\pi}{p_1}$ and $\frac{2\pi}{p_2}$

i.e. $2\pi\sqrt{\left(\frac{5a}{3g}\right)}$ and $2\pi\sqrt{\left(\frac{a}{12g}\right)}$ *i.e.* $2\pi\sqrt{\left(\frac{5a}{3g}\right)}$ and $\pi\sqrt{\left(\frac{a}{3g}\right)}$

Example 9:

A uniform rod, of mass 5m and length 2a, turns freely about one end which is fixed, to its other extremity is attached one end of a light string, of length 2a, which comes at its other end a particle of mass m, show that the periods of the small oscillations in a vertical plane are the same as those of simple pendulums of length $\frac{2a}{3}$ *and* $\frac{20a}{7}$

Solution:

Let the string BC and the rod AB make angles ϕ and θ with the vertical at any time t. The particle of mass m is tied to the end C of the string.

Now $x_c = 2a\sin\theta + 2a\sin\phi$,

$$\dot{x}_c = 2a(\cos\theta\dot{\theta} + \cos\phi\dot{\phi})$$

$$y_c = 2a\cos\theta + 2a\cos\phi.$$

$$\dot{y}_c = -2a(\sin\theta\dot{\theta} + \sin\phi\dot{\phi})$$

$\therefore$ (velocity)^2 of $m = \dot{x}_c^{\,2} + \dot{y}_c^{\,2}$

$= 4a^2(\dot{\theta} + \dot{\phi}^2 + 2\dot{\theta}\dot{\phi}).$

Again co ordinates of G are (a sin θ, a cos θ)

$\therefore$ (velocity)^2 ofG $= a^2\dot{\theta}^2$

Now let T be the kinetic energy, and W the work function of the system, then we have

Total K.E. = K.E. of rod + K.E. of particle of mass m.

$$T = \frac{1}{2}5m\left(\frac{a^2}{3}\dot{\theta}^2 + a^2\dot{\theta}^2\right) + \frac{1}{2}m.4a^2(\dot{\theta}^2 + \phi^2 + 2\dot{\theta}\dot{\phi})$$

$$= ma^2\left(\frac{16}{3}\dot{\theta}^2 + 2\dot{\phi}^2 + 4\dot{\theta}\dot{\phi}\right)$$

and W = 5m ga cos θ + mg.2a (cosθ + cosϕ)

$$= 7mga\cos\theta + 2mga\cos\phi = 7mag\left(1 - \frac{\theta^2}{2}\right) + 2mag\left(1 - \frac{\phi^2}{2}\right)$$

$\therefore$ Lagrange's θ equation is given by

$$\frac{d}{dt}\left(\frac{\partial T}{\partial \dot{\theta}}\right) - \frac{\partial T}{\partial \theta} = \frac{\partial W}{\partial \theta}$$

$$\Rightarrow \frac{d}{dt}\left(\frac{32}{3}\dot{\theta} + 4\dot{\phi}\right) = -\frac{7g}{a}\theta \Rightarrow 32\ddot{\theta} + 12\ddot{\phi} = -21\frac{g}{a}\theta \qquad ...(1)$$

Lagrange's ϕ equation is given by

$$\frac{d}{dt}(4\dot{\phi} + 4\dot{\theta}) = -\frac{2g}{a}\phi \Rightarrow i.e.\ 2\ddot{\theta} + 2\ddot{\phi} = -\frac{g}{a}\phi \qquad ...(2)$$

$\therefore$ (1) and (2) $\Rightarrow (32D^2 + 21c)\theta\ 12D^2\phi = 0$ ...(3)

and $2D^2\theta + (2D^2 + c)\phi = 0$ where $\frac{f}{a} = c$

Now eliminating 'ϕ' between (3) and (4), we get

$[(32D^2 + 21c)(2D^2 + c) - 24D^2]\theta = 0$

or $[40D^4 + 74cD^2 + 21c^2]\theta = 0$ ...(5)

Now let $\theta = A\cos(pt + B) \Rightarrow D\theta = -pA\sin(pt + B)$.

$D^2\theta = -p^2A\cos(pt + B) = -p^2\theta$ and $D^4\theta = p^4\theta$.

substituting these in (5) we get

$$(40p^4 - 74cp^2 + 21c^2)\theta = 0 \text{ i.e. } 40p^4 - 74cp^2 + 21c^2 = 0 \text{ as } \theta \neq 0$$

or $(2p^2 - 2c)(20p^2 - 7c) = 0$

i.e, $\left(2p^2 - \frac{3g}{a}\right)\left(20p^2 - 7\frac{g}{a}\right) = 0. \Rightarrow p_1^{\,2} = \frac{3g}{2a}$ and $\Rightarrow p_2^{\,2} = \frac{7g}{20a}$.

*Hence length of equivalent pendulums are

$\frac{g}{p_1^{\,2}}$ and $\frac{g}{p_2^{\,2}}$ *i.e.* $\frac{2a}{3}$ and $\frac{20}{7}a$.

Example 10:

A uniform rod, of length 2a, can turn freely about one end, which is fixed. Initially it is inclined at an angle α, to the downward drawn vertical and it is set rotating about a vertical axis through its fixed end with angular velocity w. Show that, during the motion, the rod is always inclined to the vertical at an angle which is > or< α, according as $\omega^2 >$ or $< \frac{3}{4a\cos\alpha}$ *and that in each case its motion is inclined between the inclination α and*

$$\cos^{-1}[-n + \sqrt{(2n\cos\alpha + n^2)}] \text{ when } n = \frac{a\omega^2 \sin^2\alpha}{3g}$$

If it be slightly disturbed when revolving steadily at a constant angle α show that the time of a small oscillation is

$$2\pi\sqrt{\left[\frac{4a\cos\alpha}{3g(1+3\cos^2\alpha}\right]}$$

Solution:

The rod OA is turning about the end O. Take a point P on the rod such that $OP = \xi$, and the element $PQ = \xi$,

$\therefore$ mass of element $PQ = \frac{m}{2a}d\xi$,

where m is the mass of the rod Further at any time t, let the rod be inclined at an angle θ to the vertical and let the plane through the rod and the vertical have turned though angle φ from its initial position OX, then co-ordinates of the point P are

$$x_p = \xi\sin\theta\cos\phi,\ y_p = \xi\sin\theta\sin\phi,\ z = \xi\cos\theta$$

$$\therefore v_p^{\,2} = (\text{velocity})^2 \text{ of } p = \dot{x}_p^{\,2} + \dot{y}_p^{\,2} + \dot{z}_p^{\,2} = \xi^2(\dot{\theta}^2 + \dot{\phi}^2\sin^2\theta)$$

and kinetic energy of the element $PQ = \frac{1}{2}\frac{m}{2a}v^2_p$

$$= \frac{1}{2}\frac{m}{2a}d\xi(\dot{\theta}^2 + \dot{\phi}^2 \sin^2\theta)\xi^2$$

Now, let T, be the K.E. of the rod OA, the b we have

$$T = \frac{1}{2}\frac{m}{2a}(\dot{\theta}^2 + \dot{\phi}\sin^2\theta)\int_0^{2a}\xi^2 d\xi = \frac{2ma^2}{3}(\dot{\theta} + \dot{\phi}^2\sin^2\theta)$$

or $T = \frac{2ma^2}{3}(\dot{\theta}^2 + \dot{\phi}^2 \sin^2\theta)$

Also the work function, $W = m\,ga\cos\theta + C.$

Lagrange's ϕ-equation gives

$$\frac{d}{dt}\left(\frac{4ma^2}{3}\dot{\phi}\sin^2\theta\right) = 0 \text{ i.e. } \frac{d}{dt}[\dot{\phi}\sin^2\theta] = 0 \qquad ...(1)$$

$$\Rightarrow \dot{\phi}\sin^2\theta = k \text{ (constant).} \qquad ...(2)$$

Initially $\theta = \alpha, \dot{\phi} = \theta, \quad \therefore k = \omega\sin^2\alpha.$

Thus (2) gives $\dot{\phi}\sin^2\theta = \omega\sin^2\alpha,$

and Lagrange's θ-equation is $\frac{d}{dt}\left(\frac{\partial T}{\partial\dot{\theta}}\right) - \frac{\partial T}{\partial\theta} = 0.$

* when $\theta = A(pt + B)$, the period of motion is given $T = \frac{2\pi}{p}$. If l is the length of the simple equivalent pendulum, we have

$$T = 2\pi\sqrt{(l/g)} \Rightarrow l = \frac{g}{p^2}$$

$$\Rightarrow \frac{d}{dt}\left(\frac{4ma^2}{3}\dot{\theta}\right) - \frac{2ma^2}{3}\dot{\phi}^2.2\sin\theta\cos\theta = -\,m\,ga\sin\theta.$$

$$\Rightarrow \ddot{\theta} - \dot{\phi}^2\sin\theta\cos\theta = -\frac{g}{4a}\sin\theta. \qquad ...(4)$$

Eliminating $\dot{\phi}$ between (4) and (3), we have

$$\ddot{\theta} - \frac{\omega^2\sin^4\alpha}{\sin^3\theta}\cos\dot{\theta} = -\frac{3g}{4a}\sin\theta. \qquad ...(5)$$

$$\Rightarrow \dot{\theta} + \frac{\omega^2\sin^4\alpha}{\sin^3\theta} = \frac{3g}{4a}\cos\theta + A. \qquad ...(6)$$

Initially $\theta = \alpha, \dot{\theta} = 0, \therefore A = \omega^2 \sin^2\alpha - \frac{3g}{2a}\cos\alpha$

Substituting this value of A in (6), we get

$$\dot{\theta}^2 + \frac{\omega^2 \sin^4\alpha}{\sin^2\theta} = \frac{3g}{2a}\cos\theta + \omega^2 \sin^2\alpha - \frac{3g}{2a}\cos\alpha,$$

$$\text{or } \dot{\theta}^2 = \omega^2 \sin^2\alpha\left(1 - \frac{\sin^2\alpha}{\sin^2\theta}\right) + \frac{3g}{2a}(\cos\theta - \cos\alpha)$$

$$= \frac{3ng}{a}\left(1 - \frac{\sin^2\alpha}{\sin^2\theta}\right) + \frac{3g}{2a}(\cos\theta - \cos\alpha)\left[\because n = \frac{a\omega^2 \sin^2\alpha}{3g}\right]$$

$$= \frac{3g}{2a}.\frac{\cos\alpha - \cos\theta}{\sin^2\theta}[2n(\cos\alpha + \cos\theta) - \sin^2\theta]$$

$$\text{i.e. } \dot{\theta}^2 = \frac{3g}{2a}.\frac{\cos\alpha - \cos\theta}{\sin^2\theta}[(\cos^2\theta + 2n\cos\theta + 2n\cos\alpha - 1)] \qquad ...(7)$$

From (7), we see that $\dot{\theta} = 0$, when

$(\cos\alpha - \cos\theta)[(\cos^2\theta + 2n\cos\theta + 2n\cos\alpha - 1)] = 0$

i.e. if either r $\cos\alpha - \cos\theta$ *i.e.* $\theta = \alpha$ (the initial position)

or $\cos^2 + 2n\cos\theta + 2n\cos\alpha - 1 = 0$

$$\text{i.e. } \cos\theta = \frac{-2n \pm \sqrt{[4n^2 + 4(1 - 2\cos\alpha)]}}{2}$$

$$\text{or } \cos\theta = -n + \sqrt{(1 - 3n\cos\alpha + n^2)} \qquad ...(8)$$

(the other value being inadmissible because that gives value of cos θ numerically greater that unity.

Hence the motion is included between $\theta = \alpha$ and $\theta = \theta_1$ where

$\cos\theta_1 = \{\sqrt{(1 - 2n\cos\alpha + n^2)} - n\}$

The rod will move above or below its initial position, if $\theta_1 >$ or $< \alpha$

or if $\cos\theta_1 <$ or $> \cos\alpha$

i.e. if $1 - 2n\cos\alpha + n^2 <$ or $> (n + \cos\alpha)^2$

i.e. if $\frac{3ng}{a\omega^2} <$ or $> 4n\cos\alpha$

i.e. if $\omega^2 >$ or $< \frac{3g}{4a\cos\alpha}$.

Small Oscillations about the Steady Motion : The motion will be steady if the rod goes round, inclined at the same angle α with the vertical or mathematically if $\theta=\alpha$(throughout the motion), then $\ddot{\theta}=0$. Making these substitutions in (5), we get,

$$\frac{\omega^2 \sin^4\alpha}{\sin^3\theta}\cos\theta=-\frac{3g}{4a}\sin\theta \text{ i.e. } \omega^2=\frac{3g}{4a\cos\alpha}$$

when ω^2 has this value and there are small oscillations about the position $\theta = \alpha$, then putting $\theta=\alpha+\psi$ in equation (5) we get

$$\ddot{\psi}=\frac{3g}{4a\cos\alpha}\frac{\sin^4\alpha}{\sin^3(\alpha+\psi)}\cos(\alpha+\psi)-\frac{3g}{4a}\sin(\alpha+\psi)$$

$$=\frac{3g}{4g}\left[\frac{\sin^4\alpha(\cos\alpha\cos\psi-\sin\alpha\sin\psi}{\cos\alpha(\sin\alpha\cos\psi+\cos\alpha\ \sin\psi)^3}-(\sin\alpha\cos\psi+\cos\alpha\sin\psi\right]$$

$$=\frac{3g}{4g}\left[\frac{\sin^4\alpha(\cos\alpha-\psi\ \sin\alpha\sin\psi}{\cos\alpha(\sin\alpha\cos\psi\cos\alpha)^3}-(\sin\alpha+\psi\cos\alpha\right], \text{ approximately}$$

$$=-\frac{3g\sin\alpha}{4a}[(1-\psi\tan\alpha)(1+\psi\cot\alpha)^{-3}-(1+\psi\cot\alpha], \text{ approx.}$$

$$=-\frac{3g\sin\alpha}{4}(4\cot\alpha+\tan\alpha)\psi,$$

$$\text{app.}=\frac{-3g(1+3\cos^2\alpha)}{4a\cos\alpha}\psi=-\mu\psi \text{ say}$$

$$\therefore \text{ time of small oscillation }=\frac{2\pi}{\sqrt{\pi}}=2\pi\sqrt{\left(\frac{4a\cos\alpha}{3g(1+3\cos^2\alpha)}\right)}.$$

Example 11:

A uniform bar of length 2 a is hung from a fixed point by a string of length b fastened to one end of the bar. Show that when the system makes small normal oscillations in a vertical plane, the length 1 of the equivalent simple pendulum is a root of the quadratic,

$$l^2-\left(\frac{4}{3}a+b\right)l+\frac{ab}{3}=0.$$

Solution:

At any time t, let the string OA and the rod AB make angles θ and ϕ with the vertical.

$$x_G=b\sin\theta+a\sin\phi.$$

$y_G = b\cos\theta + a\sin\phi.$

$\therefore \dot{x}_G^2 + \dot{y}_G^2 = (\text{velocity})^2$ of G

$= b^2\dot{\theta}^2 + a^2\dot{\phi}^2 + 2ab\dot{\theta}\dot{\phi}\cos(\theta - \phi)$

$= b^2\dot{\theta}^2 + a^2\dot{\phi}^2 + 2ab\dot{\theta}\dot{\phi}$ [$\because \theta$ and ϕ are small]

Now let T be the kinetic energy and W the work function of the system, then we easily obtain

$$W = mg\,[b\cos\theta + a\cos\phi]$$

and $T = \frac{1}{2}m\left[\frac{a^2}{3}\dot{\phi}^2 + b^2\dot{\theta}^2 + a^2\dot{\phi}^2 + 2ab\dot{\theta}\dot{\phi}\right]$

$$= \frac{1}{2}m\left[\frac{4a^2}{3}\dot{\phi}^2 + b^2\dot{\theta}^2 + 2ab\dot{\theta}\dot{\phi}\right]$$

$\therefore$ Lagrange's θ-equation is $\frac{d}{dt}\left(\frac{\partial T}{\partial \dot{\theta}}\right) - \frac{\partial T}{\partial \theta} = \frac{\partial W}{\partial \theta}$

$\Rightarrow \frac{d}{dt}\{m(b^2\dot{\theta} + ab\dot{\phi})\} = -\,mgb\theta.$ $\{\because \sin\theta = 0\}$

$\Rightarrow b\ddot{\theta} + a\dot{\phi} = -g\theta$ ...(1)

Lagrange's ϕ - equation is given by

$$\frac{d}{dt}\left\{\left(m\frac{4}{3}a^2\dot{\phi} + ab\dot{\theta}\right)\right\} = -\,mag\phi$$

$\Rightarrow 4a\ddot{\phi} + 3b\ddot{\theta} = -\,3g\phi.$ ...(2)

Equations (1) and (2) again can be written as

$(bD^2 + g)\,\theta + aD^2\,\phi = 0$ ...(3)

and $3bD^2\ \theta + (4\,aD^2\ 3g)\,\phi = 0.$ ...(4)

Eliminating θ between these equations, we obtain

$$[(bD^2 + g)(4aD^2 + 3g) - 3abD^4]\theta = 0$$

i.e. $[(abD^4 + (4a + 3b)gD^2 + 3g^2]\theta = 0.$ ...(5)

Now let $\theta = A\cos\left[\sqrt{\left(\frac{g}{l}\right)}t + B\right]$

where l is the length of the simple equivalent pendulum.

Then $D\theta = -\sqrt{\left(\frac{g}{l}\right)}A\sin\left[\sqrt{\left(\frac{g}{l}\right)}t + B\right]$

$$D^2\theta = -\frac{g}{l}A\cos\left[\sqrt{\left(\frac{g}{l}\right)}t + B\right] = \frac{g}{l}\theta \text{ and } D^2\theta = \frac{g^2}{l^2}\theta,$$

$$\therefore (5) \Rightarrow \left[ab\frac{g^2}{l^2} - (4a+3b)\frac{g^2}{l} + 3g^2\right]\theta = 0$$

$$\Rightarrow 3l^2 - (4a+3b)\,l + ab = 0 \qquad \{\because \theta \neq 0\}$$

$$\Rightarrow l^2 - \left(\frac{4}{3}a + b\right)l + \frac{ab}{3} = 0.$$

Example 12:

A uniform straight rod of length 2a, is freely movable about its centre and a particle of mass one-third that of the rod is attached by a light inextensible string, of length a, to one end of the rod; show that one period of principle oscillation is $\left(\sqrt{5+1}\right)\pi\sqrt{\left\{\frac{a}{g}\right\}}$.

Solution:

At time t, let θ and φ be the inclinations of the rod and the string to the vertical. Co - ordinates of C are

$x_C = a\sin\theta + a\sin\phi$ and

$y_C = a\cos\theta + a\cos\phi$.

$\therefore \dot{x}_C = a\cos\theta\dot{\theta} + a\cos\phi\dot{\phi}$ and $\dot{y}_C = -a\sin\theta\theta - a\sin\phi\dot{\phi}$

$\Rightarrow \dot{x}_C^2 + \dot{y}_C^2 = a^2\dot{\theta}^2 + a^2\dot{\phi}^2 + 2a^2\cos(\phi-\phi)\dot{\theta}\dot{\phi}$

$= a^2\dot{\theta}^2 + a^2\dot{\phi}^2 + 2a^2\dot{\theta}\dot{\phi}$

[neglecting higher powers of small quantities]

$\therefore$ (velocity)^2 of the particle C = $v_C^2 = a^2\dot{\theta}^2 + a^2\dot{\phi}^2 + 2a^2\dot{\theta}\dot{\phi}$.

And velocity of the C.G. of the rod *i.e.* of O, is zero.

Now let T, be the kinetic energy and W, the work function of the system, then we easily get $W = \frac{mg}{3}(a\cos\theta + a\cos\phi) + C$

and $T = \frac{1}{2}m\frac{a^2}{3}\dot{\theta}^2 + \frac{1}{2}\left(\frac{m}{3}\right)[a^2\dot{\theta}^2 + a^2\dot{\phi}^2 + 2a^2\dot{\theta}\dot{\phi}]$

$= \frac{ma^2}{6}[2\dot{\theta}^2 + \dot{\phi}^2 + 2\dot{\theta}\dot{\phi}]$

$\therefore$ Lagrange's θ-equation is given by

$$\frac{d}{dt}\left(\frac{2ma^2}{3}\dot{\theta}+\frac{ma^2}{3}\dot{\phi}\right)=-\frac{mga}{3}\theta \Rightarrow 2\ddot{\theta}+\ddot{\phi}=-\frac{g}{a}\theta \qquad ...(1)$$

While Lagrange's φ-equation gives $\frac{d}{dt}\left[\frac{ma^2}{3}\dot{\phi}+\frac{ma^2}{3}\dot{\theta}\right]=-\frac{mga}{3}\theta$

i.e. $\ddot{\theta}+\ddot{\phi}=-\frac{g}{a}\phi.$

Equations (1) and (2) again give

$(2D^2+c)\,\theta + D^2\,\phi = 0$ ...(3) and $D^2\,q + (D^2+c)\,\phi = 0$ ...(4)

where $c=\frac{g}{a}.$

Eliminating φ in between (3) and (4), we get

$\{d^2+c)(2D^2+c) - D^4\}\,\theta = 0$ *i.e.* $[D^4+3cD^2+c^2]\,\theta = 0.$ ...(5)

To solve (5), let $\theta = A\cos(pt+B)$ $\therefore$ $D\theta = pA\sin(pt+B),$

$D^2\theta = -p^2A\cos(pt+B) = -p^2\theta$ and $D^4\theta = p^4\theta.$

With these substitutions, (5) gives

$$(p^4-3cp^2+c^2)\,\theta = 0 \Rightarrow p^4-3cp^2+c^2=0 \qquad (\because \theta\neq 0)$$

$$\therefore p^2=\frac{3c\pm\sqrt{(9c^2-4c^2)}}{2}=\left(\frac{3\pm\sqrt{5}}{2}\right)c=\frac{(3\pm\sqrt{5}}{2}\cdot\frac{g}{a}.$$

$\therefore$ one period of principal oscillations corresponding to p_1, is given by

$$\frac{2\pi}{p_1}=2\pi\sqrt{\left(\frac{2}{3-\sqrt{5}\cdot}\frac{a}{g}\right)}=2\pi\sqrt{\left(\frac{a}{g}\right)}\sqrt{\left\{\frac{2(3+\sqrt{5}}{9-5}\right\}}$$

$$=2\pi\sqrt{\left(\frac{a}{g}\right)}\sqrt{\left(\frac{6+2\sqrt{5}}{4}\right)}=2\pi\sqrt{\left\{\frac{a}{g}\right\}}\sqrt{\left\{\frac{(\sqrt{5}+1)^2}{4}\right\}}$$

$$=(\sqrt{5}+1)\pi\sqrt{\left(\frac{a}{g}\right)}.$$

Example 13:

A mass m hangs from a fixed point by a light string of length l and a mass m′ hangs from m by a second string of length l′. For oscillations in a vertical plane, show that the periods of the principal oscillations are the values of $\frac{2\pi}{n}$ where n is given by the equation

$$n^4 - gn^2 \frac{m+m'}{m}\left(\frac{1}{l}+\frac{1}{l'}\right) + g^2 \frac{m=m'}{ml'l} = 0.$$

Solution:

At any time t, let the strings be inclined at angles 0 and ϕ to the vertical. Co-ordinates of m are (l sin θ, l cos θ).

$\therefore$ (velocity)² of $m = l^2\dot{\theta}^2$ while co-ordinates of m′ are

$x_B = l\sin\theta + l'\sin\phi, \Rightarrow$

$\dot{x}_B = l\cos\theta\dot{\theta} + l'\cos\phi\dot{\phi}$

$y_B = -l\cos\theta + l'\cos\phi \Rightarrow$

$\dot{y}_B = -(l\sin 0\dot{\theta} + l'\sin\phi\dot{\phi})$

$\therefore$ (velocity)² of $m' = \dot{x}_B^2 + \dot{y}_B^2 = l^2\dot{\theta}^2 + l^2\dot{\phi}^2 + 2ll\theta\dot{\phi}$ [$\because \theta$ find ϕ are small]

Now let T, be the kinetic energy and , W the work function, of the system, then we have

W = mgl cos θ + m′g (l cos θ + l ′ cos ϕ)

= gl (m + m′) cos θ + m′ gl′ cos ϕ

and $T = \frac{1}{2}ml^2\dot{\theta}^2 + \frac{1}{2}m'[l^2\dot{\theta}^2 + l'\theta^2 + 2ll\dot{\theta}\dot{\phi}]$

$\frac{1}{2}[(m+m')l^2\dot{\theta}^2 + m'l'^2\dot{\theta}^2 + 2m'\,ll'\dot{\theta}\dot{\phi}$

Lagrange's θ-equation is given by $\frac{d}{dt}\left(\frac{\partial T}{\partial \dot{\theta}}\right) - \frac{\partial T}{\partial \theta} = \frac{\partial W}{\partial \theta}$

$= \frac{d}{dt}[(m+m')\,l^2\dot{\theta} + m'll'\dot{\phi}] = -gl(m+m')\,\theta.$

$\Rightarrow \{m+m'\}\,l\ddot{\theta} + m'l'\ddot{\phi} = -g\,(m+m')\theta$ ...(1)

While Lagrange's ϕ - equation gives

$\frac{d}{dt}[m'l'^2\dot{\phi} + m'll'\dot{\theta}] = -m'gl'\phi$

$\Rightarrow l'\ddot{\phi} + l\ddot{\theta} = -g\phi$ ...(2)

Equation (1) and (2) again give

$(m+m')(lD^2+g)\theta + m'l'D^2\phi = 0$ ...(3)

$lD^2\theta + (l'D^2+g)\phi = 0$ ...(4)

Eliminating ϕ, we get $[(m+m')(l'D^2+g) - m'll'D^4]\theta = 0$

$$i.e.\ [mll'D^4 + (m+m')(l+l')gD^2 + (m+m')g^2]\theta = 0 \qquad ...(5)$$

Now let $\theta = A\cos(nt+B)$; $\therefore$ $D\theta = -nA\sin(nt+B)$

$$D^2\theta = -n^2A\ \text{cps}\ (nt+B) = -m^2\theta \text{ and } D^4\theta = n^4\theta \qquad ...(6)$$

$\therefore$ (5) and (6) give $mall'\,n^4 - (m+m')(l+l')\,gn^2 + (m+m')\,g^2 = 0$

$$\text{or } n^4 - \frac{m+m'}{m}\left(\frac{1}{l}+\frac{1}{l'}\right)gn^2 + \frac{(m+m')g^2}{mall'} = 0. \qquad ...(7)$$

Example 14:

A mass M hangs from a fixed point at the end of a very long string whose length l is a, to M is suspended a mass m by a string whose length l is small compound with a; prove that the time of a small oscillation of m is

$$2\pi\sqrt{\left(\frac{M}{M+m}\cdot\frac{1}{g}\right)}$$

Solution:

Here, we have $m = M$, $m' = m$, $l = a$, $l' = l$.

$$\therefore n^4 - \frac{M+m}{M}\left(\frac{1}{a}+1\right)\frac{g}{l}n^2 + \frac{(M+m)g^2}{Ml^2} = 0$$

$$i.e.\ \therefore n^4 - \frac{M+m}{M}\left(\frac{1}{a}+1\right)\frac{g}{l}n^2 + \frac{(M+m)g^2}{Ml^2}\cdot\frac{l}{a} = 0 \qquad ...(8)$$

But a is large compared to $l \therefore \frac{l}{a} \to 0$

Hence the equation (8), gives

$$n^4 - \frac{M+m}{M}\cdot\frac{g}{l}\cdot n^2 = 0 \quad i.e.\ n^2 = \frac{M+m}{M}\cdot\frac{g}{l}$$

$$\therefore \text{Time of a small oscillation} = \frac{2\pi}{n} = 2\pi\sqrt{\left\{\frac{M}{M+m}\cdot\frac{l}{g}\right\}}.$$

Example 15:

At the lowest point of a smooth circular tube, of mass M and radius a, is placed a particle of mass M′, the tube hangs in a vertical plane from its highest point, which is fixed, and can turn freely in its own plane about this point. If the system be slightly displaced, show that the periods of the two independent oscillations of the system are

$$2\pi\sqrt{\left(\frac{2a}{g}\right)} \text{ and } 2\pi\sqrt{\left(\frac{Mag^{-1}}{M+M'}\right)}.$$

And that for one principal mode of oscillations, the particle remains at res relative to the tube and for the other, the centre of gravity of the particle and the tube and for the other, the centre of gravity of the particle and the tube remain at rest.

Solution:

Let C be the centre of the tube and A the position of the particle M′ at time t when OC and CA make angle 3 θ and φ with the vertical

$\therefore x_A = a \sin\theta + a \sin\phi,$

$y_A = a\cos\theta + a\cos\phi.$

and $(\text{velocity})^2$ of A $= \dot{x}_A^2 + \dot{y}_A^2$

$= (a\cos\theta\dot{\theta} + a\cos\phi\dot{\phi})^2 + (-a\sin\theta\dot{\theta} - a\sin\phi\dot{\phi})^2$

$= a^2\dot{\theta}^2 + a^2\,\dot{\phi}h2 + 2a^2\dot{\theta}\dot{\phi}\cos(\theta - \phi) = a^2\dot{\theta}^2 + 2a^2\dot{\theta}\dot{\phi}$

[neglecting small quantities of the higher order].

Also $C \equiv (a\sin\theta, a\cos\theta)$

$(\text{velocity})^2$ of $C = (a\cos\theta\dot{\theta})^2 + (-a\sin\theta\dot{\theta})^2 = a^2\dot{\theta}^2$

Now let T, be the kinetic energy and W the work function of the system then we readily obtain $W = Mga\cos\theta + M'g = (M + M')\,ga\cos\theta + M'ga\cos\phi + K$

T = K.E. of circular tube + K.E. of particle

$= \frac{1}{2}M(a^2\dot{\theta}^2 + a^2\,\dot{\theta}^2) + \frac{1}{2}M(a^2\dot{\theta}^2 + a^2\dot{\phi}^2 + 2a^2\dot{\theta}\dot{\phi})$

$= \frac{2M + M'}{2}a^2\dot{\theta}^2 + \frac{1}{2}M'a^2\dot{\phi}^2 + M'a^2\dot{\theta}\dot{\phi}.$ ...(2)

∴ Lagrange's θ-equation gives

$\frac{d}{dt}[(2M + M')\,a^2\dot{\theta} + M'a^2\dot{\phi}] = -(M + M')ga\theta.$

$\Rightarrow (2M + M')\ddot{\theta} + M'\,\ddot{\phi} + = -(M + M')\,\frac{g}{a}\theta.$ ...(3)

Also Lagrange's φ - equation gives

$\frac{d}{dt}[M'\,a^2\dot{\phi} + M'\,a^2\dot{\theta}] = -M'ga\,\phi \Rightarrow \ddot{\phi} + \ddot{\theta} = -\frac{g}{a}\phi$ ...(4)

Equations (3) and (4) can be re-written as

$[(2M + M')\,D^2 + (M + M')\,c]\,q + M'\,D^2\,\phi = 0$ ...(5)

and $D^2\theta + (D^2 + c)\,\phi = 0$ where $c = \frac{g}{a}.$

Eliminating ϕ between these two equations, we get

$$[\{(2M + M')D^2 + (M + M')c\}(D^2 + c) - M'D^4]\theta = 0$$

i.e. $[2MD^4 + c(3M + 2M')D^2 + c^2(M + M')]\theta = 0.$ ...(7)

To solve (7),

let $\theta = A\cos(pt + B)$; $D\theta = -pA\sin(pt + B)$

$D^2\theta = -p^2A\cos(pt + B) = -p^2\theta$ and $D^4\theta = \theta^4\theta$ ...(8)

$\therefore$ (7) and (8) give $[2Mp^4 - c(3M + 2M')p^2 + c^2(M + M')\theta = 0$

i.e. $2Mp^4 - c(3M + 2M')p + c^2(M + M') = 0.$ $[\because \theta \neq 0]$

which again gives $(2p^2 - c)[Mp^2 - c(M + M')] = 0$

$\therefore p_1^2 = \frac{c}{2}$ and $p_2^2 = \frac{c(M + M')}{M}\frac{g}{a}.$ $\left(\because c = \frac{g}{a}\right)$

Hence periods of oscillations are given by

$\frac{2\pi}{p_1}$ and $\frac{2\pi}{p_2}$ i.e. by $2\pi\sqrt{(2a/g)}$ and $2\pi\sqrt{\left(\frac{M}{(M + M'}\frac{a}{g}\right)}.$

Multiplying (6) by λ and adding to (5), we have

$D^2\{(2M + M' + 1)\theta + (M' + \lambda)\phi\} = -\ \{(M + M')\theta + \lambda\phi\}$ ...(9)

Now chose λ such that

$$\frac{2M + M' + \lambda}{M' + \lambda} = \frac{M + M'}{\lambda} \Rightarrow \lambda = M' \text{ and } \lambda = -(M + M').$$

taking $\lambda = M'$, equation (9) reduces to

$$D^2\{(M + M')\theta + M'\phi\} = -\frac{1}{2}c\{M + M')\theta + M'\phi\}$$

and when $\lambda = -(M + M')$, equation (9) reduces to

$$D^2\{\theta - \phi) = -\frac{M + M'}{M}c(\theta - \phi)$$

$\therefore$ Principal co-ordinates are $q - f$ and $\{(M + M')\theta + M\text{–}\phi\}$. For the first mode, $\theta - \phi = 0$, *i.e.* $\theta = \phi$. This shows that the particle is at rest relative to the tube. For the second mode we have $(M + M')\theta + M'\phi = 0$. Further, the x-coordinates of C.G. of the particle and the tube

$$= \frac{M a\sin\theta + M'(a\sin\theta + a\sin\phi)}{M + M'}$$

$$= \frac{a}{M + M'}\{M\theta + M'(\theta + \phi)\}$$ (since θ and ϕ are small,

$\therefore \sin\theta = \theta$ and $\sin\phi = \phi$)

$$= \frac{a}{M+M'}\{(M+M')\theta + M'\phi\} = 0 \text{ [using above results]}$$

⇒ The common C.G. of the particle and the tube remains at rest.

Example 16:

A perfectly rough sphere lying inside a hollow cylinder, which rests on a perfectly rough plane, is slightly displaced from its position of equilibrium. Show that the time of a small oscillation is

$$2\pi\sqrt{\left(\frac{a-b}{g}.\frac{4M}{10M+7m}\right)}$$

where a is the radius of the cylinder, b that of the sphere, and M, m are the masses of the cylinder and the sphere.

Solution:

Let CA be a line fixed in the cylinder and C'N, a line fixed in the sphere, which were initially vertical. Let these lines, after a time t, make angles ψ and ϕ with the vertical. Further let θ be the angle which the line joining centre makes with the vertical.

Initially O was the point of contact with the horizontal plane, which is regarded as origin. There is no slipping; between the cylinder, horizontal plan e and between the cylinder, sphere; therefore, we get OB = are AB = $a\psi$ and are AP = arc NP

i.e. $a(\theta+\psi) = b(\theta+\phi)$, *i.e.* $b\phi = (a-b)\,\dot{\theta} + a\dot{\psi}$.

Referred to the horizontal and vertical through O as co-ordinate axes, we have

$xc' = a\psi + a(a-b)\sin\theta,\ yc' = a-(a-b)\cos\theta.$ (co-ordinates of c'

$\therefore$ (velocity)^2 of c'

$$\dot{x}c'^2 + \dot{y}c^2 = \{a\dot{\psi} + (a-b)\cos\theta\dot{\theta}\}^2 + \text{man}\{a-b)\sin\theta\dot{\theta}\}^2$$

$$= a^2\dot{\psi}^2 + (a-b)^2\dot{\theta}^2 + 2a(a-b)\dot{\psi}\dot{\theta}\cos\theta$$

$$= a^2\dot{\psi}^2 + (a-b)^2\dot{\theta}^2 + 2a(a-b)\dot{\psi}\dot{\theta}. \qquad ...(1)$$

Also co-ordinates of C are $(a\,\psi, a)$.

$$\therefore (\text{velocity})^2\ (a\dot{\psi})^2 = a^2\dot{\psi}^2. \qquad ...(2)$$

Now let T be the kinetic energy and $\dot{W}$, the work function. Then we have

$$W = (a-b)mg\cos\theta + C \qquad ...(3)$$

and $$T = \frac{1}{2}M\left(v^2C + a^2\dot\psi^2\right) + \frac{1}{2}m\left(v^2c' + \frac{2b^2}{5}\dot\phi^2\right)$$

$$\Rightarrow T = \frac{1}{2}M(a^2\dot\psi^2 + a^2\dot\psi^2)$$

$$+\frac{1}{2}m\left[\frac{2b^2}{5}\dot\phi + a^2\dot\psi^2 + (a-b)^2\dot\theta^2 + 2a(a-b)\dot\psi\dot\theta\right]$$

$$= Ma^2\dot\psi^2 + \frac{1}{2}m[\frac{2}{5}\{(a-b\theta + a\dot\psi\} + a^2\dot\psi^2 + (a-b)^2\dot\theta^2 + 2a(a-b)\dot\psi\dot\theta]$$

$$= \frac{10M+7m}{10}a^2\dot\psi^2 + \frac{7m}{10}[(a-b)^2\theta^2 + 2a(a-b)\dot\psi\dot\theta] \qquad ...(4)$$

$\therefore$ Lagrange's θ-equation gives

$$\frac{d}{dt}\left[\frac{7m}{5}\{(a-b)^2\dot\theta + a(a-b)\dot\psi\}\right] = -(a-b)mg\sin\theta$$

$$\Rightarrow 7(a-b)\ddot\theta + 5a\ddot\psi = -5g\theta \text{ (as } \theta \text{ is small).} \qquad ...(5)$$

Also Lagrange's ψ-equation $\frac{d}{dt}\left[\frac{10M+7m}{5}a^2\dot\psi + \frac{7m}{5}a(a-b)\theta\right] = 0$

$$\Rightarrow (10M+7m)a\ddot\psi + 7m(a-b)\ddot\theta = 0$$

$$\Rightarrow (7m(a-b)\ddot\theta + (10M+7m)a\ddot\psi = 0 \qquad ...(6)$$

Eliminating $\ddot\psi$ between(5) and (6) ,we get

$$[7(10M+7m) - 49m](a-b)\ddot\theta = -5(10M+7m)g\theta$$

or $70M(a-b)\ddot\theta = -5(10M+7m)g\theta$

or $$\ddot\theta = -\frac{(10M+7m)}{14M}\cdot\frac{g}{a-b)}\theta = -\mu\theta \text{ say,}$$

$\therefore$ time of a small oscillation $= \dfrac{2\pi}{\sqrt{\mu}} = 2\pi\sqrt{\left(\dfrac{a-b}{g}\cdot\dfrac{14M}{10M+7m}\right)}.$

Example 17:

A perfectly rough sphere, of mass m and radius b, rest at the lowest point of a fixed spherical cavity of radius a. To the highest point of the movable sphere is attached a particle of mass m and the system is disturbed. Show that the oscillations are the same as those of a simple pendulum of length

$$a-b)\frac{4m'+\frac{7}{5}m}{m+m'\left(2-\frac{a}{b}\right)}$$

Solution:

O is the centre of the fixed cavity, C the centre of the sphere and at B, a particle of m′ is attached. Initially NB was vertical, and N coincided with A.

After the time t, let BN or CN, a line fixed in the sphere make an angle ϕ with the vertical. But there is no slipping between the cylinder and the sphere.

$\therefore$ arc AP = arc NP,

i.e. $a\theta = b(\theta+\phi)$

i.e. $b\phi=(a-b)\theta \Rightarrow b\dot{\phi}=(a-b)\dot{\theta}$

Now co-ordinates of iB (i.e. of m ′) are

$x_B=(a-b)\sin\theta+b\sin\phi, y_B=(a-b)\cos\theta-b\cos\phi,$

and co-ordinates of the centre C are

$\therefore (\text{velocity})^2 \text{ of } B = \dot{x}_B^{\ 2}+\dot{y}_B^{\ 2}$

$=\{(a-b)\cos\theta\dot{\theta}+b\cos\theta\dot{\theta}\}^2+\{-(a-b)\sin\theta\dot{\theta}+b\sin\theta\dot{\theta}\}^2$

$=(a-b)^2\dot{\theta}^2+b^2\phi^2+2b(a-b)\dot{\theta}\dot{\phi}$

[neglecting small quantities of second and higher orders]

and $(\text{velocity})^2$ of C = $\{(a-b)\cos\theta\dot{\theta}\}^2+\{-(a-b)\sin\theta\dot{\theta}\}^2$

$=(a-b)^2\dot{\theta}^2$

Now let T, be the kinetic energy and W the work function of the system. then we readily obtain

$W=mg(a-b)\cos\theta+m'g\{(a-b)\cos\theta-b\cos\phi\}+D$

$=(a-b)(m+m')g\cos\theta-m'gb\cos\phi+D$

$=(a-b)(m+m')g\cos\left(\frac{b}{a-b}\phi\right)-m'gb\cos\phi+D \qquad \{\because (a-b)\theta=b.\phi\}$

and $T=\frac{1}{2}m\left[\frac{2b^2\dot{\phi}^2}{5}+(a-b)^2\dot{\theta}^2\right]+\frac{1}{2}m'\{(a-b)^2\dot{\theta}^2+b^2\dot{\phi}^2+2b(a-b)\dot{\theta}\dot{\phi}$

$=\frac{1}{2}m\left[\frac{2b^2\dot{\phi}^2}{5}+b^2\phi^2\right]+\frac{1}{2}m'\{b^2\dot{\phi}^2+b^2\dot{\phi}^2+2b^2\phi^2] \qquad [\because (a-b)\dot{\theta}=b\dot{\phi}]$

$$=\frac{b^2}{10}(7m+20m')\dot{\phi}^2.$$

Further Lagrange's ϕ-equation gives $\frac{d}{dt}\left[\frac{b^2}{5}(7m+20m')\dot{\phi}\right]$

$$=-(a-b)(m+m')g\frac{b}{a-b}\sin\left(\frac{b}{a-b}\phi\right)+m'gb\sin\phi$$

$$=-(m+m')bg\sin\frac{b\phi}{a-b}+m'gb\sin\phi$$

$$\Rightarrow\frac{b^2}{5}(7m+20m')\ddot{\phi}=-(m+m')bg.\frac{b}{a-b}\phi+m'gb\phi \text{ app.}$$

$$\Rightarrow\left(4m'+\frac{7m}{5}\right)\ddot{\phi}=-\frac{g}{a-b}\left[m+m'\left(2-\frac{a}{b}\right)\right]\phi, \text{ app.}$$

$$\Rightarrow\ddot{\phi}=-\frac{g}{a-b}\cdot\frac{m+m'\left(2-\frac{a}{b}\right)}{4m'+\frac{7}{5}m}\phi=-\mu\phi \quad [\text{form } \ddot{x}=-\mu x]$$

$\therefore$ Length of the simple equivalent pendulum $=\frac{g}{\mu}$

$$=(a-b)\frac{4m'+\frac{7}{5}m}{m+m'\left(2-\frac{a}{b}\right)}.$$

Example 18:

A perfectly tough sphere rests at the lowest point of a fixed spherical cavity of double its own radius. To the highest point of the movable sphere is attached a particle of mass 7/20 times that of the sphere and the system is disturbed. Show that the oscillations are the same as those of a simple pendulum of length 14/5 times the radius of the sphere.

Solution:

Put proceed similarly to get the required result.

Example 19:

A plank, of mass M, radius of gyration k and length 2b, can swing like a sea-saw across a perfectly rough fixed cylinder of radius a. At its ends hang two particles each of mass m, by strings of length l. Show that, as the system swings, the lengths of its simple equivalent pendulum are

$$l \text{ and } \frac{Mk^2 + 2mb^2}{(m + 2m)a}.$$

Solution:

Let the strings be AP and BQ such that their free extremities are having particles of mass m. Initially G was at D and AP, BQ were vertical.

After a time t, when the plank ψ with the horizontal. Let the strings be inclined at θ and φ to the vertical.

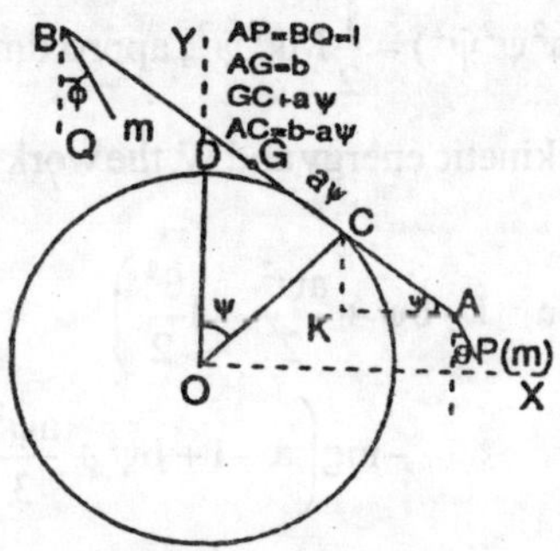

Fig. 3.9

But there is no slipping between the plank and the cylinder, so we have

$$\text{Now } xp = a\sin\psi + (b - a\psi)\cos\psi + l\sin\theta = b + l\theta - \frac{1}{2}b\psi^2 \qquad ...(1)$$

$$yp = a\cos\psi - (b - a\psi)\sin\psi - l\cos$$

$$= a(1 - \frac{1}{2}\psi^2) - (b - a\psi)\psi - l(1 - \frac{1}{2}\theta^2) \qquad ...(2)$$

$$\therefore \dot{x}_p = l\dot{\theta} - b\psi\dot{\psi} \text{ and } \therefore \dot{y}_p = -b\dot{\psi} + a\psi\dot{\psi} + l\theta\dot{\theta}$$

$$\therefore (\text{Velocity})^2 \text{ of } = \dot{x}_p{}^2 + \dot{y}_p{}^2 = l^2\dot{\theta}^2 + b^2\dot{\psi}^2 p$$

$$\text{Thus kinetic energy of m at } P = \frac{1}{2}m(l^2\dot{\phi}^2 + b^2\dot{\psi}^2).$$

$$\text{Similarly kinetic energy of m at } Q = \frac{1}{2}m(l^2\dot{\phi}^2 + b^2\dot{\psi}^2)$$

To obtain the corresponding quantities for the point Q. We shall write–ψ for ψ and φ for θ.

$$\text{Also y-coordinate of } Q = a - l + b\psi + \frac{1}{2}a\psi^2 + \frac{1}{2}l\phi^2 = yq \text{ say}$$

[put–ψ for ψ and φ for θ in (2)]

the co-ordinates of G are {a sin ψ −aψ cosψ, acosψ + aψ sinψ} (neglecting higher powers of ψ as it is small)

$$i.e. \left\{\frac{a\psi^2}{2}, a + \frac{a\psi^2}{2}\right\}.$$

$\therefore$ (velocity)²of G = $a^2\psi^2\dot{\psi}^2 [\because \dot{x} = a\dot{\psi}\psi, \dot{y} = a\psi\dot{\psi}]$

(neglecting smaller, quantities). Thus kinetic energy of the plank

$$= \frac{1}{2}M(k^2\dot{\psi}^2 + a^2\psi^2\dot{\psi}^2) = \frac{1}{2}Mk^2\dot{\psi}^2, \text{ approximately}$$

Now let T be the kinetic energy and W, the work function of the system, then we obtain

$$W = -mg\left(a - l - b\psi + \frac{a\psi^2}{2} + l\frac{\theta^2}{2}\right)$$

$$-mg\left(a - l + b\psi + \frac{a\psi^2}{3} + l\frac{\theta^2}{2}\right) - mg\left(a + \frac{a\psi^2 2}{}\right)$$

$$= K - \frac{1}{2}a(M + 2m)g\psi^2 - \frac{1}{2}m\,gl\left(\theta^2 - \phi^2\right)$$

$$\text{and } T = \frac{1}{2}m(l^2\dot{\theta}^2 + b^2\dot{\psi}^2) + \frac{1}{2}m(l^2\dot{\phi}^2 + b^2\dot{\psi}^2) + \frac{1}{2}MK^2\dot{\psi}^2$$

Lagrange's θ-equation is $\frac{d}{dt}\left(\frac{\partial T}{\partial \dot{\theta}}\right) - \frac{\partial T}{\partial \theta} = \frac{\partial W}{\partial \theta}$

$$\Rightarrow \frac{d}{dt}(ml^2\dot{\theta}^2) = -mgl\theta \Rightarrow \ddot{\theta} = -\frac{g}{l}\theta,$$

$\therefore$ length of the simple equivalent pendulum = l

Also Lagrange's ψ – aqⁿ gives

$$\frac{d}{dt}\{(Mk^2 + 2mb^2)\dot{\psi}\} = -a(M + 2m)g\psi \Rightarrow \ddot{\psi} = -ag\frac{M + 2m}{Mk^2 + 2mb^2}\psi$$

Example 20:

A solid uniform sphere has a light rod rigidl, attached to it which passes through its centre. This rod is so jointed to a fix ed vertical axis that the angle q between the rod and the axis may alter but the rod must turn with the axis. If the vertical axis be forced to revolve constant y with uniform angular velocity, show that the equation of motion is of the form

$$\dot{\theta}^2 = n^2(\cos\theta\, 0\, \cos\beta)(\cos\alpha - \cos\theta)$$

Show also that the total energy imparted to the sphere as q increase from θ_1 *to* θ_2 *varies as* $\cos^2\theta_1 - \cos^2\theta_2$.

Solution:

First of all, we reduce the revolving axis OZ to rest by introducing an additional force $m\omega^2$ NO′, along NO′ *i.e.* a force $m\omega^2 l \sin\theta$ along NO′.

After the interval of time t. Let the rod make an angle q with the vertical ONZ (taken as Z-axis. (Further let ϕ be the angle through which the sphere turn in the horizontal plane, then the co-ordinates of C.G. of the sphere, are given by

$$x_{0'} = l\sin\theta\cos\phi.\ y_0' = l\sin\theta\sin\phi,\ z_{0'} = l\cos\theta$$

$$\therefore \dot{x}_0' = l\dot{\theta}\cos\theta\cos\phi - l\dot{\phi}\sin\theta\sin\phi,$$

$$\dot{y}_0 = l\dot{\theta}\cos\theta\cos\phi + l\dot{\phi}\sin\theta\cos\phi,\ \dot{z}_0' = -l\dot{\theta}\sin\phi$$

$$\Rightarrow \dot{x}_0'^2 + \dot{y}_0'^2 + \dot{z}_0'^2 = l^2\dot{\theta}^2 + l^2\sin^2\theta\dot{\phi}^2$$

$$\therefore T = \frac{1}{2}m\left[\frac{2a^2}{5}\dot{\theta}^2 + \dot{x}_{0'}^2 + \dot{y}_{0'}^2 + \dot{z}_{0'}^2\right]$$

$$= \frac{1}{2}m\left[\frac{2a^2}{5}\dot{\theta}^2 + l^2\dot{\theta}^2 + l^2\dot{\phi}\sin^2\theta\right]$$

$$= \frac{1}{2}m\left[\left(\frac{2a^2}{5}l^2\right)\dot{\theta}^2 + l^2\omega^2\sin^2\theta\right]\ (\because \phi \neq \omega \text{ given})$$

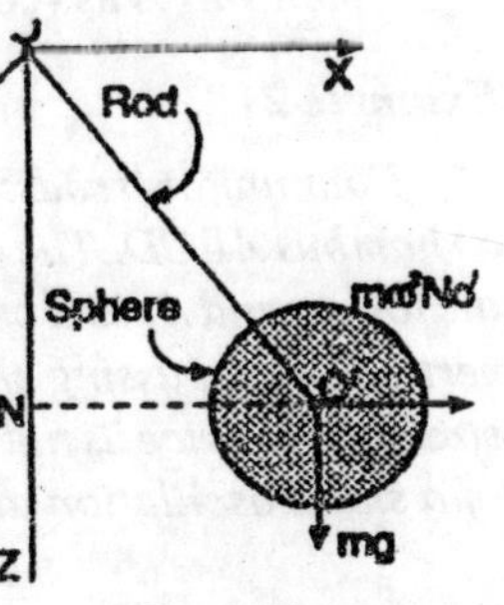

Fig. 3.10

and $\dot{W}^* = mgl\cos\theta + m\omega^2 l\sin\theta = mgl\cos\theta + m\omega^2 . 2\sin\theta\cos\theta$

$$= -mgl\sin\theta + 2m\omega^2 l^2\sin\theta\cos\theta$$

$$\Rightarrow \left(\frac{2a^2}{5} + l^2\right)\ddot{\theta} = -mgl\sin\theta + 3m\omega^2 l^2\sin\theta\cos\theta$$

Multiplying both sides by $2\dot{\theta}$ and integrating, we get

$$\left(\frac{2}{5}a^2 + l^2\right)\dot{\theta}^2 = 2gl\cos\theta - 3l^2\omega^2\cos^2\theta + D$$

$$\Rightarrow \dot{\theta}^2 = n^2(\cos\theta - \cos\beta)(\cos\alpha - \cos\theta)$$

where n is constant and α, β are the values of θ for which θ vanish.

Second Part:

K.E. + Potential Energy = T + K, when P.E. is K and is given by

$$K = T - W + C = \frac{1}{2}m\left[\left(\frac{2a^2}{5} + l^2\right)\dot{\theta}^2 + l^2\omega^2\sin^2\theta\right]$$

$- mgl \cos\theta - ml^2\omega^2 \sin^2\theta + C$

$= \frac{1}{2}m[\{2gl\cos\theta - 3l^2\omega^2\cos^2\theta + D\} + l^2\omega^2\sin^2\theta]$

$- mgl\cos\theta - ml^2\omega^2\sin^2\theta + C$

$= -\frac{1}{2}m\omega^2 l^2\cos^2\theta - \frac{1}{2}m\omega^2 l + A$ where A is constant.

$= -\frac{1}{2}m\omega^2 l^2\cos^2\theta + B$ where B is constant

∴ Total energy imparted

$$= \left[-\frac{1}{2}m\omega^2 l^2\cos^2\theta + B\right]_{\theta_1}^{\theta_2} = \frac{1}{2}m\omega^2 l^2(\cos^2\theta_1 - \cos^2\theta_2)$$

which varies as $(\cos^2\theta_1 - \cos^2\theta_2)$.

Example 21:

Four uniform rods; each of length 2a, are hinged at their ends so as to form a rhombus ABCD. The angles B and D are connected by an elastic string and the lowest end A rests on a horizontal plane while the end C slides on a smooth vertical wire passing through A; in the position of equilibrium the string is stretched to twice its natural length and the angle BAD is 2α. Show that the time of a small oscillation about this position is

$$2\pi\left\{\frac{2a(1+3\sin^2\alpha)}{3g\cos 2\alpha}\cos\alpha\right\}^{1/2}$$

Solution:

In the position of equilibrium, rods are making angles α with the vertical. When the system is slightly displaced from the position of equilibrium, let the rods make angle (α + θ) with the vertical θ being a small displacement. Now assuming the fixed and A as origin and the horizontal and vertical lines through it as co-ordinate axes, the co-ordinates of G_2 are $\{a\sin(\alpha+\theta), 3a\cos(\alpha+\theta)\}$

∴ (velocity)² of $G_2 = \{a\cos(\alpha+\theta)\dot{\theta}\}^2 + (-3a\sin(\alpha+\theta)\dot{\theta}\}^2$

$= a^2[(1+8\sin^2(\alpha+\theta)]\dot{\theta}^2$

Co-ordinates of G_1 are $\{a\sin(\alpha+\theta), a\cos(\alpha+\theta)\}$

∴ (velocity)² of $G_1 = a^2\dot{\theta}^2$

∴ Kinetic energy of the four taken together is

$$T = 2.\frac{1}{2}m.\left[\frac{a^2}{3}\dot{\theta}^2 + a^2\dot{\theta}^2\right]$$

$$+2.\frac{1}{2}m\left[\frac{a^2}{3}\dot{\theta}^2+a^2\{1+8\sin^2(\alpha+\theta)\}\dot{\theta}\right]$$

$$=\frac{8ma^2}{3}\left[1+\sin^2(\alpha+\theta)\right]\dot{\theta}^2\ (\because v_{G_1}=v_{G_4}\text{and } v_{G_2}=v_{G_3})$$

The work function W is given by $W=2\{-mga\cos(\alpha+\theta)\}$

$$+2\{-mg3a\cos(\alpha+\theta)\}-2\int_0^{2a\sin(\theta+\alpha)}\lambda\left(\frac{y-c}{c}\right)dy$$

$$=-8mga\cos(\alpha+\theta)-\frac{\lambda}{c}\{2a\sin(\alpha+\theta)-\}^2$$

Lagrange's θ equation gives

$$\frac{d}{dt}\left|\frac{16ma^2}{3}\{1+3\sin^2(\alpha+\theta)\}\dot{\theta}-16ma^2\sin(\alpha+\theta)\cos(\alpha+\theta)\dot{\theta}^2\right.$$

$$=8mga\sin(\alpha+\theta)-\frac{4\lambda}{c}a\cos(\alpha+\theta)\{2a\sin(\alpha+\theta)-c\}$$

$$\Rightarrow\frac{16ma^2}{3}(1+3\sin^2(\alpha+\theta)\}\ddot{\theta}$$

$$=8mga\sin(\alpha+\theta)-\frac{4\lambda a}{c}\cos(\alpha+\theta)\{2a\sin(\alpha+\theta)-c\}\qquad\text{...(1)}$$

Initially when $\theta=0,\dot{\theta}=0,\ddot{\theta}=0, c=a\sin\alpha$, hence (1) gives

$$\lambda=\frac{2mgc}{a\cos\alpha.}$$

Putting this value of λ in equation (1), we get

$$\frac{16ma^2}{3}\{1+3\sin^2(\alpha+\theta)\}\ddot{\theta}$$

$$=mga8\sin(\alpha+\theta)-\frac{8mg\cos(\alpha+\theta)}{\cos\alpha}\{2a\sin(\alpha+\theta)-c\}$$

*The force $m\omega^2 l\sin\theta$ also contributes to W. The distance of the point of application at O′ of this force from the vertical OZ is equal to l sin θ, hence the contribution $m\omega^2l^2\sin^2\theta$ to W is as given in (2).

** If W is the work function of the system , then P.E. = C –W.

i.e. $\frac{16ma^2}{3}\{1+3\sin^2\alpha\}\theta=8mga(\sin\alpha+\theta\cos\alpha)$

$$-\frac{8mg}{\cos\alpha}(\cos\alpha-8\sin\alpha)\{2a(\sin\alpha+\theta\cos\alpha)-a\sin\alpha\}.$$

$$= -\frac{8mg\cos 2\alpha}{\cos\alpha}\theta \text{ app.} \Rightarrow \ddot{\theta} = -\frac{3g\cos 2\alpha}{2a\cos\alpha(1+3\sin^2\alpha)}\theta \text{ app.}$$

$\therefore$ Time of a small oscillation about the position of equilibrium is given by

$$2\pi\sqrt{\left\{\frac{2a\cos\alpha(1+3\sin^2\alpha)}{3g\cos^2\alpha}\right\}}$$

Example 22:

A smooth circular wire, of mass 8 m and radius a, swings in a vertical plane, being suspended by an inextensible string of length a attached to one point of it, a particle of mass m can slide on the wire. Prove that the periods of small oscillations are

$$2\pi\sqrt{\left(\frac{8a}{3g}\right)}, 2\pi\sqrt{\left(\frac{a}{3g}\right)}, 2\pi\sqrt{\left(\frac{8a}{9g}\right)},$$

Solution:

At any time t, let the string OA, and the radius AC be inclined at angles θ and ϕ with he vertical and further let the radius to the particle (m) be inclined at an angle ψ with the vertical.

Now co-ordinates of C are

$(a\sin\theta + a\sin\phi, a\cos\theta + a\cos\phi)$.

$(\text{velocity})^2$ of $C = a^2\dot{\theta}^2 + a^2\dot{\phi}\cos(\theta-\phi)$

$$-a^2\dot{\theta}^2 + a^2\dot{\phi}^2 + 2a^2\dot{\theta}\dot{\phi} \text{ approximately } \left[\begin{array}{l}\because \dot{x}_C = a\cos\theta\dot{\theta} + a\cos\phi\dot{\phi} \\ \dot{y}_C = -a(\sin\theta\dot{\theta} + \sin\phi\dot{\phi}\end{array}\right]$$

Also co-ordinates of the particle m (*i.e.* of the pt. P) are

$x_P = a(\sin\theta + \sin\phi + \sin\psi)$,

$y_P = a(\cos\phi + \cos\phi + \cos\psi)$.

$\because (\text{celocity})^2$ of $m = a^2(\dot{\theta}^2 + \dot{\phi}^2 + \dot{\psi}^2 + 2\dot{\theta}\dot{\phi} + 2\dot{\theta}\dot{\phi} + 2\dot{\phi}\dot{\psi} + 2\dot{\psi}\dot{\theta})$ app,

Let T, be the kinetic energy and W, the work function of the system, then we readily get

$W = 8mg(a\cos\theta + a\cos\phi) + mg(a\cos\theta + a\cos\phi + a\cos\psi)$

$= mga[9\cos\theta + 9\cos\phi + \cos\psi)$

and $T = \frac{1}{2}.8m[a^2\dot{\phi}^2 + (a^2\dot{\theta}^2 + a^2\dot{\phi}^2 + a^2\dot{\phi}^2 + 2a^2\dot{\theta}\dot{\phi})]$

$$+\frac{1}{2}ma^2[\dot{\theta}^2 + \dot{\phi}^2 + \dot{\psi}^2 + 2\dot{\theta}\dot{\phi} + 2\dot{\phi}\dot{\psi} + 2\dot{\psi}\dot{\theta}]$$

i.e. $T = \frac{1}{2}m[9\dot{\theta}^2 + 17\dot{\phi}^2 + \dot{\psi}^2 + 18\dot{\theta}\dot{\phi} + 2\dot{\phi}\dot{\psi} + 2\dot{\psi}\dot{\theta}]$ ...(2)

∴ Lagrange's q and y equations give

$$9\ddot{\theta} + 9\ddot{\phi} + \ddot{\psi} = -9\frac{g}{a}\theta \quad ...(3)$$

$$9\ddot{\theta} + 17\ddot{\phi} + \ddot{\psi} = -9\frac{g}{a}\phi \quad ...(4)$$

and $\ddot{\theta} + \ddot{\phi} + \ddot{\psi} = \frac{g}{a}\psi,$

which can be rewritten as

$$(9D^2 + 9c)\,\theta + 9D^2\,\phi + D^2\,\psi = 0 \quad ...(6)$$

$$9D^2\theta + (17D^2 + 9c)\,\phi + D^2\psi = 0 \quad ...(7)$$

and $D^2\theta + D^2\,\phi + (D^2 + c)\,\psi = 0$ ...(8)

Eliminating ϕ and ψ in ...(6), (7) and (8), we get

$$\begin{vmatrix} 9D^2 + 9c & 9D^2 & D^2 \\ 9D^2 & 17D^2 + 9c & D^2 \\ D^2 & D^2 & D^2 + c \end{vmatrix} \theta = 0$$

i.e. $(8D^2 + 9c)\,[9c(2D^2 + c) + D^2(8D^2 + 9c)]\theta = 0$

i.e. $(8D^2 + 9c)\,[8D^4 + 27cD^2) + 9c^2]\theta = 0$

i.e. $(8D^2 + 9c)\,(8D^4 + 3c)\,D^2 + 3c]\theta = 0$ ...(9)

Now let $\theta = A\cos(pt + B)$, then

$D\theta = -pA\sin(pt + B)$, $D^2\theta$

$= -p^2A\cos(pt + B) = -p^2\theta$ ...(10)

∴ (9) gives $(8p^2 - 9c)\,(8p^2 - 3c)\,(p^2 - 3c) = 0$ $[\because \theta \neq \theta]$

$$\Rightarrow \left(8p^2 - \frac{9g}{a}\right)\left(8p^2 - \frac{3g}{a}\right)\left(p^2 - \frac{3g}{a}\right) = 0.$$

i.e. $p_1^2 = \frac{9g}{8a}, p_2^2 = \frac{3g}{8g}, p_3^2 = \frac{3g}{a}$

Thus periods of small oscillations are $\frac{2\pi}{p_1}, \frac{2\pi}{p_2}, \frac{2\pi}{p_3}$

i.e. $2\pi\sqrt{\left(\frac{8a}{9g}\right)}, 2\pi\sqrt{\left(\frac{8a}{3g}\right)}, 2\pi\sqrt{\left(\frac{a}{9g}\right)}$

Example 23:

A plank, 2a feet long, is placed symmetrically across a light cylinder, of radius a which rests and is free to roll on a perfectly rough horizontal plane. A heavy particle whose mass is an times that of plank is embedded in the cylinder at its lowest point. If the system is slightly displaced, show that its periods of oscillation are the values of

$$\frac{2\pi}{p}\sqrt{\left(\frac{a}{g}\right)}$$

given by the equation $4p^4 - (n + 12)\, p^2 + 3\,(n - 1) = 0$.

Solution:

C is the centre of the cylinder whose radius is a.

Let the mass of the plank be m, therefore mass of the particle embedded at the lowest point of the cylinder is nm.

Suppose θ and ϕ are the angles through which the cylinder and the plank have turned in time t, from their initial positions.

Initially G was coinciding with K which was at the highest point of the cylinder.

There is no slipping between the plank and the cylinder, hence Further there is no sliding between the cylinder and the horizontal plane,

PG = arc KP = a ($\phi = \theta$)

hence OC_1 = arc $C_1S = a\theta$, where O was the initial point of contact of the cylinder and the horizontal plane.

Taking O as origin and the horizontal and vertical through O as co-ordinates axes, we obtain $x_G = aq + a \sin f - a\,(f - q) \cos f$

$= a\theta + a\phi - a\,(\phi - \theta) = 2a\theta$

and $y_G = a + a \cos\phi + a\,(\phi - \theta) \sin\phi = 2a - a\theta\phi + a\,\dfrac{\phi^2}{2}$

Further co-ordinates of the particle nm (*i.e.* of the point S)

arc $\equiv \{a\theta - a\sin\theta, a - \cos\theta\}$

$\therefore$ (velocity)^2 of (nm) $= (a\dot{\theta} - a\cos\theta\dot{\theta})^2 + (a\sin\theta\dot{\theta})^2,$

$$= (a^2 + a^2 - 2a^2\cos\theta)\dot{\theta}^2.$$

Now let T, be the kinetic energy and W, the work function of the system, then we readily obtain

$$W = -n\,mg\,(a - a\cos\theta) - mg\left(2a - a\theta\phi + a\frac{\phi^2}{2}\right)$$

$$= -\,nmga\frac{\theta^2}{2} - mga\left(\frac{\phi^2}{2} - \theta\phi\right) - 2mga$$

$$\text{and } T = \frac{1}{2}m\left[\frac{a^2}{3}\dot{\phi}^2 + 4a^2\dot{\theta}^2\right] + \frac{1}{2}nm[2a^2 - 2a^2\cos\theta]\dot{\theta}^2$$

$$= \frac{1}{2}m\left[\frac{a^2}{3}\dot{\phi}^2 + 4a^2\dot{\theta}^2\right] + \frac{1}{2}nm.2a^2\dot{\theta}^2\frac{\theta^2}{2}$$

$$= \frac{1}{2}m\left[\frac{a^2}{3}\dot{\phi}^2 + 4a^2\dot{\theta}^2\right]$$, approximately, (neglecting the second part)

$\therefore$ Lagrange's q - equation is given by $\frac{d}{dt}\left(\frac{\partial T}{\partial\dot{\theta}}\right) - \frac{\partial T}{\partial\dot{\theta}} = \frac{\partial W}{\partial\theta}$

$$\Rightarrow \frac{d}{dt}(4ma^2\dot{\theta}) = -\,nmga\theta + mga\phi \Rightarrow 4\ddot{\theta} = -\frac{g}{a}(n\theta - \phi) \qquad ...(1)$$

Further Lagrange's f-equation gives

$$\frac{d}{dt}\left(\frac{ma^2}{3}\dot{\phi}\right) = -\,mg(\phi - \theta) \Rightarrow \ddot{\phi} = -\frac{3g}{a}(\phi - \theta) \qquad ...(2)$$

Equations (1) and (2) can be re-written at $(4D^2 + nc)\,\theta - c\phi = 0$ ...(3)

and $3cq - (D^2 + 3c)\,\phi = 0$ where $c = (g/a)$ ...(4)

Eliminating f in between (3) and (4), we get

$$[(4D^2 + nc)\,(D^2 + 3c) - 3c^2\,]\,\theta = 0$$

$$\Rightarrow [4D^2 + c(n + 12)\,D^2 + 3\,(n - 1)\,c^2]\,\theta = 0 \qquad ...(5)$$

Now if the periods of oscillation are the values of

$\frac{2\pi}{p}\sqrt{\left(\frac{a}{g}\right)}$ *i.e.* values of $\frac{2\pi}{\sqrt{\left(\frac{g}{a}p^2\right)}}$,

then the solution of the above equation must be of the form

$$\theta = A\cos\left[\sqrt{\left(\frac{g}{a}\right)}pt + B\right]$$

$$\therefore D\theta = -\sqrt{\left(\frac{g}{a}\right)}pA\sin\left[\sqrt{\left(\frac{g}{a}\right)}pt + B\right]$$

$$D^2\theta = -\left(\frac{g}{a}\right)pA\cos\left[\sqrt{\left(\frac{g}{a}\right)}pt + B\right]$$

$$= -\left(\frac{g}{a}\right)p^2\theta = -cp^2\theta \text{ and } D^4\theta = c^2p^4\theta.$$

Substituting these values in (5) we get

$$[4c^2p^4 - c^2(n+12)p^2 + 3(n-1)c^2]\theta = 0$$

$$\Rightarrow 4p^4 - (n+12)p^2 + 3(n-1) = 0 \qquad (\because \theta \neq 0)$$

Example 24:

To a point of a solid homogeneous sphere, of mass M, is freely hinged one end of a homogeneous rod, of mass nM; and the other end is freely hinged to a fixed point. If the system makes small oscillations under gravity about the position of equilibrium, the centre of a sphere and the rod being always in a vertical plane passing through the fix point, show that the periods of the principal oscillations are the values of $\frac{2\pi}{p}$ *given by the equation*

$$2ab(6+7n)p^4 - p^2g\{10a(3+n) + 21b(2+n)\} + 15g^2(2+n) = 0,$$

where a is the length of the rod and b is the radius if the sphere.

Solution:

At any time t, let the rod and the sphere have turned through angel θ and ϕ to vertical, where OA = a, AC = b.

Now co - ordinates of C are

$$x_C = a\sin\theta + b\sin\phi,\ y_C = a\cos\theta + b\cos\phi$$

$$\therefore \text{(velocity)}^2 \text{ of C} = \dot{x}_C^2 + \dot{y}_C^2 = a^2\dot{\theta}^2 + b^2\dot{\phi}^2 + 2ab\dot{\theta}\dot{\phi}\cos(\theta - \phi)$$

$$= a^2\dot{\theta}^2 + b^2\dot{\phi}^2 + 2ab\dot{\theta}\dot{\phi} \qquad [\because \theta \text{ and } \phi \text{ are small}]$$

Also the co-ordinates of G are $\left(\frac{a}{2}\sin\theta, \frac{a}{2}\cos\theta\right)$

$$\therefore \text{(velocity)}^2 \text{ of G} = \frac{a^2}{4}\dot{\theta}^2$$

Now let T be, the kinetic energy and W, the work function of the system, then we readily obtain

$$W = n\,Mg\frac{a}{2}\cos\theta + Mg(a\cos\theta + b\cos\phi)$$

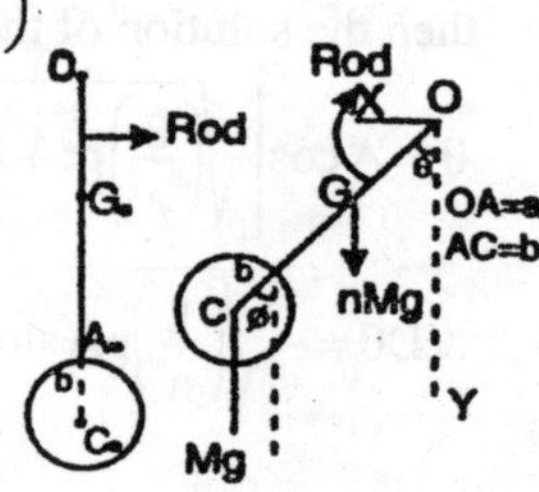

Fig. 3.11

$$= \frac{1}{2} a(n+2)\, Mg \cos\theta + bMg \cos\phi$$

and $$T = \frac{1}{2} M \left[\frac{2b^2}{5} \dot{\phi}^2 + (a^2\dot{\theta}^2 + b^2\dot{\theta}^2 + 2ab\dot{\theta}\dot{\phi} \right] + \frac{1}{2} n.M \left[\frac{a^2}{12}\dot{\theta}^2 + \frac{a^2}{4}\dot{\theta}^2 \right]$$

$$= \frac{1}{6} a^2 (n+3)\, M\dot{\theta}^2 + \frac{7b^2}{10} M\dot{\phi}^2 + abM\dot{\theta}\dot{\phi}$$

$\therefore$ Lagrange's q-equation is given by $\frac{d}{dt}\left(\frac{\partial T}{\partial \dot{\theta}}\right) - \frac{\partial T}{\partial \theta} = \frac{\partial W}{\partial \theta}$

$$\Rightarrow \frac{d}{dt}\left\{ \frac{1}{3} a^2 (n+3)\, M\dot{\theta} + abM\dot{\phi}. \right\} = -\frac{1}{2} a(n+2) Mg\, \theta \text{ app.}$$

$$\Rightarrow 2a(n+3)\ddot{\theta} + 6b\ddot{\phi} = -3(n+2)g\theta \qquad ...(1)$$

While Lagrange's ϕ-equation gives

$$\frac{d}{dt}\left\{ \frac{7b^2}{5} M\dot{\phi} + abM\dot{\theta} \right\} = -3(n+2)g\theta$$

$$\Rightarrow 7b\ddot{\phi} + 5a\ddot{\theta} = -5g\phi \qquad ...(2)$$

These can be re-written as

$$\{2a\,(n+3)D^2 + 3\,(n+2)\,g\}\,\theta + 6b\,D^2\,\phi = 0 \qquad ...(3)$$

and $$5aD^2\theta + (7bD^2 + 5g)\,\phi = 0 \qquad ...(4)$$

Eliminating ϕ between (3) and (4), we get

$$[2ab\,(7n+6)\,D^4 + \{10a\,(n+3) + 21b\,(n+2)\}\,gD^2 + 15\,(n+2)\,g^2]\,\theta = 0 \qquad ...(5)$$

To solve (5), let us put

$\theta = A\cos(pt + B), \therefore D\theta = -pA\sin(pt + B).$

$D^2\theta = -p^2 A\cos(pt + B) = -p^2\theta$ and $D^2\,\theta = p^4\theta.$

Substituting these values in (5), we have

$$2ab\,(7n+6)p^4 - \{10\,(n+3)\,a + 21b\,(n+2)\}\,p^2 g + 15\,(n+2)\,g^2 = 0.$$

Example 25:

A hollow cylindrical garden roller is fitted with a counterpoise which can turn on the axis of the cylinder; the system is placed on the rough horizontal plane and oscillates under gravity, if $\frac{2\pi}{p}$ be the time of a small oscillation, show that p is given by the equation $p^2[2M + M')\,k^2 - M'\,h^2] = (2M + M')\,gh$ where M and M′ are the masses of the roller and counterpoise, k is the radius of gyration of M′ about the axis of the cylinder and h is the distance of its centre of mass from the axis.

Solution:

Suppose O′ is the centre of the cylindrical roller and G is the centre of gravity of the counterpoise, whose mass is M′. Obviously the line O′ K is a line fixed in the roller and the line O′ G is fixed in the counterpoise which were initially vertical. Suppose they make angles θ and φ with the vertical at the time t. Initially K was at O.

There is no slipping between the cylinder and the horizontal plane, hence OB = arc KB = aθ. Now assuming O as origin and the horizontal and vertical through O as co-ordinates axes, we have co-ordinates of G:-

$x_G = a\theta + h\sin\phi,\ y_G = a - h\cos\phi,$

$\therefore$ (velocity)^2 of $G = \dot{x}_G^2 + \dot{y}_G^2 = (a\dot{\theta} + h\cos\phi\dot{\phi})^2 + (h\sin\phi\dot{\phi})^2$

$= a^2\dot{\theta}^2 + h^2\dot{\phi}^2 + 2ah\dot{\theta}\dot{\phi}$ [neglecting higher powers of φ]

But radius of gyration of the counterpoise about O′ is k, where O′G = h. Hence the square of radius of gyration about G is $(k^2 - h^2)$.

Also (velocity)^2 of O′ = $(a\dot{\theta})^2 = a^2\dot{\theta}^2$. [$\therefore$ co-ordinates of O′ are (aθ, a)]

Now let T, be the kinetic energy and W, the work function of the system then we get

$$T = \frac{1}{2}M(a^2\dot{\theta}^2 + a^2\dot{\theta}^2) + \frac{1}{2}M'[(k^2 - h^2)\dot{\phi}^2 + a^2\dot{\theta}^2 + h^2\dot{\phi}^2 + 2ah\dot{\theta}h]$$

$$= \frac{M + M'}{2}a^2\dot{\theta}^2 + \frac{1}{2}M'k^2\dot{\phi}^2 + M'ah\dot{\theta}\dot{\phi}$$

$M = M'gh\cos\phi + D.$

$\therefore$ Lagrange's θ-equation gives $\frac{d}{dt}[(2M + M')a^2\dot{\theta} + M'ah\dot{\phi}] = 0$

$\Rightarrow (2M + M')a\ddot{\theta} + M'h\ddot{\phi} = 0$ ...(1)

while Lagrange's φ-equation gives

$\frac{d}{a}[M'k^2\dot{\phi} + M'ah\dot{\theta}] = -M'gh\phi \Rightarrow k^2\ddot{\phi} + ah\ddot{\theta} = -gh\phi$

$\Rightarrow ah\ddot{\theta} + k^2\ddot{\phi} = -gh\phi,$ ...(2)

$O'O = a,\quad O'G = h$

Now eliminating $\ddot{\theta}$ between (1) and (2), we get

$[Mh^2 - (2M + M')k^2]\ddot{\phi} = (2M + M')gh\phi.$

or $[(2M + M')\,k^2 - M'\,h^2]\;\ddot{\phi} = -\,(2M + M')gh\phi$ ...(3)

But, if $\dfrac{2\pi}{p}$ is the time of small oscillation, then we assume $\phi = A\cos(pt + b)$

$\therefore \dot{\phi} = -\,pA\sin(pt + B)$ and $\ddot{\phi} = -\,p^2A\cos(pt + B) = -\,p^2\theta$

$\therefore$ Equation (3) gives

$-\,p^2\,[(2M + M')\,k^2 - M'\,h^2] = -\,(2M + M')\,gh$ $\qquad [\because \phi \neq 0]$

Example 26:

Two equal rods AB and BC; each of length l, smoothly jointed at B, are suspended from A and oscillate in a vertical plane through A. Show that the periods of normal oscillations are

$$\frac{2\pi}{n} \text{ where } n^2 = \left(3 \pm \frac{6}{\sqrt{7}}\right)\frac{g}{l}.$$

Solution:

At any time t, let the rod AB and BC be inclined at angles θ and φ to the vertical.

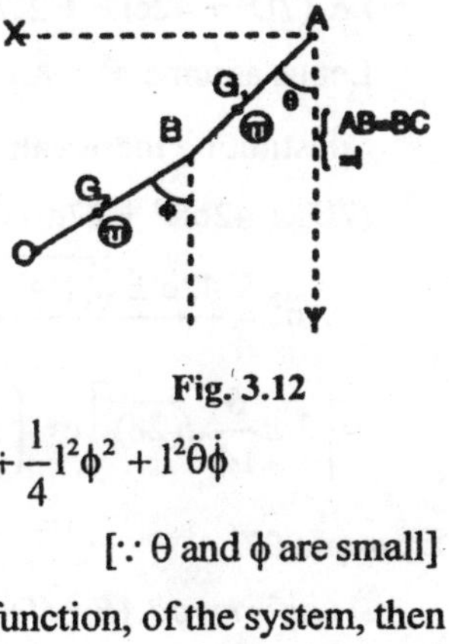

$\therefore$ Co-ordinates of G_1 are $\left(\frac{1}{2}\sin, \frac{1}{2}\cos\theta\right)$

$$\therefore v_{G_1}^2 = \left(\frac{1}{2}\cos\theta\dot{\theta}\right)^2 + \left(-\frac{1}{2}\sin\theta\dot{\theta}\right)^2 = \frac{l^2}{4}\dot{\theta}^2$$

$$x_{G_2} = l\sin\theta + \frac{1}{2}\sin\phi,\; y_{G_2} = l\cos\theta + \frac{1}{2}\phi$$

Fig. 3.12

$$\therefore x_{G_2}^2 = l^2\dot{\theta}^2 + \frac{1}{2}l^2\dot{\phi}^2 + l^2\dot{\theta}\dot{\phi}\cos(\theta - \phi) = l^2\theta^2 + \frac{1}{4}l^2\phi^2 + l^2\dot{\theta}\dot{\phi}$$

$[\because \theta$ and ϕ are small$]$

now, let T, be the kinetic energy and W, the work function, of the system, then we have $W = mgl\cos\theta + mg\left(l\cos\theta + \frac{1}{2}\cos\phi\right)$

$$= \frac{1}{2}mgl(3\cos\theta + \cos\phi)$$

and $T = \frac{1}{2}m\left[\frac{1}{12}l^2\dot{\theta}^2 + \frac{1}{2}l^2\dot{\theta}^2\right] + \frac{1}{2}m\left\{\frac{1}{12}l^2\dot{\phi}^2 + l^2(\dot{\theta}^2 + \frac{1}{4}\dot{\phi}^2 + \dot{\theta}\dot{\phi})\right\}$

$$= \frac{1}{2}ml^2\left(\frac{4}{3}\dot{\theta}^2 + \frac{1}{3}\dot{\phi}^2 + \dot{\theta}\dot{\phi}\right)$$

$\therefore$ Lagrange's θ-equations is

$$\frac{d}{dt}\left(\frac{\partial T}{\partial \dot{\theta}}\right)-\frac{\partial T}{\partial \theta}=\frac{\partial W}{\partial \theta}\Rightarrow\frac{d}{dt}\left(\frac{4}{d}l\dot{\theta}+\frac{1}{2}l\dot{\phi}\right)=-\frac{3}{2}g\theta$$

$$\Rightarrow 8\ddot{\theta}+3\ddot{\phi}=-\frac{9g}{l}\theta$$

While Lagrange's ϕ equation gives

$$\frac{d}{dt}\left(\frac{1}{3}l\dot{\phi}+\frac{1}{2}l\dot{\theta}\right)=-\frac{1}{2}g\phi\Rightarrow 3\ddot{\theta}+2\ddot{\phi}=-\frac{3g}{l}\phi$$

Equations (1) and (2) can be written as

$(8D^2 + 9c)\,\theta + 3D^2\phi = 0$

and $3D^2\theta + (2D^2 + 3c)\,\phi = 0$ where $c = \left(\frac{g}{l}\right)$

Eliminating ϕ between (3) and (4), we get

$(8D^2 + 9c)\,(2D^2 + 3c) \;- 9D^4]\theta = 0$

i.e. $(7D^2 + 42cD^2 + 27c^2)\,\theta = 0$

Let us assume, $\theta = A\cos(nt + B) = -\;n^2\theta$ and $D^4\theta = n^4\theta$

Substituting these values in (5), we get

$(7D^4 + 42cD^2 + 27c^2)\,\theta = 0$ *i.e.* $7n^2 \;-\; 42cn^2 \;- 27c^2) = 0 \quad [\because \theta \neq 0]$

$$\text{i.e. } n^2=\frac{42c\pm\sqrt{[\{(42c)^2-4(7)(27c^2)\}]}}{14}$$

$$=\left[3\pm\frac{6}{14}\sqrt{(28)}\right]c=\left(3\pm\frac{6}{\sqrt{7}}\right)c=\left\{3\pm\frac{6}{\sqrt{7}}\right\}\frac{g}{l}.$$

Example 27:

A uniform rod AB, of length 2a can turn freely about a point distance c from its centre, and is at rest at an angle α to the horizon when a particle is hung by a light string of length l from one end. If the particle be displaced slightly in the vertical plane of the rod show that it will oscillate in the same time as a simple pendulum of length

$$l\frac{a^2+3ac\cos^2\alpha+3c^2\sin^2\alpha}{2^2+3ac}$$

Solution:

Let M be the mass and G the centre of gravity of the rod. Further let O be the point about which it nac turn where OG = c. Let BP be a string of length l and m the mass of the particle tied to the end P of the string BP.

Initially rod was making an angle α with the horizontal and the string was vertical.

Let B_0 be the initial position of B so that $\angle B_0OX = \alpha$, After a time t let the rod make an angle θ with OB_0 *i.e.* an angle)$\alpha + \theta$) with the horizontal and let the string be inclined at an angle θ with the vertical.

Initially the system was at rest, hence taking moments about O, (in this position), we get $Mc = m(a - c)$.

Assuming O as origin and the horizontal and the vertical through O as co-ordinates axes, we obtain the following results

$$x_p = (a - c)\cos(\alpha + \theta) + l\sin\phi.\ y_p = (a - c)\sin(\alpha + \theta) + l\cos\phi.$$

$$\therefore (\text{velocity})^2 \text{of } P = \{-(a - c)\sin(\alpha + \theta)\dot{\theta} + l\sin\theta\dot{\theta}\}^2$$

$$+\{(a - c)\cos(\alpha + \theta)\dot{\theta} - l\sin\phi\dot{\phi}\}^2$$

$$= (a - c)^2\dot{\theta}^2 + l^2\dot{\phi}^2 - 2l(a - c)\dot{\theta}\dot{\phi}\sin(\alpha + \theta + \phi)$$

$$= (a - c)^2\dot{\theta}^2 + l^2\dot{\phi}^2 + 2l(a - c)\dot{\theta}\dot{\phi}\sin\alpha$$

(neglecting small quantities of the higher order)

Also co-ordinates of G (the C.G. of the rod) are

$$\{-c\cos(\alpha + \theta), -c\sin(\alpha + \theta)\}$$

$$\therefore (\text{velocity})^2 \text{of } G = \{c\sin(\alpha + \theta)\dot{\theta}\}^2 + \{-c\cos(a + \theta)\dot{\theta}\}^2 = c^2\dot{\theta}^2.$$

Now let T, be the kinetic energy and W, the work function of the system, then we easily obtain

$$W = mg\ \{(a - c)\sin(\alpha + \theta) + l\cos\phi] - Mgc\sin(\alpha + \theta) + D$$

$$= mgl\cos\phi + D$$

[the first and the last terms cancel, because m (a – c) = Mc]

$$\text{and } T = \frac{1}{2}M\left[\frac{a^2}{3}\dot{\theta}^2 + c^2\dot{\theta}^2\right] + \frac{1}{2}m[(a - c)^2\dot{\theta}^2$$

$$+l^2\dot{\phi}^2 - 2l(a - c)\dot{\theta}\dot{\phi}\sin\alpha]$$

$\therefore$ Lagrange's θ-equation gives

$$\frac{d}{dt}\left[\left\{M\left(\frac{a^2}{3} + c^2\right) + m(a - c)^2\right\}\dot{\theta} - ml(a - c)\ddot{\phi}\sin\alpha\right] = 0$$

$$\Rightarrow \left\{M\left(\frac{a^2}{3} + c^2\right) + m\,(a - c)^2\right\}\ddot{\theta} - ml(a - c)\ddot{\phi}\sin\alpha = 0.$$

$$\Rightarrow\left\{M\left(\frac{a^2}{3}+c^2\right)+mc\,(a-c)\right\}\ddot{\theta}-mcl\ddot{\phi}\sin\alpha=0 \quad [\because m(a-c)=Mc]$$

$\Rightarrow (a^2+3ac)\ddot{\theta}-3lc\sin\alpha\ddot{\phi}=0.$ While Lagrange's ϕ equation gives

$$\frac{d}{dt}\left\{ml^2\dot{\phi}-ml(a-c)\dot{\theta}\sin\alpha\right\}=-mgl\phi$$

$$\Rightarrow l\ddot{\phi}-(a-c)\ddot{\theta}\sin\alpha=-g\phi \qquad ...(2)$$

Eliminating θ in (1) and (2), we have

$$l\ddot{\phi}-(a-c)\sin\alpha\frac{3lc\sin\alpha}{a^2+3ac}\ddot{\phi}=-g\phi$$

i.e. $\Rightarrow \dfrac{a^2+3ac-3c(a-c)\sin^2\alpha}{a^2+3ac}l\ddot{\phi}=-g\phi$

$$\Rightarrow\ddot{\phi}=-\frac{g}{l(a^2+3ac\cos^2\alpha+3c^2\sin^2\alpha)}\phi=-\mu\phi\text{ (say)}$$

$\therefore$ Length of the simple equivalent pendulum $=\dfrac{g}{\mu}$

$$=\frac{a^2+3ac\cos^2\alpha+3c^2\sin^2\alpha}{a^2+3ac}l.$$

Example 28:

A uniform rod AB of length 8a is suspended from a fixed point O by means of light inextensible string, of length 13a, attached to B. If the system is slightly displaced in a vertical plane, show that $(\theta+3\phi)$ and $(12\theta-13\phi)$ are principal co-ordinates where θ and ϕ are the angles which the rod and string respectively make with the vertical. Also show that periods of small oscillations are

$$2\pi\sqrt{\left(\frac{a}{g}\right)}\text{ and }2\pi\sqrt{\left(\frac{52}{3g}\right)}.$$

Solution:

We have

$$x_G=13a\sin\phi+4a\sin\theta$$

and $y_G=13a\cos\phi+4a\cos\phi$

$$\therefore \dot{x}_G^2+\dot{y}_G^2=169a^2\dot{\phi}^2+16a^2\dot{\theta}^2$$

$$+104a^2\dot{\theta}\dot{\phi}\cos(\theta-\phi)$$

Thus $T=\dfrac{1}{2}m[k^2\dot{\theta}^2+(\dot{x}_G^2+\dot{y}_G^2)]=\dfrac{1}{2}ma^2\left[\dfrac{64}{3}\dot{\theta}^2+169\dot{\phi}^2+104\dot{\theta}\dot{\phi}\right]$

and the work function

$W = mg\,(13a\cos\phi + 4a\cos\theta)$

$\therefore$ Lagrange's θ-equation gives

$$\frac{d}{dt}\left(\frac{\partial T}{\partial \dot{\theta}}\right) - \frac{\partial T}{\partial \theta} \Rightarrow 61\ddot{\theta} + 39\ddot{\phi} = -\frac{3g}{a}\theta \qquad ...(1)$$

While Lagrange's θ-equation gives $4\ddot{\theta} + 13\ddot{\phi} = -\frac{g}{a}\phi$ ...(2)

Equations (1) and (2) $\Rightarrow D^2(\theta + 3\phi) = -\frac{3g}{52a}(\theta + 3\phi)$

and $D^2(12\theta - 13\phi) = -\frac{g}{a}(12\theta + 13\phi)$

Now putting $q + 3\phi = X$ and $12\theta - 13\theta = Y$ in these equations, we get D^2X

$$= -\frac{3g}{52a}X \text{ and } D^2Y = -\frac{g}{a}\cdot Y;$$

which obviously represent two independent simple harmonic motions. Hence X and Y are principal co-ordinates, that is

$(\theta + 3\phi)$ and $(12\theta - 13\phi)$ are principal co-ordinates.

Also, periods of small oscillations are given by

$$2\pi\sqrt{\left(\frac{52a}{3g}\right)} \text{ and } 2\pi\sqrt{\left(\frac{a}{g}\right)}$$

Example 29:

A ring slides on a smooth circular hoop of equal mass and of radius a which can turn in a vertical plane about a fix point O in its circumference. If θ *and* ϕ *be the inclinations to the vertical of the radius through O and of the radius through the ring, prove that principal co-ordinates are* $(2\theta + \phi)$ *and* $\phi - \theta)$, *and the periods of small oscillations are*

$$2\pi\sqrt{\left(\frac{a}{2g}\right)} \text{ and } 2\pi\sqrt{\left(\frac{2a}{g}\right)}.$$

Solution:

Let the mass of the hoop and the ring be m. In a displaced position, let O′ be the centre of the hoop and P the position of the ring which slides on the hoop.

$\therefore$ Co-ordinates of the point P are given by

$x_p = a\,(\sin\theta + \sin\phi)$

$y_p = a\,(\cos\theta + \cos\phi)$

$\Rightarrow \dot{x}_P^2 + \dot{y}_P^2 = a^2(\dot{\theta}^2 + \dot{\phi}^2 + 2\dot{\theta}\dot{\phi})$

when θ and ϕ are small.

also co-ordinates of $O' = a^2\dot{\theta}^2$

Thus T = Energy of circular hoop + Energy of ring

$$= \frac{1}{2}m(a^2\dot{\theta}^2 + a^2\dot{\theta}^2) + \frac{1}{2}ma^2(\dot{\theta}^2 + \dot{\phi}^2 + 2\dot{\theta}\dot{\phi})$$

$$= \frac{1}{2}ma^2(3\dot{\theta}^2 + \dot{\phi}^2 + 2\dot{\theta}\dot{\phi})$$

Also the work function

W = mga cos θ + mg (a cos θ + a cos ϕ) = mga (2 cos θ + cos ϕ).

∴ Lagrange's θ-equation gives $3\ddot{\theta} + \ddot{\phi} = -\frac{2g}{a}\theta$ ...(1)

Lagrange's f-equation gives $\ddot{\theta} + \ddot{\phi} = -\frac{g}{a}\phi$ ...(2)

Now adding (1) and (2) and multiplying (2) by 2 and subtracting (1) from that, we get $D^2(2\theta + \phi) = -\frac{g}{2a}(2\theta + \phi)$

and $D^2(\phi - \theta) = -\frac{2g}{a}(\phi - \theta)$

Taking 2θ + ϕ = X and ϕ − θ = Y, we get

$$D^2X = -\frac{g}{2a}X \text{ and } D^2Y = -\frac{2g}{a}Y;$$

which obviously represent two independent simple harmonic motions. Thus X and Y are principal co-ordinates, that is (2θ + ϕ) and (ϕ − θ) are principal co-ordinates.

Also, periods of small oscillations are given by

$$2\pi\sqrt{\left(\frac{2a}{g}\right)} \text{ and } 2\pi\sqrt{\left(\frac{a}{2g}\right)}.$$

Example 30:

A square ABCD formed by four rods each of length 2l and mass hinged at their ends, rests on a horizontal frictionless table. An impulsive of magnitude I is applied to the vertex A in the direction AD Find the equations of motion, and prove that the K.E. developed immediately after the application of the impulsive forces is

$$T = (I^2/2m)$$

Solution:

When the square is struck, its shape will in general be a rhombus. Suppose that at any time t, the angels made by sides AD (or BC) and BA (or CD) with the x-axis are θ_1 and θ_2 respectively, while the co-ordinates of the centre M are (x, y).

*Suppose that the force F_v acting on a system are such that $\lim_{\tau\to 0}\int_0^{\tau} F_v dt = I_v$

where t represents a time interval, Then we call F_v impulsive forces and I_v are called Impulse.

** If we call P_α to be the generalised impulse, (3) can be written as

Hence x, y, θ_1, θ_2, are the generalised co-ordinates.

From the adjoining diagram, we see that the position vectors of the centre E,F, G.H of the rods are given respectively by

$$r_E = (x - l\cos\theta_1)i + (\dot{y} - l\sin\theta_1)j,$$

$$r_F = (x + l\cos\theta_2)i + (y - l\sin\theta_2)j,$$

$$r_G = (x + l\cos\theta_2)i + (y - l\sin\theta_1)j,$$

$$\text{and } r_H = (x - l\cos\theta_2)i + (y + l\sin\theta_1)j.$$

$$\because v_E = \dot{r}_E = (\dot{x} - l\sin\theta_1\dot{\theta}_1)i + (\dot{y} - l\cos\theta_1\dot{\theta}_1)j,$$

$$v_F = \dot{r}_F = (\dot{x} - l\sin\theta_2\dot{\theta}_2)i + (\dot{y} - l\cos\theta_2\dot{\theta}_2)j,$$

$$v_G = \dot{r}_G = (\dot{x} - l\sin\theta_1\dot{\theta}_1)i + (\dot{y} + l\cos\theta_1\dot{\theta}_1)j,$$

$$v_H = \dot{r}_H = (\dot{x} + l\sin\theta_2\dot{\theta}_2)i + (\dot{y} + l\cos\theta_2\dot{\theta}_2)j.$$

$$\text{Now, K.E. of the rod AB} = \frac{1}{2}m\dot{r}_E^2 + \frac{1}{3}ml^2\dot{\theta}_1^2\frac{1}{2} = T_{AB} \text{ say}$$

$$\text{K.E. of the rod CB} = \frac{1}{2}m\dot{r}_F^2 + \frac{1}{3}ml^2\dot{\theta}_1^2\frac{1}{2} = T_{BC} \text{ say}$$

$$\text{K.E. of the rod CD} = \frac{1}{2}m\dot{r}_G^2 + \frac{1}{3}ml^2\dot{\theta}_2^2\frac{1}{2} = T_{CD} \text{ say}$$

$$\text{K.E. of the rod DA} = \frac{1}{2}m\dot{r}_H^2 + \frac{1}{3}ml^2\dot{\theta}_1^2\frac{1}{2} = T_{DA} \text{ say}$$

$$\therefore \text{K.E. of system } \left(\frac{\partial T}{\partial}\right)_2 = (4m\dot{x})_2 = 4m\dot{x}, \left(\frac{\partial T}{\partial \dot{y}}\right)_2 = (4m\dot{y})_2 = 4m,$$

$$\frac{1}{2}m(4\dot{x}^2 + 4\dot{y}^2 + 2l^2\dot{\theta}_1^2 + 2l^2\dot{\theta}_2^2) + \frac{ml^2}{3}(\dot{\theta}_1^2 + \dot{\theta}_2^2).$$

$$= 2m(\dot{x}^2 + \dot{y}^2) + \frac{4}{3}ml^2(\dot{\theta}_1^2 + \dot{\theta}_2^2). \quad ...(1)$$

Let us now assume that initially the rhombus is a square at rest with its sides parallel to the co-ordinate axes and its centre located at the origin.

Then, we get $x = 0 = y,\ \theta_1 = \frac{\pi}{2}, \theta_2 = 0, \dot{x} = 0,\ \dot{y} = 0, \dot{\theta}_1 = 0, \dot{\theta}_2 = 0.$

Now if we use the notation, $(\,)_1$ and $(\,)_2$ to denote quantities before and after the impulse is applied, we have

$$\left(\frac{\partial T}{\partial \dot{x}}\right)_1 = (4m\dot{x})_1 = 0 \left(\frac{\partial T}{\partial \dot{y}}\right)_1 = (4m\dot{y})_1 = 0$$

$$\left(\frac{\partial T}{\partial \dot{\theta}}\right)_1 = \left(\frac{8}{3}ml^2\dot{\theta}_1\right) = 0, \left(\frac{\partial T}{\partial \dot{\theta}_2}\right) = \left(\frac{8}{3}ml^2\dot{\theta}_2\right) = 0$$

and $\left(\frac{\partial T}{\partial \dot{x}}\right)_2 = (4m\dot{x})_2 = 4m\dot{x}, \left(\frac{\partial T}{\partial \dot{y}}\right)_2 = (4m\dot{y})_2 = 4m,$

$$\left(\frac{\partial T}{\partial \dot{\theta}_1}\right)_2 = \left(\frac{8}{3}ml^2\dot{\theta}_1\right)_2 = \frac{8}{3}ml^2\dot{\theta}_1 \left(\frac{\partial T}{\partial \dot{\theta}_2}\right)_2 = \frac{8}{3}ml^2\dot{\theta}_2.$$

Hence Lagrange's equations are

$$\left(\frac{\partial T}{\partial \dot{x}}\right)_2 - \left(\frac{\partial T}{\partial \dot{x}}\right)_1 = p_x \Rightarrow 4m\dot{x} = P_x \quad ...(2)$$

$$\left(\frac{\partial T}{\partial \dot{y}}\right)_2 - \left(\frac{\partial T}{\partial \dot{y}}\right)_1 = p_y \Rightarrow 4m\dot{y} = P_y \quad ...(3)$$

$$\left(\frac{\partial T}{\partial \dot{\theta}_1}\right)_2 - \left(\frac{\partial T}{\partial \dot{\theta}_1}\right)_1 = p_{\theta_1} \Rightarrow \frac{8}{3}ml^2\dot{\theta}_1 = P_{\theta_1}. \quad ...(4)$$

$$\left(\frac{\partial T}{\partial \dot{\theta}_1}\right)_2 - \left(\frac{\partial T}{\partial \dot{\theta}_2}\right)_1 = p_{\theta_1} \Rightarrow \frac{8}{3}ml^2\dot{\theta}_2 = P_{\theta 2}. \quad ...(5)$$

Now we shall find the value of P_x, P_y, p_{θ_1} and p_{θ_2}

we have $P_\alpha = \Sigma I_v \bullet \frac{\partial r_v}{\partial q_\alpha}$ where I_v are the impulsive forces.

$$\therefore P_x = I_A \bullet \frac{\partial r_A}{\partial x} + I_B \bullet \frac{\partial r_B}{\partial x} + I_c \bullet \frac{\partial r_c}{\partial x} + I_D \bullet \frac{\partial r_D}{\partial x} \quad ...(6)$$

$$P_y = I_A \bullet \frac{\partial r_A}{\partial y} + I_B \bullet \frac{\partial r_B}{\partial y} + I_c \bullet \frac{\partial r_c}{\partial y} + I_D \bullet \frac{\partial r_D}{\partial y} \quad ...(7)$$

$$P_{\theta_1} = I_A \cdot \frac{\partial r_A}{\partial \theta_1} + I_B \cdot \frac{\partial r_B}{\partial \theta_1} + I_c \cdot \frac{\partial r_c}{\partial \theta_1} + I_D \cdot \frac{\partial r_D}{\partial \theta_1} \quad ...(8)$$

$$P_{\theta 2} = I_A \cdot \frac{\partial r_A}{\partial \theta_2} + I_B \cdot \frac{\partial r_B}{\partial \theta_2} + I_c \cdot \frac{\partial r_c}{\partial \theta_2} + I_D \cdot \frac{\partial r_D}{\partial \theta_1} \quad ...(9)$$

where

$$r_A = (x - l\cos\theta_1 - l\cos\theta_2)\,i + (y - l\sin\theta_1 + l\sin\theta_2)\,j \quad ...(10)$$

$$r_B = (x - l\cos\theta_1 + l\cos\theta_2)\,i + (y - l\sin\theta_1 - l\sin\theta_2)\,j \quad ...(11)$$

$$r_C = (x + l\cos\theta_1 + l\cos\theta_2)\,i + (y + l\sin\theta_1 - l\sin\theta_2)\,j \quad ...(12)$$

$$r_D = (x + l\cos\theta_1 - l\cos\theta_2)\,i + (y + l\sin\theta_1 + l\sin\theta_2)\,j \quad ...(13)$$

But initially the impulsive force at A is in the direction of the positive y-axis, we have

$$I_A = Ij. \quad ...(14)$$

$\therefore$ Equation (6), (7), (8) and (9) $\Rightarrow$

$$P_x = 0, P_y = I, P_{\theta_1} = -Il\cos\theta_1 \text{and} P\theta_2 = Il\cos\theta_2 \quad ...(15)$$

Thus equation (2) and (3),(4) and (5) give

$$4m\dot{x} = 0, 4m\dot{y} = I, \frac{8}{3}ml^2\dot{\theta}_1 = -Il\cos\theta_1, \frac{8}{3}ml^2\dot{\theta}_2 = Il\cos\theta_2 \quad ...(16)$$

Second Part

We have $\dot{x} = 0, \dot{y} = \frac{1}{4m'}\dot{\theta}_1 = -\frac{3I}{8ml}\cos\theta_1$ and $\dot{\theta}_2 = \frac{3I}{8ml}\cos\dot{\theta}_2$

$$\therefore T = 2m(x^2 + y^2) + \frac{4}{3}ml^2(\dot{\theta}^2{}_1 + \dot{\theta}_2^2)$$

$$= 2m\left(0 + \frac{I^2}{16m^2}\right) + \frac{4}{3}ml^2\left[\frac{9I^2}{64m^2l^2}\cos^2\theta_1 + \frac{9I^2}{64m^2l^2}\cos^2\theta_2\right] \quad ...(17)$$

But immediately after the application of the impulsive forces,

$\theta_1 = \frac{1}{2}\pi$ and $\theta_2 = 0$ approximately, so (17) gives $T = \frac{I^2}{2m}$.

Example 31:

Three equal uniform rods, AB, BC, CD are freely joined at B and C and the ends A and B are fastened to smooth, fixed pivots whose distance apart is equal to the length of either rod. The frame being at rest in the form of the square, a blow J is given perpendicular to AB at its middle point and in the plane of square. Show that the energy set up is $\frac{3J^2}{40m}$ where m is the mass of each rod.

Find also the blows at the joints B and C.

Solution:

The blow J is given at G_1 the C.G. of AB, at right angles to AB

The rods AB and CD will turn through the same angle θ but the rod BC will remain parallel to AD.

Now let T be the K.E. of the system, then we have

$$T = 2.\frac{1}{2}m\left[\frac{a^2}{3}\dot{\theta}^2 + a^2\dot{\theta}^2\right] + \frac{1}{2}m(2a\dot{\theta})^2 = \frac{10ma^2}{3}\dot{\theta}^2.$$

∴ Lagrange's θ-equation gives

$$\left(\frac{\partial T}{\partial \dot{\theta}}\right) - \left(\frac{\partial T}{\partial \dot{\theta}}\right) = J \Rightarrow \frac{20ma^2}{3}\dot{\theta} = Ja$$

$$i.e.\ \dot{\theta} = \frac{3J}{20ma} \therefore T = \frac{10ma^2}{3}.\frac{9J^2}{400m^2a^2} = \frac{3J^2}{40m}.$$

Second Part:

Let P and Q be the impulses at B and C respectively. With directions, as shown in the figure, then considering the motion of AB and taking moments about A, we get

Change in the angular momentum about the axis through A

= moments of the impulses about this axis

$$i.e.\ m\frac{4a^2}{3}\dot{\theta} = Ja - P2a \Rightarrow P = \frac{1}{2}J - \frac{2ma}{3}$$

$$\therefore P = \frac{1}{2}J - \frac{2ma}{3}\frac{3J}{20ma} = \frac{2J}{5}$$

Again considering the motion of CD and taking moments about D, we obtain

$$m = \frac{4a^2}{3}\dot{\theta} = Q2a \Rightarrow Q = \frac{2ma}{3}\dot{\theta} = \frac{3J}{20ma} = \frac{1}{10}J.$$

REVISION AT A GLANCE

(1) Generalised Co-ordinates

Suppose that a particle or a system of N-particles moves subject to possible constraints, as for example a particle moving along a circular wire or a rigid body moving along an inclined plane, then there will be necessarily a minimum number of independent co-ordinates then needed to specify the motion. These co-ordinates denoted by $q_1, q_2, \ldots.. q_n$ are called generalised co-ordinates. These may be distances, angles or quantities to them.

(2) Degrees of Freedom

The number of co-ordinates required to specify the position of a system of one or more particles is called the number of degrees of freedom of the system.

(3) Transformation Equations

Let $r_v = x_v i + y_v j + z_v k$ be the position vector of vth particle with respect to xyz co-ordinate system. The relationships of the generalised co-ordinates $q_1, q_2, \ldots q_n$ to the position co-ordinates are given by the transformation equations.

$$\left.\begin{array}{l} x_v = x_v(q_1, q_2, \ldots, q_n, t) \\ y_v = y_v(q_1, q_2, \ldots, q_n, t) \\ z_v = z_v(q_1, q_2, \ldots, q_n, t) \end{array}\right\} \quad \ldots(1)$$

where t denotes the time in vector (1) can be written as

$$r_v = r_v(q_1, q_2, \ldots, t)$$

where the function in (1) or (2) are continuous and have continuous derivatives.

(4) Classification of Mechanical Systems

(a) *Scleronmic system :* The mechanical system in which the moving constraints are involved and the time t does enter explicitly is called a Rhenomic system.

(b) *Rhenomic systm :* The mechanical system in which t, the time, does not enter explicitly in equations (1) to (2) is called a sceleronimic system.

(c) *Holonomic system and Non Holonomic system :* Let $q_1, q_2, \ldots q_n$ denote the generalised co-ordinates describing a system and let t denote the time. If all the constraints of the system m can be expressed as equations having the form $f(q_1, q_2, \ldots q_n\, t) = 0$. or their equivalent, then the system is said to be Holonomic otherwise it is be Non-Holonomic system.

(d) *Conservative and non conservative system :* If the forces acting on the system are derivable from a potential function [or potential energy V], then the system is called conservative, otherwise it is non-conservative.

(5) Kinetic Energy and Generalised Velocities

The K.E. of the system is $T = \frac{1}{2}\Sigma_{v=1}^{n} m_v \dot{r}_v^{\,2}$

The K.E. of the system can be written as a quadratic form in the generalised $\dot{q}_\alpha$ If the system is independent of time explicitly *i.e.* Sclemomic then the system is Rheonomic, linear terms in q_α are also present.

(6) Generalised Forces

If W is the total work done on a system of particles by forces F acting on the Vth particle then

$$dW = \Sigma_{\alpha=1}^{n} \phi_\alpha dq_\alpha \text{ where } \phi_\alpha = \Sigma_{v=1}^{n} F_v \bullet \frac{\partial r_v}{\partial q_\alpha}$$

is called the generalised force associated with generalised coordinates q_α

(7) Lagrange's Equations

$$\frac{d}{dt}\left(\frac{\partial T}{\partial \dot{q}_\alpha}\right) - \frac{\partial T}{\partial q_\alpha} = \phi_1 = \frac{\partial W}{\partial q_\alpha}$$

For a = 1, 2, ..., n, we have n different equations which are called Lagrange's equations.

Note: The quantity $q_\alpha = \left(\frac{\partial T}{\partial \dot{q}_\alpha}\right)$ is called the generalised momentum associated with the general co-ordinate q_α

(8) If the Forces are Derivable from a Potential V, then

$$\phi_\alpha\left(\frac{\partial W}{\partial q_\alpha}\right) = -\frac{\partial V}{\partial q_\alpha},$$

since the potential, or potential energy is a function of q's only (and possible the time t) then, we have

$$\frac{d}{dt}\left(\frac{\partial L}{\partial \dot{q}_\alpha}\right) - \frac{\partial T}{\partial q_\alpha} = -\frac{\partial V}{\partial q_\alpha} \Rightarrow \frac{d}{dt}\left[\frac{\partial}{\partial \dot{q}_\alpha}(T - V)\right] - \left(\frac{\partial T}{\partial q_\alpha} - \frac{\partial V}{\partial q_\alpha}\right) = 0$$

$$\Rightarrow \frac{d}{dt}\left(\frac{\partial L}{\partial \dot{q}_\alpha}\right) - \frac{\partial L}{\partial q_\alpha} = 0 \text{ where } L = T - V \quad ...(19)$$

The function L defined by L = T V is said to be Lagrangian function.

(9) Generalising Momentum

We defined $P_\alpha = \frac{\partial T}{\partial \dot{q}_\alpha}$

to be the generalised momentum associated with generalised co-ordinate q_α. We usually refer P_α as the momentum conjugate to q_α or the conjugate to momentum.

In case the system is conservative, we have

$$T = L + V \Rightarrow (\partial T / \partial \dot{q}_\alpha) = (\partial L / \partial \dot{q}_\alpha) + (\partial V / \partial \dot{q}_\alpha) = (\partial L / \partial \dot{q}_\alpha)$$

because V, the P.E. system does not depend upon q_α

$$\therefore q_\alpha = (\partial L/\partial \dot{q}_\alpha)$$

(10) Lagrange's Equation with Impulsive Forces

$$\Rightarrow \left(\frac{\partial T}{\partial \dot{q}_\alpha}\right) - \frac{\partial T}{\partial q_{1\alpha}} = \Sigma I_v \bullet \frac{\partial r_v}{\partial q_\alpha} = p_\alpha \text{ (say)}$$

where subscripts 1 and 2 denote respective quantities before and after the application of the impulsive forces.

These equations are known as Lagrange's equations under impulsive forces.

EXERCISES

1. A square ABCD formed of four freely jointed uniform rods, is rotating about its centre of gravity on smooth horizontal table with angular velocity ω when the joint A is suddenly fixed. Show that the initial angular velocities of the rods are equal and that 3 / 5 of the kinetic energy immediately lost.
2. A uniform straight rod of length 2a, is freely movable about, its on the and a particle of mass one fourth that of the rod is attached by a light inextensible string of length 3a, to one end of the rod, find the period of principle oscillations.
3. Obtain Lagrange's equations of motion for a system under finite forces and hence deduce the same under impulsive forces.
4. A hollow circular roller of radius a mass M has attached to the centre of its axis a particle of mass m by a light a rod of length b. The particle is free to swing about the axis a plane perpendicular to the axis. The roller is at rest on a horizontal plane rough enough to prevent slipping, with rod held at an angle a with the downward vertical. If the rod is then released prove that the centre of the roller will oscillate through a distance

$$\frac{2mba^2 \sin\alpha}{M(a^2 + k^2) + ma^2}.$$

where k is the radius of gyration of the roller about the axis.
5. A homogeneous rod OA, of mass m_1 and length 2a, is freely at O to a fixed point, as its other end is freely attached another homogeneous rod AB, of mass m_2 and length 2b; the system moves under gravity, find equations to determine motion.

6. A thin circular ring of a radius a and M lies on a smooth horizontal plane and two light elastic strings are attached to it at ends of a diameter. The other ends of the string being fastened fixed points in the diameter produced. Show that for small oscillations in the plane of the ring the periods are the values of $2\pi/p$ given by

$$\frac{Mlp^2}{2T} - = 0 \text{ or } \frac{b}{l-b} \text{ or } \frac{l}{a}$$

where b is the natural length l the equilibrium length .and T the equilibrium tension of each string.

7. A heavy uniform rod of mass m and length 2a rotating in a vertical plane falls and strikes a smooth horizontal plane. If u and ω βε its linear and angular velocities and θ the inclination to the vertical just before impact, prove that the impulse J is given by

$$(1 + 3\sin^2\theta)j = m(u + a\omega\sin\theta).$$

8. A rhombus of smoothly jointed equal uniform rods of length 2a lies on a smooth horizontal table. It is struck by a blow J perpendicular to one of its sides at a point distant c from the middle point , show that the angular velocity of the side instantly becomes $\frac{3jc}{8ma^2}$ where m is the mass of each side.

4

INITIAL MOTION

INTRODUCTION

Some times we have problems in which a system of bodies is supported in equilibrium. If one of the supports of the body be suddenly removed or gives way the reactions at the other supports are instantaneously altered due to the fact that accelerations of the body are altered. *The motion just after one of the supports gives way is called the Initial Motion.*

We are required to find out the values of initial tensions, initial accelerations, initial reactions and initial radii of curvatures. For this we have to consider the motion of the body immediately after the removal of the support.

The manner of finding the initial motion of a system is the same as in case of usual motion.

We simply write down the equations of motion and the geometrical equations connecting the displacements. As we are to simply investigate the initial motion we neglect everything except the finite quantities of first powers.

Differentiate twice each of the geometrical equations and simplify the result by substituting the initial values of the co-ordinates, initial angular and linear velocities are neglected.

The differential coefficients are eliminated from the dynamical equations and initial reaction and initial tensions are found out.

SOLVED EXAMPLES

Example 1:

An equilateral triangle is suspended from a point by three strings, each equal in length to a side of the triangle, attached to its angular points, if one of the strings be cut, show that the tensions of the other two are diminished in the ration 12 : 25.

Solution:

Let the triangle ABC be suspended from a fixed point O by three strings AO, BO and CO each of length l say. The length of each string Δ ABC ∴ AB = BC = AC = l. If G be the C.G. of the Δ ABC, then in this position OG is vertical.

Let h be the length of the medium AD or OD whereas D is the middle point of BC.

Let m be the mass of the triangle ABC and T_0 the tension in each string. Resolving forces vertically, we have

OA = a

$$3T_0 \cos\angle AOG = mg$$

$$\text{i.e. } 3T_0 \frac{OG}{OA} = mg$$

$$\text{i.e. } 3T_0 \sqrt{\frac{2}{3}} = mg$$

$$\text{or } T_0 = \frac{1}{\sqrt{6}} mg \quad \text{...(i)}$$

$$OD = AD = \frac{a\sqrt{3}}{2}, \therefore AG = \frac{2}{3}AD = \frac{a}{\sqrt{3}}$$

$$\text{so, } OG = \sqrt{(OA^2 - AG^2)}$$

$$= \sqrt{\left(a^2 - \frac{a^2}{3}\right)} = a\sqrt{\frac{2}{3}}$$

$$DG = \frac{1}{2}AG = \frac{a}{2\sqrt{3}}.$$

Let α be the angle which OD make with OG (the vertical line) then

$$\cos\alpha = \frac{DG}{OD} = a\sqrt{\frac{2}{3}} \Big/ \left(\frac{a\sqrt{3}}{2}\right) = \frac{2\sqrt{2}}{3}$$

$$\text{and } \sin\alpha = \frac{DG}{OD} = \frac{a}{2\sqrt{3}} \Big/ \left(\frac{a\sqrt{3}}{2}\right) = \frac{1}{3}$$

When one string say O A is cut: Let after a small time t, OD make an angle (α + θ) with the vertical and AD make an angle θ with the horizontal, where θ and f are small.

Taking the fixed point O as the origin and the horizontal and vertical through O as the axes, the coordinates (x, y) of G are

$$x = OD\sin(\alpha+\theta) - DG\cos\phi = \frac{a\sqrt{3}}{2}\sin(\alpha+\theta) - \frac{a}{2\sqrt{3}}\cos\phi$$

$$y = OD\cos(\alpha+\theta) + DG\sin\phi = \frac{a\sqrt{3}}{2}\cos(\alpha+\theta) + \frac{a}{2\sqrt{3}}\sin\phi$$

where $OD = (a\sqrt{3/2})$ and $DG = (a/2\sqrt{3})$.

Since θ and ϕ are small neglecting squares and higher powers, we get

$$x = \frac{a\sqrt{3}}{2}(\sin\alpha + \theta\cos\alpha) - \frac{a}{2\sqrt{3}}; \; y = \frac{a\sqrt{3}}{2}(\cos\alpha - \theta\sin\alpha) + \frac{a}{2\sqrt{3}}\phi$$

$$\left.\begin{aligned} \therefore \ddot{x} &= \frac{a\sqrt{3}}{2}\ddot{\theta}\cos\alpha, \\ \ddot{y} &= -\frac{a\sqrt{3}}{2}\ddot{\theta}\sin\alpha + \frac{a}{2\sqrt{2}}\ddot{\phi}. \end{aligned}\right\} \text{There are initial values for } \ddot{x} \text{ and } \ddot{y}.$$

Now the equations of motion are

$$m\ddot{x} = -2T\cos 30^\circ \sin(\alpha+\theta), \quad \text{...(1)}$$

$$m\ddot{y} = mg - 2T\cos 30^\circ \cos(\alpha+\theta) \quad \text{...(2)}$$

$$\text{and } mk^2\ddot{\phi} = 2T\cos 30^\circ .DG\sin(90-\alpha-\theta+\phi) \quad \text{...(3)}$$

$$\text{where } k^2 = \frac{1}{3}\left[\left(\frac{AD}{3}\right)^2 + 2\left(\frac{AD}{6}\right)^2\right] = \frac{1}{18}AD^2 = \frac{a^2}{24} \text{ i.e. } k^2 = \frac{a^2}{24}$$

Equation (1), (2) and (3) reduce to (for small values of θ and ϕ)

$$\left.\begin{aligned} & m\frac{a\sqrt{3}}{2}\ddot{\theta}\cos\alpha = -2T\cos 30^\circ \sin\alpha && \text{...(4)} \\ & m\left(-\frac{a\sqrt{3}}{2}\ddot{\theta}\sin\alpha + \frac{a}{2\sqrt{3}}\ddot{\phi}\right) = mg - 2T\cos 30^\circ \cos\alpha && \text{...(5)} \\ & \text{and } m\frac{a^2}{24}\ddot{\phi} = 2T\cos 30\left[\frac{a}{2\sqrt{3}}\sin(90-\alpha\right] && \text{...(6)} \end{aligned}\right\}$$

These are the equations of initial motion.

Substituting values of $\ddot{\theta}$ and $\ddot{\phi}$ from (4) and (6) in (5), we have

$$\frac{2T\cos 30\sin^2\alpha}{\cos\alpha} + \frac{1}{2\sqrt{3}\cdot}48T\cos 30.\frac{1}{2\sqrt{2}}\cos\alpha$$

$$= mg - 2T\cos 30\cos\alpha.$$

$$\text{i.e. } 2T\cos 30\left[\frac{\sin^2\alpha}{\cos\alpha} + 3\cos\alpha\right] = mg,$$

$$\text{i.e. } 2T\frac{\sqrt{3}}{2}\left[\frac{1}{9\cdot}\frac{3}{2\sqrt{2}} + \frac{6\sqrt{2}}{3}\right] = mg,$$

$$\text{i.e. } T\left[\frac{1}{12} + 2\right]\sqrt{6} = mg \text{ or } T = \frac{12mg}{25\sqrt{6}\cdot} \quad \text{(ii)}$$

$$\text{From (i) and (ii) } T/T_0 = \frac{12mg}{25\sqrt{6}} / \frac{mg}{\sqrt{6}} = \frac{12}{25} \text{ i.e. } T : T_0 = 12 : 25$$

Example 2:

A number of uniform straight rods of the same weight and length freely jointed end to end, are in a horizontal straight line with the extreme end of the last rod fixed. If the supports are all removed at once, and if $\omega_n, \omega_n + \omega_n + 2$ *are the initial angular accelerations of any three adjacent rods, then prove that* $\omega_n + 4\,\omega_n + \omega_n + \omega_n + 2 = 0$.

Solution:

Let m be the mass and 2a the length of each rod. Let AB, BC, CD be the three adjacent rods, and reactions at the joints are R_n, $R_n + 1$, $R_n + 2$, $R_n + 3$ per unit mass of the rods. Let U_n, $U_n + 2$, $U_n + 1$, $U_n + 2$ be the vertical accelerations of the C.G.'s of the three rods. Let ω_n, $\omega_n + 1$, $\omega_n + 2$, be the angular accelerations of the three rods. For the rod AB,

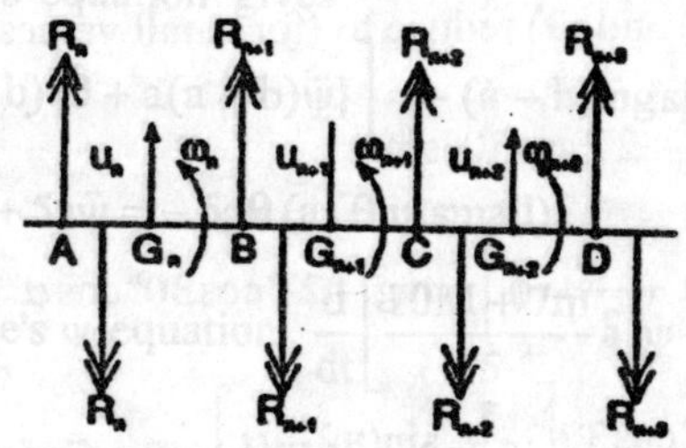

Fig. 4.1

$$\begin{cases} U_n = R_{n+1} - R_n - g & (1)\ \text{(motion of } G_n) \\ \dfrac{a^2}{3}\omega_n = aR_{n+1} + aR_n & (2)\ \text{(taking moment about } G_n) \end{cases}$$

For the rod BC,

$$\begin{cases} U_{n+1} = R_{n+2} - R_{n+1} - g & (3)\ \text{(motion of } G_{n+1}) \\ \dfrac{a^2}{3}\omega_{n+1} = aR_{n+2} + aR_{n+1} & (4)\ \text{(taking moment about } G_{n+2}) \end{cases}$$

For the rod CD,

$$\begin{cases} U_{n+2} = R_{n+3} - R_{n+2} - g & (5)\ \text{(motion of } G_{n+2}) \\ \dfrac{a^2}{3}\omega_{n+2} = aR_{n+3} + aR_{n+2} & (6)\ \text{(taking moment about } G_{n+2}) \end{cases}$$

Since the acceleration of the end point B of the rod AB is the same as that of the same point B of the rod BC,

$$\therefore U_n + a\omega_n = U_{n+1} - a\omega_{n+1} \qquad \text{...(7)}$$

Substituting in (7) from (1), (2) (3) and (4), we have

$$R_{n+1} - R_n - g + 3R_{n+1} - g - 3R_{n+2} - 3R_{n+1}$$

i.e. $2R_{n+2} + 8R_{n+1} + 2R_{n=0}$

i.e. $R_{n+2} + 4R_{n+1} + R_n = 0.$ ...(8)

It follows that $R_{n+3} + 4R_{n+2} + R_{n+1} = 0$

{Putting n = n + 1 in equation (8)}

or $R_{n+3} - R_{n+2} + 5R_{n+2} + R_{n+1} = 0$

or $R_{n+3} + (4R_{n+1} + R_n) + 5R_{n+1} = 0$ [from (8)]

i.e. $(R_{n+3} + R_{n+2}) + 4(R_{n+2} + R_{n+1}) + (R_{n+1} + R_n) = 0$

i.e. $\frac{a}{3}[\omega_{n+2} + 4\omega_{n+1} + \omega_n] = 0$ [from (2), (4) and (6)]

i.e. $\omega_{n+2} + 4\omega_{n+1} + \omega_n = 0$. Hence the required result.

Example 3:

An elliptic lamina is supported with its plane vertical and transverse axis horizontal by two weightless pins passing through the foci. If one pin be released, show that if the eccentricity of the ellipse be $\sqrt{(2/5)}$, the pressure on the other pin is initially unaltered.

Solution:

Let originally the elliptic lamina is supported by two points at S and S′ with its plane vertical and major axis AA′ horizontal. By symmetry reaction of each pin will be vertical and same. Let R_0 be the reaction of each pin Let m be the mass of the lamina. Resolving forces vertically, we have $2R_0 = mg$

or $$R_0 = \frac{1}{2}mg.$$ ...(1)

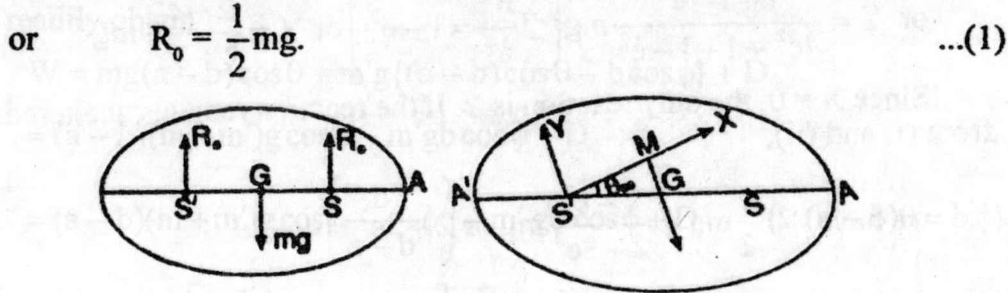

Fig. 4.2

When one of the pin is released say at S, then the lamina turns about the remaining pin at S′. Let S′ A make an angle θ with the horizontal after time 't', here θ is small.

With the focus S′ as the origin and horizontal and vertical lines through S′ as the axes, the co-ordination of C.G. *i.e.* point G are

$$\left.\begin{aligned} x &= S'G\cos\theta = ae\cos\theta = ae, \\ y &= S'G\sin\theta = ae\sin\theta = ae\theta. \end{aligned}\right\} \text{neglecting squares and higher powers of } \theta.$$

$\therefore \ddot{x} = 0, \ddot{y} = ae\ddot{\theta}$ for initial values.

Let X and Y be the horizontal and vertical components of the reaction at S′. Equations of motions at the lamina are

$$\left.\begin{aligned} m\ddot{x} &= X \\ m\ddot{y} &= mg - Y \end{aligned}\right\} \text{these given motion of the C.G. 'G'}$$

and $m.\dfrac{a^2+b^2}{4}.\ddot{\theta}$ X ae sin θ + X ae cos θ (taking moment about the centre of gravity G).

Equations of initial motion are obtained by taking sin θ = θ, cos θ = 1 and putting initial values of $\ddot{x}$ and $\ddot{y}$ in the last three equations.

i.e. $$X = 0 \qquad ...(1)$$

$$mae\, q = mg - Y \qquad ...(2)$$

and $$\frac{a^2+b^2}{4}\ddot{\theta} = Yae.$$

From (1), (2) and (3) on eliminating $\ddot{\theta}$, we get

$$\frac{4ae}{a^2+b^2} = \frac{mg-Y}{ae\,Y} \text{ or } 4a^2e^2\,Y = mg\,(a^2+b^2) - (a^2+b^2)Y$$

$$\text{or } [4a^2e^2 + (a^2+b^2)]Y = (a^2+b^2)\,mg \text{ or } Y = \frac{a^2+b^2}{4a^2e^2+a^2+b^2}mg$$

$$\text{or } Y = \frac{1+1-e^2}{4e^2+1+1-e^2}mg\left(\because \frac{b^2}{a^2} = 1-e^2\right) \text{ or } Y = \frac{2-e^2}{2+3e^2}mg$$

Since X = 0, the only reaction is Y. If the reaction remains unaltered, then from (i) and (ii),

we have $$\frac{1}{2}mg = \frac{2-e^2}{2+3e^2}mg \text{ or } 2+3e^2 = 4-2e^2$$

or $$5e^2 = 2 \text{ or } e = \sqrt{\left(\frac{2}{5}\right)}.$$

Example 4:

A uniform rod AB of mass m and length 2a has attached to it at its ends two strings; each of length l, and their other ends are attached to two fixed points

O and O'; in the same horizontal line, the rod rests in a horizontal position and the strings are inclined at an angle α to the vertical The string O'B is now cut; find the change in the tension of the string OA and the instantaneous angular accelerations of the string and rod.

Solution:

Originally, suppose T_0 is the tension in string. In the position of equilibrium, resolving forces vertically, we have

$$2T_0 \cos\alpha = mg, \text{ i.e. } T_0 = \frac{mg}{2\cos\alpha}.$$

When the string O' B is cut. Let the string and the rod turn through small angle θ and φ respectively from their original positions *i.e.* at time t let the string makes an angle (α – θ) with the vertical and the rod makes an angle φ with the horizontal, and then let T be the tension in the string OA.

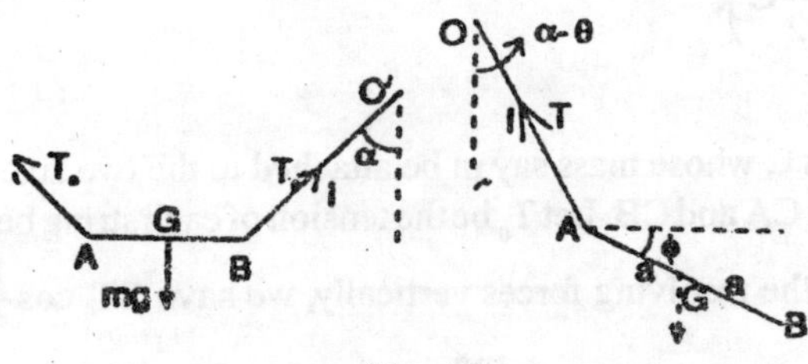

Fig. 4.3

Referred to O as origin and the horizontal and vertical lines through O as co-ordinates axes, the co-ordinates of G the C.G. of the rod are given by

$$x = l\sin(\alpha - \theta) + a\cos\phi = l(\sin\alpha\cos\theta - \sin\theta) + a\cos\phi$$

$$= l(\sin\alpha - \theta\cos\alpha) + a$$

to a first order approximation of θ and φ since θ and φ are small and

$$y = l\cos(\alpha - \theta) + a\sin\phi = l(\cos\alpha + \theta\sin\alpha) + a\phi.$$

Differentiating x and y twice, we have

$$\ddot{x} = -l\ddot{\theta}\cos\alpha \ddot{y} = l\ddot{\theta}\sin\alpha + a\ddot{\phi}$$

The equations of initial motion are

$$m\ddot{x} = -T\sin(\alpha - \theta) \text{ i.e. } ml\ddot{\theta}\cos\alpha = T\sin\alpha, \quad ...(1)$$

$$m\ddot{y} = mg - T\cos(\alpha - \theta) \text{ i.e. } m(l\ddot{\theta}\sin\alpha + a\ddot{\phi}) = mg - T\cos\alpha \quad ...(2)$$

and $m\frac{a^2}{3}\ddot{\phi} = Ta\sin\{90 - \phi - (\alpha - \theta)\}$

i.e. $ma\ddot{\phi} = 3T\cos\alpha$ ...(3)

Substituting values of $\ddot{\theta}$ and $\ddot{\phi}$ from (1) and (3) in (2), we have

$T = \dfrac{mg\cos\alpha}{1+3\cos^2\alpha}$. Then from (1) and (3), we have

$$\dot{\theta} = \frac{g}{l}\cdot\frac{\sin\alpha}{1+3\cos^2\alpha} \text{ and } \ddot{\phi} = \frac{3g}{a}\cdot\frac{\cos\alpha}{1+3\cos^2\alpha}.$$

Example 5:

Two strings of equal lengths have each an end tied to a weight C, and their other ends tied to two points A and B in the same horizontal line. If one string be cut, show that the tension of the other will be instantaneously altered in the ration 1 : 2 $\cos^2\left(\frac{1}{2}C\right)$.

Solution:

Let the weight C whose mass say m be attached to the two fixed points A and B by two string CA and CB. Let T_0 be the tension of each string before string is being cut. Here the resolving forces vertically, we have $2T_0\cos\frac{1}{2}C = mg$

i.e. $$2T_0 = \frac{mg}{2\cos\frac{1}{2}C}$$

When one string CB is cut: Let the other remaining string CA make an angle $90 - \frac{1}{2}C + \theta$ with the horizontal line AB after a short interval of time t and let the tension now be T. Here θ is small If AC = l, then co-ordinates of C, w.r.t. origin A are

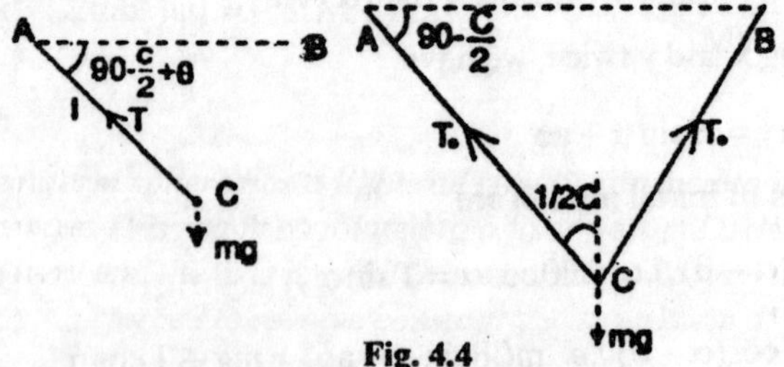

Fig. 4.4

$$x = l\cos\left(90 - \frac{C}{2} + \theta\right) = l\sin\left(\frac{C}{2} - \theta\right) = l\left(\sin\frac{C}{2}\cos\theta - \cos\frac{C}{2}\sin\theta\right)$$

$= l\left(\sin\frac{C}{2} - \theta\cos\frac{C}{2}\right)$ since θ is small so we can take cos θ = 1, sin θ = θ

$y = l\sin\left(90 - \frac{C}{2}\cos\theta\right) = l\cos\left(\frac{C}{2} - \theta\right)$

$= l\left(\cos\frac{C}{2}\cos\theta + \sin\frac{C}{2}\sin\theta\right) = l\left(\cos\frac{C}{2} + \theta\sin\frac{C}{2}\right)$ since θ is small.

$\therefore \ddot{x} = -\ddot{\theta}l\cos\frac{C}{2}$ and $\ddot{y} = \ddot{\theta}l\sin\frac{C}{2}$

Equations of motion of the weight at C are

$$m\ddot{x} = -T\cos\left(90 - \frac{C}{2} + \theta\right) \qquad ...(1)$$

$$\text{and } m\ddot{x} = mg - T\sin\left(90 - \frac{C}{2} + \theta\right) \qquad ...(2)$$

taking q zero on R.H.S of (1) and (2), they reduce to

$\ddot{\theta}l\cos\frac{C}{2} = -\frac{T}{m}\sin\frac{C}{2}\Big]$ {For initial motion putting values

and $\ddot{\theta}l\sin\frac{C}{2} = g - \frac{T}{m}\cos\frac{C}{2}\Big]$ of $\ddot{x}$ and $\ddot{y}, \theta = 0$ in (1) and (2)}

Eliminating $\ddot{\theta}$ between these two equations, we get

$$\frac{\cos\frac{C}{2}}{\sin\frac{C}{2}} = \frac{t\sin\frac{C}{2}}{mg - T\cos\frac{C}{2}} \quad i.e.\ T\left(\cos^2\frac{C}{2} + \sin^2\frac{C}{2}\right) = mg\cos\frac{C}{2}$$

$$\text{or} \qquad T = mg\cos\frac{C}{2} \qquad ...(ii)$$

Hence from (i) and (ii), we have $T_0 : T = 1 : 2\cos^2\frac{C}{2}$.

Example 6:

The ends of a heavy beam are attached by cords of equal length to two fixed points in a horizontal line, the cords making an angle of 30° with the beam. If one of the cords be c t, show that the initial tension of the other is two seventh of the weight of the beam.

Solution:

Let the beam PQ = 2a be attached by two cords PR and QS to the two fixed points R and S, each string is inclined to origin at 30°.

Let PR = QS = l. Let T_0 be the tension in the string originally

When one cord Q S is cut : Let the remaining cord PR make an angle $(30+\theta)$ with the horizontal while the rod has turned through an angle ϕ where θ and ϕ are small.

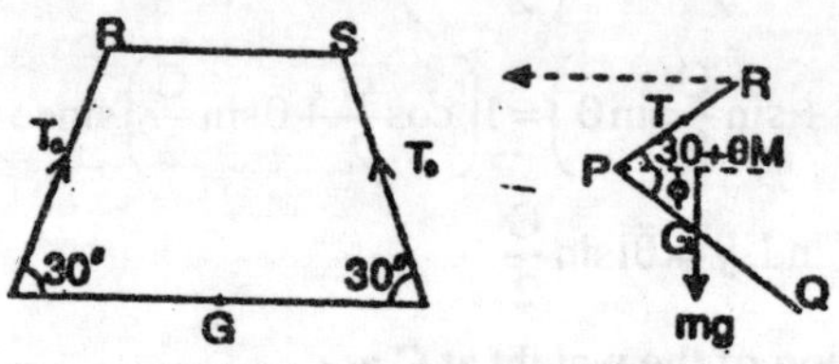

Fig. 4.5

Let (x,y) be the coordinates of the centre of gravity G of the rod, then

$$x = l\cos(30+\theta)\ a\cos\phi = l\left(\frac{\sqrt{3}}{2}-\frac{1}{2}\theta\right)-a\Big]\ \theta \text{ and } \phi$$

$$y = l\sin(30+\theta) + a\sin\phi = l\left(\frac{1}{2}+\frac{\sqrt{3}}{2}\theta\right)+a\dot{\phi}\Big]\ \text{being small}$$

$$\therefore \ddot{x} = -\frac{1}{2}\ddot{\theta} \text{ and } \ddot{y} = \frac{l\sqrt{3}}{2}\ddot{\theta}+a\ddot{\phi}$$

Equations of motion of the rod AB are (for initial motion)

$$m\ddot{x} = -T\cos(30+\theta)\ \textit{i.e.}\ \frac{\sqrt{3}}{2}\ddot{\theta}+a\ddot{\phi} = g-\frac{1}{2}\frac{T}{m} \quad ...(1)$$

$$m\ddot{y} = mg - T\sin(30+\theta)\ \textit{i.e.}\ \frac{\sqrt{3}}{2}\ddot{\theta}+a\ddot{\phi} = g-\frac{1}{2}\frac{T}{m} \quad ...(2)$$

$$\text{and } m\frac{a^2}{3}\ddot{\phi} = Ta\sin(30+\theta+\phi)\ \textit{i.e.}\ \frac{a\ddot{\phi}}{3} = \frac{1}{2}\frac{T}{m} \quad ...(3)$$

Substituting the values of $\ddot{\theta}$ and $\ddot{\phi}$ from (1) and (3) in (2), we get

$$\frac{3T}{2m}+\frac{3T}{2m} = g-\frac{T}{2m} \text{ or } T = \frac{2mg}{7}.$$

Example 7:

A uniform circular disc is supported in a vertical plane by two threads attached to the ends of a horizontal diameter, each of which makes an angle α with the horizontal. If one of the threads be cut, show that tension of the other is altered in the ration $2\sin^2\alpha : (1+2\sin^2\alpha)$.

Solution:

Originally the diameter AB of the disc is horizontal and AO and BO′ are the two threads, each inclined at an angle a to the horizontal. The point O and O′ are fixed.

Let OA = O′ B = l.

The radius of the disc = a and its mass m.

Let T_0 be the tension in each of the thread when the disc is thus supported. Resolving forces vertically, we get

$$2T_0 \sin\alpha = mg, \text{ i.e. } T_0 = \frac{mg}{2\sin\alpha}. \quad \text{...(i)}$$

When one of the threads say BO′ is cut. Let the remaining thread AO be inclined to the horizontal at angle $(\alpha + \theta)$ and let the diameter AB make an angle ϕ to the horizontal after time t, when θ and ϕ are small.

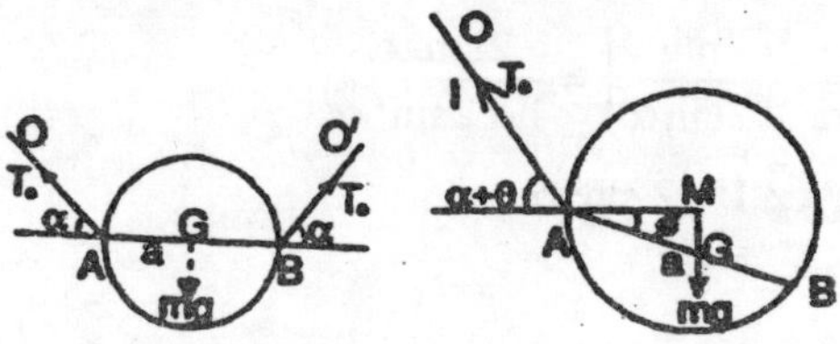

Fig. 4.6

Let T be the tension in the string AO.

Taking O as origin and the horizontal and vertical lines through O as co-ordinate axes, the co-ordinates (xy) of the centre of gravity G are given

by $x = l\cos(\alpha + \theta) + a\cos\phi,\ y = l\sin(\alpha + \theta) + a\sin\phi$

$$\left.\begin{aligned} x &= l(\cos\alpha - \theta\sin\alpha) + a \\ y &= l(\sin\alpha + \theta\cos\alpha) + a\phi \end{aligned}\right\} \text{since } \theta \text{ and } \phi \text{ are small}$$

Differentiating these equations twice, we have

$$\left.\begin{aligned} \ddot{x} &= -\ddot{\theta} l \sin\alpha \\ \ddot{y} &= \ddot{\theta} l \cos\alpha + a\ddot{\phi} \end{aligned}\right\} \text{for initial values.}$$

Equations of motion are

$$m\ddot{x} = -T\cos(\alpha + \theta), m\ddot{y} = mg - T\sin(\alpha + \theta)$$

and $m\frac{a^2}{2}\ddot{\phi} = Ta\sin(\alpha + \theta - \phi)$ (taking moment about G).

Hence for initial motion the equations are $-\ddot{\theta} l \sin\alpha = \frac{T}{m}\cos\alpha$ ...(1)

$$\ddot{\theta} l \cos\alpha + a\ddot{\phi} = g - \frac{T}{m}\sin\alpha \quad ...(2)$$

and $$\frac{a\ddot{\phi}}{2} = \frac{T}{m}\sin\alpha \quad ...(3)$$

Putting the values of $\ddot{\theta}$ and $\ddot{\phi}$ from (1) and (3) in (2), we have

$$\frac{T}{m}\frac{\cos^2\alpha}{\sin\alpha} + \frac{2T\sin\alpha}{m} = g - \frac{T\sin\alpha}{m}.$$

or $(\cos^2\alpha + 3\sin^2\alpha)T = mg\sin\alpha$

i.e. $(1+2\sin^2\alpha)T = mg\sin\alpha$ *i.e.* $T = \frac{mg\sin\alpha}{1+2\sin^2\alpha}$

Hence from (i) and (ii), we have

$$\frac{T}{T_0} = \frac{mg\sin\alpha}{1+2\sin^2\alpha} / \left\{\frac{mg}{2\sin\alpha}\right\} = \frac{2\sin^2\alpha}{1+2\sin^2\alpha}$$

or $T : T_0 = 2\sin^2\alpha : 1 + 2\sin^2\alpha$.

Example 8:

A uniform beam is supported in a horizontal position by two props placed at its ends; if one prop be removed show that the reaction of the other suddenly changes to one-quarter of the weight of the beam.

Solution:

Suppose in the original position the rod AB is in a horizontal position and kept in equilibrium by two props at A and B. Let AB = 2a and mass be m let R be the reaction of each prop. Resolving forces vertically we have 2R = mg or $R = \frac{1}{2mg}$.

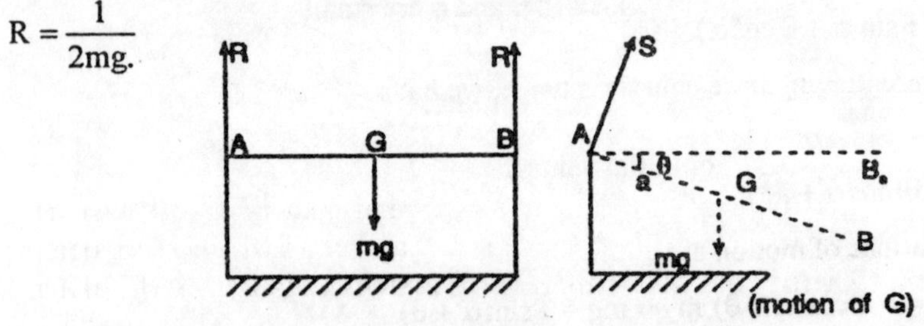

Fig. 4.7

When the prop, at B is removed : Let the beam AB turn through a small angle θ from its original position, and then let the reaction at A be S which acts at right angles to AB. Obviously G describes a circle of radius a about A.

Equations of motion are $m\,a\,\ddot{\theta} = mg\cos\theta - S$ and $m\frac{4a^2}{3}\ddot{\theta} = mga\cos\theta$ (taking moments about A) Since θ is small, neglecting squares and higher powers of θ, the above two equations, reduce to

$$\left.\begin{array}{ll} ma\ddot{\theta} = mg - R & (1) \\ m\frac{4a^2}{3}\ddot{\theta}mga, & (2) \end{array}\right\} \text{these are equations of initial motion.}$$

Eliminating $\ddot{\theta}$ between (1) and (2), we have $S = \frac{1}{4}mg$

Example 9:

A square lamina is suspended by vertical strings tied to two adjacent corners, two edges of the square being vertical. If one string is cut, shown that the tension of the other is instantaneously altered in ratio 5 : 4.

Solution:

Originally the square ABCD is hung by two fixed points O and O′, then $AG = a\sqrt{2}$ where AB = CD = 2 a. Let the mass of square be m. Let the length of each string be l. If T_0 be the tension of each of the strings in this position.

Resolving forces vertically, we have $2T_0 = mg$ *i.e.* $T_0 = \frac{1}{2}mg$ ...(i)

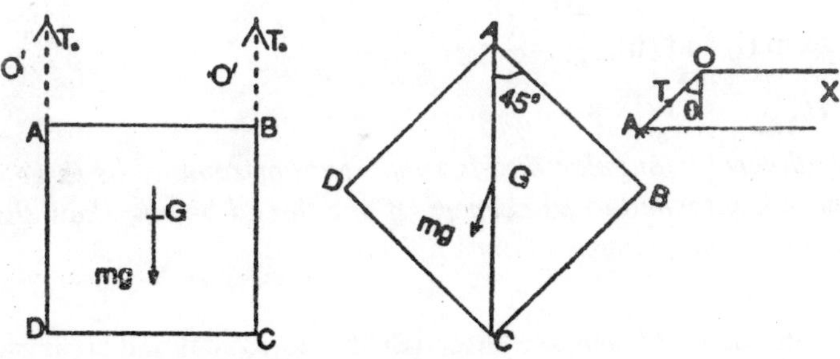

Fig. 4.8

When the strings say B O′ is cut: Let the remaining string AB make an angle θ with the vertical and the string AB makes an angle ϕ with the horizontal after a time t where θ and ϕ are small. Let T be the tension in string AO. Taking O as origin and the horizontal and vertical lines through O as co-ordinate axes, the coordinates of the centre of gravity G of the square are given by.

$$\ddot{x} = l\sin\theta - a\sqrt{(2)}\cos(45^\circ + \phi), \ddot{y} = l\cos\theta + a\sqrt{(2)}\sin(45^\circ + \phi)$$

$$\left.\begin{aligned}\ddot{x} &= l\theta - a\sqrt{(2)}\left(\frac{1}{\sqrt{2}} - \frac{\phi}{\sqrt{2}}\right)\\ \ddot{y} &= l + a\sqrt{2}\left(\frac{1}{\sqrt{2}} + \frac{\phi}{\sqrt{2}}\right)\end{aligned}\right\}\text{ For initial motion; } \sin\theta \text{ and } \phi \text{ are small}$$

taking $\sin\theta = 0$ and $\cos\theta = 1$ and $\sin\phi = \phi$, $\cos\phi = 1$.

Differentiating twice these equations, we get $\ddot{x} = l\ddot{\theta} + a\ddot{\phi}$ and $\ddot{y} = a\ddot{\phi}$
Again the equations of motion of the square are

$$m\ddot{x} = T\sin\theta \qquad ...(1)$$

$$m\ddot{y} = mg - T\cos\theta \qquad ...(2)$$

and $m\dfrac{2a^2}{3}\ddot{\phi} = Ta\sqrt{2\sin(45+\theta-\phi)}$.

These are $\ddot{x} = 0$ and $\ddot{y} = g - \dfrac{T}{m}$ (taking $\theta = 0$, $\phi = 0$) and $\dfrac{2a}{3}\ddot{\phi} = \dfrac{T}{m}$

$$\text{or}\quad\left.\begin{aligned}&l\ddot{\theta} + a\ddot{\phi} = 0, a\ddot{\phi} = g - \frac{T}{m}\\ &\text{and } \frac{2a}{3}\ddot{\phi} = \frac{T}{m}\end{aligned}\right\}\text{ equations of initial motion.}$$

Eliminating φ between the last two equations, we get

$$g - \frac{T}{m} = \frac{3T}{2m} \text{ or } T = \frac{2mg}{5} \qquad ...(ii)$$

Now from (i) and (ii), $\dfrac{T_0}{T} = \dfrac{1}{2}mg/\dfrac{2}{5}mg = \dfrac{5}{4}$

Example 10:

An equilateral triangular disc is supported horizontally be three equal vertical threads attached to its corners. If one thread be cut, show that the tension of each of the other is at once halved.

Solution:

Let the equilateral triangular disc ABC be horizontal and supported by three vertical threads AO, BO_1, CO_2. By symmetry tension in each of these strings is equal. Let T_0 be the tension in each string and m the mass of disc. In the position resolving forces vertically, we have

$$3T_0 = mg \quad T_0 = \frac{1}{3}mg$$

When one thread say CO_2 is cut: Suppose θ is the inclination of each of the remaining two strings to the vertical and ϕ is the angle which median CO makes with the horizontal where θ and ϕ are small.

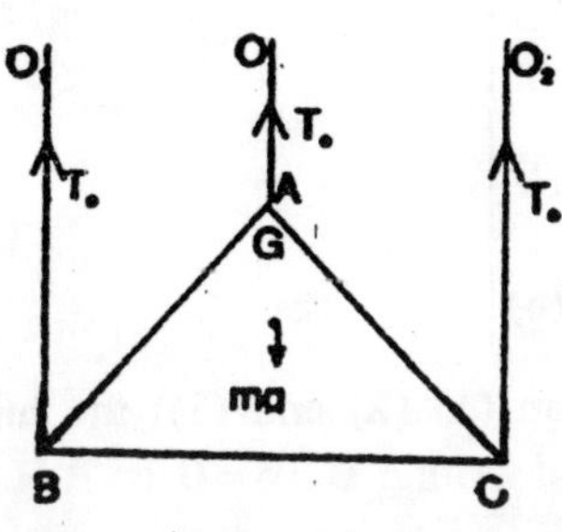

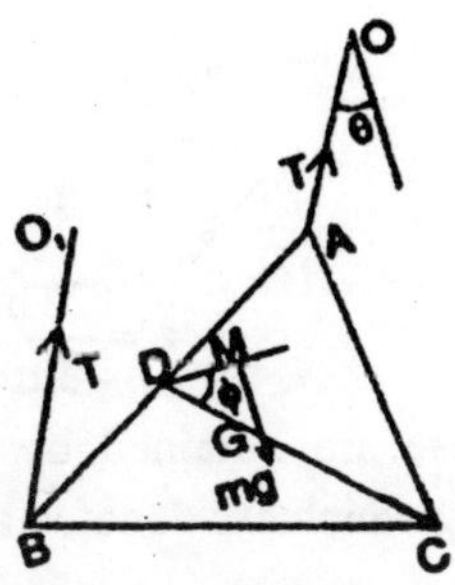

Fig. 4.9

Let T be the tension in each of two remaining string AB and BO_1. Let CD $= h \therefore GD = \frac{1}{3}h$, where G -is the CG. of the triangle ABC. Let AD = BD = l, the co-ordinates of C. G. 'G' referred to O, as origin and horizontal and vertical lines through O as co-ordinates axes are $x = OA\sin\theta - GD\cos\phi$

$$\left.\begin{aligned} &= l\sin\theta - \frac{1}{3}h\cos\phi \\ &= l\theta - \frac{1}{3}h, \\ y &= OA\cos\theta + GD\sin\phi \\ &= l\cos\theta + \frac{1}{3}h\sin\phi \\ &= l + \frac{1}{3}h\phi \end{aligned}\right]$$

since θ and φ are small, neglecting square and higher posers of θ and φ.

$$\left.\begin{aligned} &\therefore \ddot{x} = l\ddot{y} \\ &\text{and } \ddot{y} = \frac{1}{3}h\ddot{\phi} \end{aligned}\right\} \text{these give initial values of } \ddot{x} \text{ and } \ddot{y}$$

Equations of motion of Δ ABC are

$$\left.\begin{aligned} m\ddot{x} &= -2T\sin\theta \quad ...(1) \\ m\ddot{y} &= mg - 2T\cos\theta \quad ...(2) \end{aligned}\right\}$$

these are equations of motion of the centre of gravity G of the Δ ABC.

and $mk^2\ddot{\phi} = 2T.\frac{h}{3}\sin(90 - \theta + \phi)$ by taking moments about G

The initial equations (1), (2) and (3) are

$$\left.\begin{aligned} &I\ddot{\theta} = 0 && \text{...(4)} \\ &\frac{1}{3}h\ddot{\phi} = g - \frac{2T}{m} && \text{...(5)} \\ &k^2\ddot{\phi} = \frac{2Th}{3m} && \text{...(6)} \end{aligned}\right\}$$

These are obtained by putting in (1) (2) and (3)) the initial values o$\ddot{x}$ and $\ddot{y}$ which are denoted above and writing $\theta = \phi = 0$ on R.H.S.

Eliminating $\ddot{\phi}$ from (5) and (6), we have. $\frac{h}{3k^2} = \frac{3m[g-(2T/m)]}{2Th}$

$$\left.\begin{aligned} &\text{but } mk^2 = \frac{m}{3}\left[\left(\frac{h}{3}\right) + \left(\frac{h}{6}\right)^2\right] \\ &\text{or } k^2 = \frac{h^2}{18} \end{aligned}\right\}$$

as system is kinetically equivalent to three particles each equal to m/3 placed at middle points of each sides:

Hence on putting the values of k^2 in equation (7), we have

$$\frac{6}{h} = \frac{3mg[-2T/m)]}{2Th} \text{ or } 4T = mg - 2T \text{ or } T = \frac{1}{6}mg$$

$\therefore$ From (i) and (ii) $\quad \frac{T}{T_0} = \frac{\frac{1}{6}mg}{\frac{1}{3}mg} = \frac{1}{2}$

i.e. tension of each of the two string is now half of its original value.

Example 11:

A particle is suspended by three equal string each of length a, from three points forming an equilateral triangle of side 2b, in a horizontal plane. If one string be cut, the tension of each of the other will instantaneously changed in the ration $(3a^2 - 4b^2) : 2(a^2 - b^2)$.

Solution:

Let A, B and C be the vertices of the equilateral Δ ABC to which the ends of three equal string are attached and p the particle to which the other ends are attached. Each side of the triangle ABC is 2b. The three sides of the Δ ABC lie in the horizontal plane, because of symmetry the particle P is vertically below G, where G is the C.G. of the Δ ABC.

Given PA = PB = PC = a $\therefore$ $AG = \frac{2}{3}AD = \frac{2}{3}\cdot 2b\sin 60^\circ = \frac{2b}{\sqrt{3}}$

Again from right angled Δ APG

$$PC = \sqrt{[AP^2 - AG^2)]} = \sqrt{\left(a^2 - \frac{4b^2}{3}\right)} = \sqrt{\left(\frac{3a^2 - 4b^2}{3}\right)}$$

Let m be the mass of the particle P and the tension of each string T_0 (originally).

Resolving forces vertically, we have

$$3T_0\cos(\angle APG) = mg \text{ i.e. } T_0 = \frac{mg}{3\cos(\angle APG)} = \frac{1}{2}mg\frac{AP}{PG}$$

When the strings is cut: Let the string PA be cut, then the particle P begins to describe a circle with radius PD and centre D, where D is the middle point of BC.

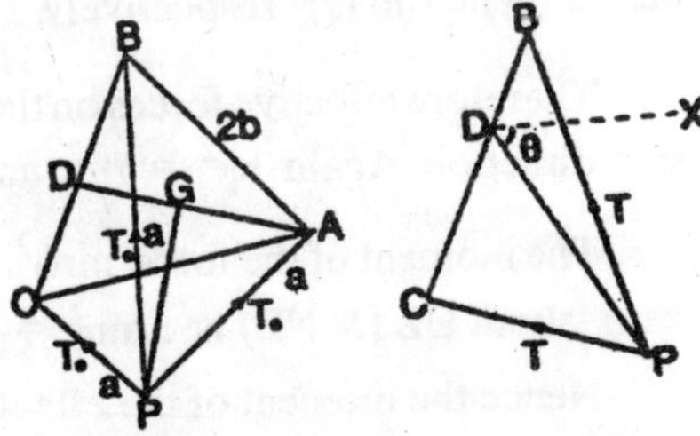

Fig. 4.10

Let T be the tension in each of the remaining string suppose θ be the angle when PD makes with the horizontal at any time t. Due to symmetry the resultant of these two tensions is along PD and its value is

$$2T\cos(\angle BPD), \text{ where } \cos\angle BPD = \frac{PD}{PB} \text{ and } PD^2 = a^2 - b^2.$$

Considering motion of the particle P

$$m.PD,\dot{\theta}^2 = 2T\cos\angle BPD - mg\sin\theta$$

$$\therefore mPD\ddot{\theta}_0^2 = 2T\cos\angle BPD - mg\sin\theta_0. \qquad \text{[for initial values]}$$

$$\text{or } 0 = 2t\cos\angle BPD - mg\frac{PG}{PD}\left(\text{since initially } \dot{\theta}_0 = 0, \sin\theta_0 = \frac{PG}{PD}\right)$$

$$\therefore T = mg\frac{PG}{2PD\cos\angle BPD} = mg\frac{PG.PB}{2PD^2}$$

$$\therefore \frac{T}{T_0} = \frac{PG.PB}{2PD^2}\cdot\frac{3PG}{AP} = \frac{3PG^2}{2PD^2} \text{ as } AP = BP$$

$$= \frac{3}{2\cdot 3(a^2 - b^2)}\frac{3a^2 - 4b^2}{} = (3a^2 - 4b^2) : 2(a^2 - b^2).$$

MOTION ABOUT A FIXED AXIS

A rigid body is rotating about a fixed axis. To find the moment of the effective forces about the axis of rotation.

Let the axis of rotation be OZX, perpendicular to the plane of the paper. Take a plane AOZ through OZ and fixed in space, cutting the plane of the paper along OA. Let this plane be taken as the plane of reference. Let q be the angle, which another plane ZOG through the axis fixed in the body makes with the plane AOZ. Take a particle of mass m at Q and let the plane through OZ and Q cut the plane of the paper along OP. Let the angle between ZOP and ZOG be α. When body rotates about OZ, a remains constant. Let the angle between the plane ZOP and the plane ZOA be ϕ. Now $\theta + \alpha = \phi \therefore \theta = \phi$ and $\ddot{\theta} = \ddot{\phi}$

The accelerations of the particle of mass m are $r\dot{\phi}^2$ and $r\ddot{\phi}$ along QN and perpendicular to QN respectively.

Therefore effective forces on the particles are $mr\dot{\phi}^2$ and $mr\ddot{\phi}$ in the above said direction. Again $r\dot{\phi}^2 = r\dot{\theta}^2$ and $r\ddot{\phi} = r\ddot{\theta}$.

The moment of the force $mr\dot{\phi}^2$ about OZ is zero and moment of the force $mr\ddot{\phi}$ about OZ (& NZ) is $r.mr\ddot{\phi} = mr^2\ddot{\phi} = mr^2\ddot{\theta}$.

Hence the moment of the effective forces of the whole body about OZ is $\Sigma mr^2\ddot{\theta} = \ddot{\theta}\,\Sigma mr^2 = Mk^2\ddot{\theta}$, where k is the radius of gyration of the body about OZ.

Moment of Momentum About the Axis of Rotation

Velocity of the particle m is $r\dot{\phi}$ perpendicular to QN. Therefore the moment of momentum of the particle about OZ is $mr^2\dot{\phi}$ or $mr^2\dot{\theta}$.

Hence the moment of momentum of the whole body about OZ is

$$\Sigma mr^2\dot{\phi} = (\Sigma mr^2)\dot{\theta} = \dot{\theta}\,\Sigma mr^2 = Mk^2\dot{\theta}$$

GENERAL CASE OF CENTRE OF PERCUSSION

Let us take the fixed axis as the axis of y. Also let centre of gravity G lie in the xy-plane, so that coordinates of G are $(\bar{x}, \bar{y}, 0)$.

If Q is the point where the blow is applied then take a plane through Q and perp. to xy-plane as the xz-plane so that co-ordinates of Q may be $(\xi, 0, \xi)$. Now consider any other point P of mass m o the body at a distance r from Oy at any angle θ with z-axis. The coordinates of P will be

$$x = r\sin\theta,\ y = \text{const.},\ z = r\cos\theta$$

if before the blow, angular velocity is ω and the velocity component along the axes are u, v, w respectively, then we have

$$\dot{x} = u = r\cos\theta, \dot{\theta} = z\omega \ \dot{y} = v = 0, \dot{z} = w = -r\sin\theta.\dot{\theta} = -x\omega$$

If after the blow, the angular velocity is w and velocity component along the axes becomes as u′, v′, w′, then

$$u' = z\omega', v' = 0, w' = -x\omega'.$$

If X, Y, Z are the components of the blow at the point Q, then equations of motion will be

$$\begin{aligned} X &= \Sigma m(u' - u) = \Sigma mz(\omega' - \omega) \\ &= (\omega' - \omega)\Sigma mz \\ &= (\omega' - \omega)\bar{z}\,\Sigma m = M(\omega' - \omega)\bar{z} \\ &= 0 \ (\text{since } \bar{z} = 0) \qquad \ldots(1) \end{aligned}$$

$$\begin{aligned} Y &= \Sigma m(v' - v) \\ &= 0 \ (\text{since } v' = 0 \text{ and } y = 0) \qquad \ldots(2) \end{aligned}$$

$$\begin{aligned} Z &= \Sigma m(w' - w) = -(\omega' - \omega)\Sigma mx \\ &= -(\omega' - \omega)\bar{x}\,\Sigma mx = -M(\omega' - \omega)\bar{x} \qquad \ldots(3) \end{aligned}$$

$$\begin{aligned} -Y\xi &= \Sigma m\{y(w' - w) - z(v' - v)\} \\ &= -(\omega' - \omega)\Sigma mxy = -(\omega' - \omega)F \qquad \ldots(4) \end{aligned}$$

$$\Rightarrow \quad F = 0 \qquad (\because Y = 0)$$

$$\begin{aligned} \xi X - \xi Z &= \Sigma m\{z(u' - u) - x(w' - w)\} \\ &= -(\omega' - \omega)\Sigma m(z^2 + x^2) \\ &= Mk^2(\omega' - \omega) \qquad \ldots(5) \end{aligned}$$

[Mk^2 is the M.I. of the body about y-axis]

$$\begin{aligned} \xi Y &= \Sigma m\{x(v' - v) - y(u' - u)\} \\ &= -(\omega' - \omega)\Sigma mzx = -(\omega' - \omega)D \end{aligned}$$

$$\Rightarrow \quad D = 0 \qquad [\because Y = 0] \quad \ldots(6)$$

Thus we get X = 0, Y = 0, which implies that blow has no components parallel to the axes of x and y.

Hence the blow must be perp. to xy-plane which contains the fixed axis and the instantaneous position of the centre of gravity. Also we see that F = 0 and D = 0 which implies that the y-axis which is also the axis of the body is a principal axis at the point where the plane through the line of action of the blow perp. to the fixed axis cuts it.

This is a necessary condition for the existence of the centre of percussion. So if the fixed axis is not a principal axis at some point, then there is no centre of percussion.

Using equation (3) and (5), we get $\xi = \frac{k^2}{x}$ ...(7)

The obvious conclusion from the relation (7) is that the distance of the centre of percussion from the fixed axis is the same as that of the centre of oscillation.

Points to remember in finding out the centre of percussion of a body for fixed axis.

(i) *Find the point where the fixed axis is principal axis.*

(ii) *Take a distance* $\frac{k^2}{x}$.

(iii) *Draw an axis perp. to the plane containing the fixed axis and C.G. at a distance* $\frac{k^2}{x}$ *below the point where fixed axis is principal axis.*

(iv) *Any point on this line is a centre of percussion of the body for the fixed axis.*

REACTION OF THE AXIS OF ROTATION

A body moves about a fixed axis under the action of forces and both the body and the forces are symmetrical with respect to the plane through the C.G. perpendicular to the axis, find the reactions of the axis of rotation.

Let O be the point where the plane through G perpendicular to the axis of rotation meets this axis. By symmetry the actions on the axis reduce to a single force at O, the centre of suspension. Let the components of this single force be X and Y along and perpendicular to GO respectively.

Now G describes a circle round O as centre, its acceleration along and perpendicular to GO are $h\dot{\theta}^2$ and $h\ddot{\theta}$. Equations of motion of C.G. are

$$Mh\dot{\theta}^2 = X - Mg\cos\theta \quad ...(1)$$

$$Mh\ddot{\theta} = Y - Mg\sin\theta \quad ...(2)$$

By taking moments about O, $Mk^2\ddot{\theta} = -Mgh \sin q$ where k is the radius of gyration about the axis.

Y is obtained by eliminating $\ddot{\theta}$ from (2) and (3), By integrating (3) and determining the constant from the initial conditions, and then from (1), we can find X.

Resultant reaction $R = \sqrt{(X^2 + Y^2)}$ and $\tan \phi = (X/Y)$

where ϕ is the angle which the direction of R makes with GO.

Note: On resolving X and Y horizontally and vertically.

The horizontal reaction = $X \sin \theta - Y \cos \theta$

Vertical reaction = $X \cos \theta + Y \sin \theta$.

THE COMPOUND PENDULUM

To determine the motion of a body acted on by the force of gravity only and moving about a fixed horizontal axis.

Let us take plane of the paper as the plane through the centre of gravity G of the body and perpendicular to the fixed axis. Let the plane meet the axis in C. Let θ be the angle between the vertical and CG *i.e.* q is the angle between a plane fixed in space and a plane fixed in the body.

Let CH = h. The forces on the body are:

(i) its weight M g acting downward through G.

(ii) the reaction of C of the fixed axis.

We take moments about the fixed axis to eliminate this reaction.

The equation of motion is $Mk^2\theta = -Mgh \sin \theta$

$$\Rightarrow \frac{d^2\theta}{dr^2} = -\frac{gh}{k^2}\sin\theta = -\frac{gh}{k^2}\theta \text{, (θ being small)} \qquad ...(1)$$

Equation (1) shows that motion is S.H.M. Hence the time of complete oscillation of compound pendulum is $2\pi\sqrt{\left(\frac{k^2}{gh}\right)}$

Simple Equivalent Pendulum

We know that equation of motion of a particle of any mass suspended by a string of length l is

$$\frac{d^2\theta}{dt^2} = -\frac{g}{t}\sin\theta = -\frac{g}{l}\theta \qquad \text{(θ being small)}$$

The time of complete oscillation is $2\pi\sqrt{\left(\frac{l}{g}\right)}$.

If $2\pi\sqrt{\left(\frac{l}{g}\right)} = 2\pi\sqrt{\{k^2/(gh)\}}$, then $l = (k^2/h)$.

This length (k2/h) in the case of a compound pendulum is called the length of the simple equivalent pendulum.

TO SHOW THAT THE CENTRES OF SUSPENSION AND OSCILLATION ARE CONVERTIBLE

Let us take O and O' as the centre of suspension and oscillation respectively.

$$\therefore \quad OO' = \frac{k^2}{h} \text{ where } OG = h,$$

and k is radius of gyration of the body about the axis through O. Now if K is the radius of gyration of the body about an axis through G parallel to the axis of rotation, then $Mk^2 = MK^2 + M.OG^2$

$$\Rightarrow \quad Mk^2 = MK^2 + Mh^2$$

$$\Rightarrow \quad k^2 = K^2 + h^2$$

$$\therefore \quad OO' = \frac{K^2 + h^2}{h} = \frac{K^2 + OG^2}{OG}$$

$$\Rightarrow OO'.OG = K^2 + OG^2 \Rightarrow K^2 = OG\,(OO' - OG) = OG.O'G \qquad ...(1)$$

Let OO″ be the centre of oscillation when the body rotates about a parallel axis through O′. We can show as above that

$$K^2 = O'G.\,O''G \qquad ...(2)$$

From (1) and (2), we observe that O″ is simply the point O. Thus if the body were suspended from a parallel axis through O′, O is the centre of oscillation. This proves the theorem.

MINIMUM TIME OF OSCILLATION OF A COMPOUND PENDULUM

If K is the radius of gyration of th body about an axis through G parallel to the axis of rotation, then $k^2 = K^2 + h^2$.

$$l = \frac{k^2}{h} = \frac{K^2 + h^2}{h} = \frac{K^2}{h} + h$$

The time of oscillation of a compound pendulum will be least when the length of the simple equivalent pendulum is minimum. For that

$$\frac{dl}{dh} = \frac{d}{dh}\left(h + \frac{K^2}{h^2}\right) = 0$$

$$\Rightarrow \quad 1 - \frac{K^2}{h^2} = 0 \Rightarrow h = K.$$

The length of simple equivalent pendulum in this case

$$l = \frac{K^2 + h^2}{h} = \frac{K^2 + K^2}{K} = 2K.$$

In case h = 0 or ∞ i.e. if the axis of suspension either passes through G or be at infinite, the corresponding simple equivalent pendulum is of infinite length, thus the time of oscillation is infinite.

MOTION ABOUT A FIXED AXIS: IMPULSIVE FORCES

Consider a rigid body under the effect of impulsive forces. Let w and w′ be the angular velocities about the axis just before and just after the action of impulsive forces. Now change in moment of momentum about the axis = Mk^2 $(\omega' - \omega)$. Also let L the moment of external impulses about the axis of rotation, then we have $Mk^2 (\omega' - \omega) = L$ (since change in moment of momentum of the body about the axis is equal to the moment of the impulsive forces about it).

KINETIC ENERGY

The kinetic energy of the particle of mass m is $\frac{1}{2}mr^2\dot{\phi}^2$.

Hence K.E. of the whole body is

$$\Sigma\frac{1}{2}mr^2\dot{\phi}^2 = \Sigma\frac{1}{2}mr^2\dot{\phi}^2 = \frac{1}{2}\dot{\theta}^2\Sigma mr^2 = \frac{1}{2}Mk^2\dot{\theta}^2.$$

EQUATION OF MOTION

The impressed forces include besides the external forces, the reactions on the axis of rotation OZ. We take moment about OZ, so that this reaction could be avoided *i.e.*, the moment of the effective forces about OZ will be equal to the moment of the external forces about OZ. Thus $Mk^2\ddot{\theta} = L$, where L represents the moment of all external forces about OZ. Above equation is called the equation of motion of the body. In the case of impulsive forces if ω_1 and ω_2 be angular velocities of the body just before and just after the action of the impulses, L the moment of the impulses then we have $K_2(\omega_2 - \omega_1) = L$.

CENTRE OF PERCUSSION

If a body, rotating about a given axis, is so struck that there is not impulsive pressure on the axis, then any point on the line of action of the force is called a *centre of percussion.* If the line of action of the blow is known, the axis about which the body begins to turn is called the axis of *spontaneous rotation.* Obviously this combines with the position of the fixed axis in the first case.

CENTRE OF PERCUSSION OF A ROD

Consider a rod AB of length 2b. Let it be suspended freely from one end A. Let a horizontal blow of impulse P be applied to it at the point C where AC

= x. If X is the impulsive action at A and ω the angular velocity communicated to the rod, then the equation of motion are

$$Mk^2\omega = Px \quad ...(1)$$

$$M(a\omega - 0) = P + X \; ...(2)$$

where aω is the velocity with which G moves.

Now if the blow has been given through the centre of perscussion then $X = 0$ and equation (2) becomes $Ma\omega = P$.

Substituting this value of P in (1), we get

$$x = \frac{k^2}{a}$$

= length of the equivalent simple pendulum

CENTRE OF SUSPENSION

Through C, if a line be drawn perpendicular to the axis of rotation cutting it at C, then C is called the *Centre of suspension.*

Centre of Oscillation

If O is the ponit on CG produced such that $CO = l = \frac{k^2}{h}$ (the length of the simple equivalent pendulum) then the point O is called the centre of oscillation.

SOLVED EXAMPLES

Example 1:

Find the centre of percussion of a triangle ABC which is free to move about its side BC.

Solution:

To find out the point where BC is a principal axis. Let us proceed like this. Draw AD, the median and AL the perp. from A on BC. Let O be the mid point of DL. Then, by the elementary knowledge of M.I. and P.I., BC is a principal axis at the ponit O. Let the mass of the ΔABC be m. The triangle of mass m is kinetically equivalent to the particles each of mass $\frac{m}{3}$ placed at the mid points D, E and F. Let AL = P, then

$$mk^2 = \frac{m}{3}\left(\frac{1}{2}p\right)^2 + \frac{m}{3}\left(\frac{1}{2}p\right)^2 + \frac{m}{3}(0)$$

$$= \frac{1}{6}mp^2 \Rightarrow k^2 = \frac{1}{6}p^2.$$

But the depth of C.G. of below BC = h = $\frac{1}{3}$p.

Hence depth of the centre of percussion below BC along a vertical through O = $(k^2/h) = \frac{1}{2}$p.

Particular Case: If the triangle ABC is an equilateral triangle, then the ponit D and O coincide. In this case $k^2 = \frac{1}{6}p^2$, $h = \frac{1}{3}p$

Hence the depth of the centre of percussion below BC along the median bisecting BC is = $\frac{k^2}{h} = \frac{1}{2}p$.

Example 2:

Find how an equilateral lamina must be struck that it may commence to rotate about a side.

Solution:

The triangle ABC rotate about the side BC. The blow should be given at the centre of percussion when BC is the axis of rotation of the lamina. Here BC is the principal axis of triangle at its middle point (points D, O, L will coincide).

Again $k^2 = \frac{1}{6}p^2$; $h = \frac{1}{3}p$; where p is the height of the triangle.

∴ Depth of the centre of percussion below BC along the median bisecting BC is $\frac{k^2}{h}$ *i.e.,* $\frac{1}{2}p$.

Hence the blow should be given at the middle point of the median bisecting the side about which the lamina rotates.

Example 3:

Find the position of th centre of percussion of a sector of a circle, axis in the plane of the sector, perp. to its symmetrical radius and passing through the centre of the circle.

Solution:

Consider the sector AOB of a circle of radius a.

Let ∠AOB = 2α. Let a line OY perp. to the plane of the sector be the axis of rotation.

Then M.I. of the sector AOB about

$$OY = 2\int_0^{\alpha}\int_0^{\alpha} \rho r^2 \cos^2\theta \, r\, d\theta\, dr$$

$$= \rho \frac{a^4}{4} \int_0^{\alpha} (1+\cos 2\theta)\, d\theta$$

$$= \rho \cdot \frac{a^4}{4}(\alpha + \sin\alpha \cos\alpha)$$

$$= \frac{Ma^2}{4\alpha}(\alpha - \sin\alpha\cos\alpha),$$

since mass of the sector $M = \rho.\alpha a^2$.

$$\therefore \qquad Mk^2 = \frac{Ma^2}{4\alpha}(\alpha + \sin\alpha\cos\alpha)$$

$$\Rightarrow \qquad k^2 = \frac{a^2}{4\alpha}(\alpha + \sin\alpha\cos\alpha)$$

Distance of C.G. from $O = h = \dfrac{2a}{3} \cdot \dfrac{\sin\alpha}{\alpha}$

Hence distance of centre of percussion from O

$$= \frac{k^2}{h} = \frac{3a}{8}\left(\frac{\alpha + \sin\alpha\cos\alpha}{\sin\alpha}\right)$$

Example 4:

A straight uniform rod can turn freely about one end O, hangs from O vertically. Find the least angular velocity with which it must begin to move so that it may perform complete revolution in a vertical plane.

Solution:

Let the rod OA at any instant t make an angle q with the initial vertical position OX. Let G be the centre of gravity and GN perp. to OZ. Let OA = a and mass of the rod be m. The equation of motion is

$$mk^2\ddot{\theta} = -mg\left(\frac{a}{2}\right)\sin\theta$$

∵ Moment of effective forces about the axis of rotation = $mk^2\ddot{\theta}$ and moment of external forces about the axis of rotation = $-mg(a/2)\sin\theta$

$$\Rightarrow 2a\ddot{\theta} = -3g\sin\theta\left(\because k^2 = \frac{a^2}{3}\right)$$

Multiplying the above equation by $\ddot{\theta}$ and integrating, we get

$$a\dot{\theta}^2 = 3g\cos\theta + C \qquad ...(1)$$

Let $\dot{\theta} = \omega$ when $\omega = 0 \therefore a\omega^2 = 3g + C \qquad ...(2)$

Hence from (1) and (2), we get $a\dot{\theta} = a\omega^2 - 3g(1 - \cos\theta)$

we required that $\dot{\theta} = 0$ when $\theta = \pi \therefore 0 = a\omega^2 - 6g \Rightarrow \omega = \sqrt{(6g/a)}$.

Example 5:

A perfectly rough circular horizontal board is capable of revolving freely round a vertical axis through the centre. a man whose weight is equal to that of the board walks on and around it at the edge. When he has completed the circuit, what will be his position in space.

Solution:

Let any time t, θ and ϕ be the angles described by the board and man respectively and let F be the action between the feet of the man and the board. Equation of motion for the man is

$$ma\ddot{\phi} = F \qquad ...(1)$$

Equation of motion for the board is

$$mk^2\ddot{\theta} = -Fa \qquad ...(2)$$

On eliminating F between (1) and (2), we get

$$a^2\ddot{\phi} + k^2\ddot{\theta} = 0 \Rightarrow 2\ddot{\phi} + \ddot{\theta} = 0 \qquad \left(\because k^2 = \frac{a^2}{2}\right)$$

Integrating twice the above equation and considering that initially both man and the board were at rest, we get $2\phi + \theta = 0$.

Therefore when $\phi - \theta = 2\pi$ (after completing the circuit)

we get, $3\phi = 2\pi \Rightarrow \phi = 2\pi/3$.

This is the angle is space described by the man.

Example 6:

A uniform rod AB is freely movable on a rough inclined plane whose inclination to the horizon is i and whose coefficient of friction is μ, about a smooth pin fixed through the end A; the bar is held in the horizontal position in the plane and allowed to fall from this position, if θ be the angle through which it falls from rest show that (sin θ/θ) = μ cot i.

Solution:

Let any instant t, the position of the rod be AB, making an angle q with the initial horizontal position. The external forces acting on the rod, perp. to the plane, are the normal reaction R and resolved part of its weight *i.e.* mg cos i. External forces acting on the rod in the plane are, (i) the resolved part of its weight, mg sin i acting down the line of greatest slope through G (centre of gravity). (ii) the friction $\mu R = \mu mg \cos i$ acting perp. to AB through G; (iii) the reaction at A. We take moments about A to avoid reaction, so

$$mk^2\ddot{\theta} = mg \sin i.a \cos\theta - \mu\, mg \cos ia$$

$$\Rightarrow k^2\ddot{\theta} = ga (\sin i \cos\theta - \mu \cos i),\text{ where 2a is length of the rod.}$$

Multiplying the above equation by 2θ and integrating, we get

$$k^2\ddot{\theta} = 2ag \sin i \sin\theta - 2\mu ag\theta \cos i + D.$$

When $\theta = 0$, $\dot{\theta} = 0 \therefore D = 0$. Hence $k^2\dot{\theta}^2 = 2ag \sin i \sin\theta - 2\mu ag\, \theta \cos i$

Rod will come to rest when $\dot{\theta} = 0$.

$\therefore 0 = 2ag \sin\theta - 2\,\mu ag \cos i \Rightarrow (\sin\theta/\theta) = \mu \cot i.$

Example 7:

A uniform vertical circulate plate fo radius a, is capable of revolving about a smooth horizontal axis through its centre; a rough perfectly flexible chain, whose mass is equal to that of the plate and whose length is equal to its circumference hangs over its rim in equilibrium, if one end be slightly displaced show that the velocity of the chain when the other end reaches the plate is $\left(\frac{\pi ag}{6}\right)^{1/2}$

Solution:

Let x be the distance described in time t. Let v be the velocity of the string and θ be the angular velocity of the plate, then $v = \dot{x} = a\dot{\theta}$. Let m be the mass of the plate and that of the string, then K.E. of the string $= \frac{1}{2}mv^2$. K.E. of the plate

$$= \frac{1}{2}mk^2\dot{\theta}^2 = \frac{1}{2}mk^2\frac{v^2}{a^2}$$

$$= \frac{1}{2}m\frac{a^2}{2}\cdot\frac{v^2}{a^2} = \frac{1}{4}mv^2 \qquad \left[\because k^2 = \frac{a^2}{2}\right]$$

Hence, the total K.E. generated $= \frac{1}{2}mv^2 + \frac{1}{4}mv^2 = \frac{3}{4}mv^2$.

At time t, length of the string hanging to the right is $\left(\frac{\pi a}{2} + x\right)$ and hanging to the left is $\left(\frac{\pi a}{2}-x\right)$. The weights of these two portion are respectively $\frac{mg}{2\pi a}\left(\frac{\pi a}{2}+x\right)$ and $\frac{mg}{2\pi a}\left(\frac{\pi a}{2}-x\right)$.

The depths of the C.G's of these portions below AB are

$$\frac{1}{2}\left(\frac{\pi a}{2}+x\right) \text{ and } \frac{1}{2}\left(\frac{\pi a}{2}-x\right).$$

Hence when x is the displacement, work function on the right is

$$W_1 = \frac{mg}{2\pi a}\left(\frac{\pi a}{2}+x\right)\cdot\frac{1}{2}\left(\frac{\pi a}{2}+x\right)$$

Work function of the left is

$$W_2 = \frac{mg}{2\pi a}\left(\frac{\pi a}{2}-x\right)\cdot\frac{1}{2}\left(\frac{\pi a}{2}-x\right)$$

$\therefore$ Total work function

$$W = W_1 + W_2$$

$$= \frac{mg}{4\pi a}\left(\frac{\pi a}{2}+x\right)^2 + \frac{mg}{4\pi a}\left(\frac{\pi a}{2}-x\right)^2 \quad ...(1)$$

In the initial position *i.e.* when x = 0

$$W_0 = 2\frac{mg}{4\pi a}\frac{\pi^2 a^2}{4} = \frac{1}{8}mg\pi a \quad \text{[from (1)]}$$

Hence total work done

$$= W - W_0$$

$$= \frac{mg}{4\pi a}\left[\left(\frac{\pi a}{2}+x\right)^2 + \left(\frac{\pi a}{2}-x\right)^2 - \frac{1}{2}\pi^2 a^2\right]$$

$$= \frac{mgx^2}{2\pi a}$$

Therefore energy equation gives

$$\frac{3}{4}mv^2 = \frac{mgx^2}{2\pi a} \Rightarrow v^2 = \frac{2gx^2}{3\pi a}.$$

When $x = \frac{\pi a}{2}$ (*i.e.* when other end reaches the plate)

$$v^2 = \frac{1}{6}\pi ag \Rightarrow v = \left(\frac{1}{6}\pi ag\right)^{1/2}$$

Example 8:

One end of a light string is fixed to a point of the rim fo a uniform circular disc of radius a and mass m and the string is wounded several times round the rim. The free end is attached to a fixed ponit and the disc is held so that the part of the string not in contact with it, is vertical. If the disc be let go, find the acceleration and the tension of the string.

Solution:

Let the free end be attached to the fixed point P. Let A be the initial position of the centre of gravity G. Let T be the tension of the string. There being no horizontal force the C.G. will move vertically downwards. Let x be the distance moved by G in time t and during this period, q be the angle turned through some radius.

$$\therefore \quad mg - T = m\ddot{x} \quad ...(1)$$

and

$$Ta = mk^2\ddot{\theta} = m\frac{a^2}{2}\ddot{\theta} \quad ...(2)$$

Again $\quad x = a1, = \ddot{x} = a\ddot{\theta}$

On eliminating T and $\ddot{\theta}$ from (1), (2) and (3), we get

$$mga = ma\ddot{x} + m\frac{a}{2}\ddot{x} \Rightarrow \ddot{x} = \frac{2g}{3}$$

Substituting this value in (1), we get $T = \frac{1}{3}mg$.

Example 9:

Two unequal masses m_1 and m_2 ($m_1 > m_2$) are suspended by a light string over a circular pulley of mass M and radius a. There is no slipping and the friction of the axis may be neglected. If f be the acceleration; show that this is constant, and if k^2 be the radius of gyration of the pulley about the axle, show that $k^2 = \frac{a^2}{Mf}[(g - f)m_1 - (g + f)m_2]$

Solution:

Let in time t, m1 move a distance x downwards and m_2 move a distance x upwards. Let θ be the angle through which the pulley has rotated in time t. Since $x = a\theta$, $\therefore \ \ddot{x} = a\ddot{\theta}$

Equation of motion of m_1 and m_2 are

$$m_1\ddot{x} = m_1 g - T_1 \quad ...(1)$$

and

$$m_2\ddot{x} = T_2 - m_2 g \quad ...(2)$$

Equation of motion of the pulley is

$$mk_2\ddot{\theta} = T_1a - T_2a$$

(Moment is taken about the axle)

$$\Rightarrow \qquad M\frac{k^2}{a^2}\ddot{x} = T_1 - T_2 \qquad \left(\because \ddot{\theta} = \frac{\ddot{x}}{a}\right)$$

Adding (1), (2) and (3), we get $\ddot{x}\left(m_1 + m_2 + M\frac{k^2}{a^2}\right) = m_1g - m_2g$

$$\Rightarrow \ddot{x} = f = \left(m_1 + m_2 + M\frac{k^2}{a^2}\right) = m_1g - m_2g$$

From above we get $f(m_1 + m_2) + \frac{Mk^2}{a^2}f = (m_1 - m_2)g$

$$\Rightarrow \qquad k^2 = \frac{a^2}{Mf}[(m_1 - m_2)g - (m_1 + m_2)f]$$

$$= \frac{a^2}{mf}[(g - f)m_1 - (g + f)m_2].$$

Pressure on the pulley $= T_1 + T_2$.

Again on subtracting (1) from (2), we get

$$(m_2 - m_1)\ddot{x} = T_2 + T_1 - (m_1 + m_2)g$$

$$\Rightarrow \qquad T_2 + T_1 = (m_2 - m_1)\ddot{x} + (m_1 + m_2)g$$

$$= (m_2 - m_1)f + (m_1 + m_2)g.$$

Example 10:

A fine string has two masses M and M' tied to its ends and passes over a rough pulley, of mass m, whose centre is fixed. If the string does not slip over the pulley, show that M will descend with acceleration.

$$\frac{M - M'}{M + M' + (mk^2/a^2)}g.$$

where a is the radius and k the radius of gyration of the pulley.

If the policy be not sufficiently rough to prevent sliding, and M be the descending mass, show that its acceleration is $\frac{M - M'e^{\mu\pi}}{M + M'e^{\mu\pi}}g$ *and that pulley will now spin with an angular acceleration equal to*

$$\frac{2MM'ga(e^{\mu\pi} - 1)}{mk^2(M + M'e^{\mu\pi})}.$$

Solution:

First Part: when the pulley is rough enough to prevent sliding.

The equations of motion of masses and pulley are

$$M\ddot{x} = Mg - T \qquad ...(1)$$

and
$$M'\ddot{x} = T' - M'g \qquad ...(2)$$

and moment of effective forces about the axis of rotation

$$= mk^2\ddot{\theta} = (T - T')a \qquad ...(3)$$

Again
$$x = a\theta,\ \ddot{x} = a\ddot{\theta},$$

$\therefore$
$$mk^2 \frac{\ddot{x}}{a^2} = T - T' \qquad ...(4)$$

Adding (1), (2) and (4), we get $\ddot{x}\,[M + M' + (mk^2/a^2)] = (M - M')g$

$$\Rightarrow \text{Acceleration} = \ddot{x} = \frac{(M - M')g}{M + M' + (mk^2/a^2)}$$

Second Part: When the pulley is not sufficiently rough to prevent sliding, then we can not take $x = a\theta$. In this case, from Statics, we have

$$T = T'e^{\mu\pi} \qquad ...(5)$$

Solving (1), (2) and (5), we have

$$T = \frac{2MM'\,ge^{\mu\pi}}{M + M'\,e^{\mu\pi}}T'$$

$$= \frac{2MM'g}{M + M'e^{\mu\pi}}$$

and
$$\ddot{x} = \frac{M - M'\,e^{\mu\pi}}{M + M'e^{\mu\pi}}g$$

Further putting above values of T and T' in (3), we get

$$\ddot{\theta} = \frac{2ga\,(e^{\mu\pi} - 1)}{mk^2} \cdot \frac{MM'}{M + M'e^{\mu\pi}}.$$

Example 11:

Two unequal masses, M and M' rest on two rough planes inclined at an angles a and b to the horizon; they are connected by a fine string passing over a small pulley, of mass ma and radius a, which is placed at the common vertex of the two planes; show that the acceleration of either mass is

$$\frac{g[M(\sin\alpha - \mu\cos\alpha) - M'(\sin\beta + \mu'\cos\beta)}{M + M' + (mk^2/a^2)}$$

where μ and μ' are the coefficients of friction, k is the radius of gyration of the pulley about its axis and M is the mass which moves downwards.

Solution:

Suppose in time t, the mass M moves a distance x downwards, and also M moves a distance x upwards. Let the pulley turn through an angle θ in the same t.

$\therefore x = a\theta,\ \dot{x} = a\dot{\theta},\ \ddot{x} = a\ddot{\theta}$. The equation of motion of the masses M and M' are

$$M\ddot{x} = Mg \sin a - mg\,\mu \cos a - T \quad ...(1)$$

$$M''\ddot{x} = T' - M' g \sin b - M'g\,\mu' \cos b \quad ...(2)$$

Equation of motion of pulley is $mk^2\ddot{\theta} = (T - T')\,a$

$$\Rightarrow \quad \frac{mk^2\ddot{x}}{a^2} = T - T' \qquad \left(\because \ddot{\theta} = \frac{\ddot{x}}{a}\right) \quad ...(3)$$

Adding (1), (2) and (3), we get

$$\left(\frac{mk^2}{a^2} + M + M'\right)\ddot{x} = g\,[M(\sin\alpha - \mu\cos\alpha) - M'(\sin\beta - \mu'\cos\beta)]$$

$$\Rightarrow \ddot{x} = \frac{g[M(\sin\alpha - \mu\cos\alpha) - M'(\sin\beta + \mu'\cos\beta)]}{M + M' + \dfrac{mk^2}{a^2}}.$$

Example 12:

A uniform circular disc is free to turn about a horizontal axis through its centre perp. to its plane. A particle of mass m is attached to a point in the edge fo the disc. If the motion starts from the position in which radius to the particle makes an angle α with the upward vertical, find the angular velocity when m is in its lowest position. Take the mass of the disc as M.

Solution:

The circular disc is turning about the fixed horizontal axis OX, through its centre O. Let w be the angular velocity when m is in its lowest position, say L then energy principle gives,

Chains in K.E. = work done by forces

$$\Rightarrow \left(\frac{1}{2}ma^2\omega^2 + \frac{1}{2}M\frac{a^2}{2}\omega^2\right) - 0 = mg\,(a + a\cos\alpha).$$

or $$a\omega^2\,(2m + M) = 4g\,(1 + \cos\alpha)$$

or $$\omega = 2\frac{\sqrt{2}}{\sqrt{(2m + M)}}\sqrt{(g/a)}\cos\frac{\alpha}{2}$$

Example 13:

A solid homogeneous cone of height h and vertical angle 2a oscillates about a horizontal axis through its vertex. Show that the length of the simple equivalent pendulum is $\frac{1}{5}h(4+\tan^2\alpha)$.

Solution:

Let OX be the horizontal axis through the vertex O. Let us take a circular disc PQ of thickness δx at distance x from O. Moment of Inertia of disc about OX

$$= (\rho\pi x^2 \tan^2\alpha\delta x)\left(\frac{1}{4}x^2\tan^2\alpha + x^2\right)$$

Therefore M.I. of whole cone about OX

$$Mk^2 = \rho\pi\tan^2\alpha\left(1+\frac{1}{4}\tan^2\alpha\right)\int_0^h x^4 dx$$

$$= \rho x\tan^2\alpha\left(1+\frac{1}{4}\tan^2\alpha\right)\frac{1}{5}h^5$$

$$= \frac{1}{20}\rho\pi\tan^2\alpha(\tan^2\alpha+4)h^5$$

$$= \frac{3}{20}M(\tan^2\alpha+4)h^2 \qquad \left(\because M = \frac{1}{3}\pi h^3\tan^2\alpha\,\rho\right)$$

$$\therefore\; k^2 = \frac{3}{20}(\tan^2\alpha+4)h^2.$$

Again $OG = \frac{3}{4}h$.

Therefore the length of the simple equivalent pendulum *i.e.*

$$l = \frac{k^2}{OG} = \frac{1}{5}(\tan^2\alpha+4)h.$$

Example 14:

A solid homogeneous cone of height h and semi-vertical angle a, oscillates about a diameter of its base. Show that the length of the simple equivalent pendulum is $\frac{1}{5}h(2+3\tan^2\alpha)$.

Solution:

We observe that M.I. of the cone about AB

$$= \int_0^h \rho\pi x^2 \tan^2\alpha \, dx \left[\frac{x^2 \tan^2\alpha}{4} + (h-x)^2\right]$$

$$= \int_0^h \frac{\rho\pi \tan^2\alpha}{4} [x^4 \tan^2\alpha + 4x^2 (h-x)^2] \, dx$$

$$= \frac{\rho\pi \tan^2\alpha}{4} \int_0^h (x^4 \tan^2\alpha + 4x^4 - 8hx^3 + 4h^2x^2) dx$$

$$= \frac{1}{4}\rho\pi \tan^2\alpha \left(\frac{h^5}{5}\tan^2\alpha + 4\frac{h^5}{5} - 8h\frac{h^4}{4} + 4h^2\frac{h^3}{3}\right)$$

$$= \frac{1}{4}\rho\pi \tan^2\alpha \, h^5 \left[\frac{1}{5}\tan^2\alpha + \frac{2}{15}\right]$$

$$= \frac{1}{60}\rho\pi h^4 \tan^2\alpha \, [3\tan^2\alpha + 2]$$

$$= \frac{1}{20} Mh^2 (3\tan^2\alpha + 2), \text{ since } M = \frac{1}{3}\pi h^3 \tan^2\alpha . \rho$$

$$\therefore Mk^2 = \frac{1}{20} Mh^2 (3\tan^2\alpha + 2)$$

$\Rightarrow k^2 = \frac{1}{20} h^2 (3\tan^2\alpha + 2)$, where k is the radius of gyrating of the cone about AB. Hence length of the simple equivalent pendulum

$$= \frac{k^2}{\text{distance of G from AB}} = \frac{k^2}{(h/4)} = \frac{1}{5} h (3\tan^2\alpha + 2).$$

Example 15:

An elliptical lamina is such that when it swings about one latus rectum as a horizontal axis, the other latus rectum passes through the centre of oscillation, prove that the eccentricity is 1/2.

Solution:

When one of the focus say H, is the centre of suspension then the other focus H′ is the centre of oscillation. LHL′ is the latus rectum (horizontal axis) about which the elliptic lamina oscillates.

∵ The length of the simple equivalent pendulum

$$l = HH' = 2ae, \qquad \text{...(1)}$$

Also HG = ae and Mk² = Moment of inertia of the body about the axis of the rotation

$$\text{LHL}' = M\left[\frac{a^2}{4} + a^2e^2\right]$$

$$\Rightarrow \qquad k^2 = \frac{1}{4}a^2(1+4e^2)$$

$$\therefore \qquad l = \frac{k^2}{HG} = \frac{1}{4}\frac{a^2(1+4e^2)}{ae} \qquad \text{...(2)}$$

From (1) and (2), we get $2ae = \frac{1}{4}\frac{a^2(1+4e^2)}{ae}$

$\Rightarrow 8e^2 = 1 + 4e^2$

$\Rightarrow 4e^2 = 1 \Rightarrow e = \frac{1}{2}$.

Example 16:

A uniform elliptic board swings about a horizontal axis at right angles to the plane of the board and passing through one focus. If the centre of oscillation be the other focus prove that its eccentricity is $\sqrt{(2/5)}$.

Solution:

Here $Mk^2 = M\left[\frac{1}{4}(a^2+b^2) + a^2e^2\right]$

$\therefore$ length of simple equivalent pendulum

$$l = \frac{k^2}{HG}$$

$$\Rightarrow \qquad \frac{k^2}{ae} = \frac{1}{4ae}(a^2+b^2+4a^2e^2) \qquad \text{...(1)}$$

Also $\qquad l = 2ae \;\therefore\; 2ae = \frac{1}{4ae}(a^2+b^2+4a^2e^2)$

$\Rightarrow \qquad 8a^2e^2 = a^2 + b^2 + 4a^2e^2 = a^2 + (1-e^2)a^2 + 4a^2e^2$

$\Rightarrow \qquad 4a^2e^2 = 2a^2 \Rightarrow e = \sqrt{(2/5)}$.

Example 17:

A flat circular disc of radius a has a hole in it of radius b whose centre is at a distance c from the centre of the disc $(c < a - b)$. *The disc is free to oscillate in a vertical plane about a smooth horizontal circular rod of radius b passing through the hole. Show that the length of the equivalent pendulum is*

$c + \frac{1}{2}\frac{a^4 - b^4}{a^2c}$.

Solution:

Let O′ be the centre of the hole in the disc whose centre is O.

OO′ = c (given). The disc is oscillated in a vertical plane about a smooth horizontal circular rod of radius b passing through O′.

If h be the depth of C.G. of the body from O′, then

$$h = \frac{\rho g\pi a^2 c - \rho\pi b^2 .0}{\rho\pi a^2 - \rho\pi b^2} = \frac{a^2 c}{a^2 - b^2}$$

Let k be the radius of gyration about the axis of rotation, then we have

$$(\rho\pi a^2 - \rho\pi b^2)k^2 = \rho\pi a^2\left(\frac{a^2}{2} + c^2\right) - \rho\pi b^2 \cdot \frac{b^2}{2}$$

$$\Rightarrow \qquad k^2 = \frac{a^4 + 2a^2c^2 - b^4}{2(a^2 - b^2)}$$

$$\therefore \qquad l = \frac{k^2}{h}$$

$$= \left[\frac{a^4 + 2a^2c^2 - b^4}{2(a^2 - b^2)}\right] \Big/ \left[\frac{a^2 c}{(a^2 - b^2)}\right]$$

$$= \frac{a^4 + 2a^2c^2 - b^4}{2a^2c} = c + \frac{1}{2}\frac{a^4 - b^4}{a^2c}.$$

Example 18:

A bent lever, whose arms are of length a and b, the angle between them being a, makes small oscillations in its own plane about the fulcrum, show that the length of the corresponding simple pendulum is

$$\frac{2}{3}\frac{a^3 + b^3}{\sqrt{(a^4 + 2a^2b^2\cos\alpha + b^4)}}.$$

Solution:

Let G_1 and G_2 be the centres of gravity of the arms OA and OB of the lever. Let OA = a and OB = b. Also let OA be the axis of x and a perp. line OY the axis of y.

Then the co-ordinates of G_1 and G_2 will be $\left(\frac{1}{2}a, 0\right)$ and $\left(\frac{1}{2}b\cos\alpha, \frac{1}{2}b\sin\alpha\right)$ respectively.

Now if $(\bar{x}, \bar{y})$ is the C.G. of the lever, then

$$\bar{x} = \frac{a\omega \cdot \frac{1}{2}a + b\omega \cdot \frac{1}{2}b\cos\alpha}{a\omega + b\omega}$$

$$= \frac{1}{2}\frac{a^2 + b^2\cos\alpha}{a+b};$$

where w is the weight of unit length of the rod.

$$\bar{y} = \frac{a\omega.0 + b\omega.\frac{1}{2}b\sin\alpha}{a\omega + b\omega}$$

$$= \frac{1}{2}\frac{b^2\sin\alpha}{a+b}$$

Also the distance of C.G. $(\bar{x}, \bar{y})$ from O (0, 0) is

$$\sqrt{(\bar{x}^2, \bar{y}^2)} = \frac{1}{2(a+b)}\sqrt{\{a^4 + 2a^2b^2\cos\alpha + b^4\}}$$

Now if k is the radius of gyration about the axis of rotation through O, then we have

$$(a+b)\,\omega k^2 = a\omega.\frac{4}{3}\left(\frac{1}{2}a\right)^2 + b\omega.\frac{4}{3}\left(\frac{1}{2}b\right)^2$$

$$\Rightarrow \qquad k^2 = \frac{a^3 + b^3}{3(a+b)}.$$

Hence the length of the simple pendulum

$$= \frac{k^2}{\text{Dist. of C.G. of the lever from O}}$$

$$= \frac{1}{3}\frac{a^3+b^3}{a+b}\cdot\frac{2(a+b)}{(a^4 + 2a^2b^2\cos\alpha + b^4)^{1/2}}$$

$$= \frac{2}{3}\frac{a^3+b^3}{(a^4 + 2a^2b^2\cos\alpha + b^4)^{1/2}}.$$

Example 19:

A uniform triangular lamina can oscillate in its own plane about the angle A. Prove that the length of the simple equivalent pendulum is

$$\frac{3(b^2+c^2) - a^2}{4\sqrt{\{2(b^2+c^2) - a^2\}}},$$

the axis through A being horizontal.

Solution:

Let AH be perpendicular to the plane of the lamina so that it oscillates in its own plane about AH. Instead of the triangular lamina of mass m, we can have three particles each of mass 1/3m placed at the mid points D, E, F of the sides respectively. Distance of D from AH is

$$AD = [AL^2 + LD^2]^{1/2} = [AL^2 + (BD - BL)^2]^{1/2}$$

$$= [AL^2 + BD^2 + BL^2 - 2BD.BL]^{1/2}$$

$$= [(AL^2 + BL^2) + BD^2 - 2BD.BL]^{1/2}$$

$$= \left[(AB)^2 + \left(\frac{1}{2}BC\right)^2 - 2\left(\frac{1}{2}BC\right).AB\cos B\right]^{1/2}$$

$$= \left(c^2 + \frac{a^2}{4} - ac\cos B\right)^{1/2}$$

$$= \left(c^2 + \frac{a^2}{4} - ac.\frac{a^2 + c^2 - b^2}{2ac}\right)^{1/2}$$

$$= \left(\frac{2b^2 + 2c^2 - a^2}{4}\right)^{1/2}$$

Distance of E from AH = EA = b/2

Distance of F from AH = FA = c/2

M.I. of the triangle about AH

$$= \frac{1}{3}m\left(\frac{2b^2 + 2c^2 - a^2}{4} + \frac{b^2}{4} + \frac{c^2}{4}\right)$$

$$= \frac{1}{12}m(3b^2 + 3c^2 - a^2)$$

$$\therefore \quad mk^2 = \frac{m}{12}[3b^2 + 3c^2 - a^2]$$

$$\Rightarrow \quad k^2 = \frac{3b^2 + 3c^2 - a^2}{12}$$

Hence length of the simple equivalent pendulum

$$= \frac{k^2}{\text{Dist. of C.G. from AH}}$$

$$= \frac{k^2}{AG} = \frac{k^2}{\frac{2}{3}AD}$$

$$= \frac{k^2}{\frac{2}{3}\cdot\frac{1}{2}(2b^2 + 2c^2 - a^2)^{1/2}}$$

$$= \frac{3k^2}{\sqrt{(2b^2 + 2c^2 - a^2)}}$$

$$= \frac{3(3b^2 + 3c^2 - a^2)}{12\sqrt{(2b^2 + 2c^2 - a^2)}}$$

$$= \frac{3(b^2 + c^2) - a^2}{4\sqrt{(2b^2 + 2c^2) - a^2)}}.$$

Example 20:

An ellipse of axis a, b and a circle of radius b are cut from the same sheet of thin uniform metal and are superposed and fixed together with their centres coincident. This free to move in its own vertical plane about one and of the major axis. Show the length of the equivalent simple pendulum is $\frac{5a^2 - ab + 2b^2}{4a}$.

Solution:

Mass of the circle= $\pi b^2\rho$

Now taking k to be the radius of gyration of the body about a line through A perpendicular to lamina, we have

$$(\pi ab + \pi b^2)\rho k^2 = \pi b^2\rho\cdot\left(a^2 + \frac{b^2}{2}\right) + \pi ab\,\rho\left(a^2 + \frac{a^2 + b^2}{4}\right)$$

$$\Rightarrow \quad 4\pi b(a + b)\rho k^2 = \pi b^2\rho(4a^2 + 2b^2) + \pi ab\rho(5a^2 + b^2),$$

$$\Rightarrow \quad k^2 = \frac{b(2b^2 + 4a) + a(5a^2 + b^2)}{4(a + b)}$$

$$= \frac{5a^3 + 4a^2b + ab^2 + 2b^3}{4(a + b)}$$

$$= \frac{5a^2(a + b) - ab(a + b) + 2b^2(a + b)}{4(a + b)}$$

$$= \frac{(a+b)(5a^2 - ab + 2b^2)}{4(a+b)}$$

$$= \frac{1}{4}(5a^2 - ab + 2b^2)$$

Hence length of the equivalent simple pendulum

$$= \frac{k^2}{\text{Dist. of C.G. of the system from A}}$$

$$= \frac{k^2}{a} = \frac{5a^2 - ab + 2b^2}{4a}.$$

Example 21:

A uniform rod of mass m and length 2a can oscillate about a horizontal axis through one end. A circular disc of mass 24 m and radius 1/3 a can have its centre clamped to any point of the rod and its plane contains the axis of rotation. Show that for oscillations under gravity the length of the simple equivalent pendulum lies between (a/2) and 2a.

Solution:

Let AB be the rod axis of rotation pass through A. Let the centre C o the disc, be clamped at a distance x from A.

The distance of C.G. of the system *i.e.* of the rod and the disc together,

$$h = \frac{ma + 24m.x}{m + 24m} = \frac{2a^2 + 24x^2}{25}$$

then if k is the radius of gyration then

$$(m + 24m)\,k^2 = m\frac{4}{3}a^2 + 24m \times \left[\left(\frac{1}{4}\cdot\frac{a}{3}\right)^2 + x^2\right]$$

$$\Rightarrow \qquad k^2 = \frac{4a^2 + 2a^2 + 72x^2}{3 \times 2} + \frac{2a^2 + 24x^2}{25}.$$

Hence length of the simple equivalent pendulum.

$$l = \frac{k^2}{h} = \left(\frac{2a^2 + 24x^2}{25}\right) \Big/ \left(\frac{a + 24x}{25}\right)$$

$$\Rightarrow \qquad l = \frac{2a^2 + 24x^2}{a + 24x} \qquad ...(1)$$

For maximum or minimum of $l\,\frac{dl}{dx} = 0$

$$\Rightarrow \frac{dl}{dx} = \frac{48x(a+24x) - 24(2a^2 + 24x^2)}{(a+24x)^2} = 0$$

$\Rightarrow (24x^2 + 2ax - 2a^2) = 0 \Rightarrow 24x^2 + 8ax - 6ax - 2a^2 = 0$

$\Rightarrow 8x(3x + a) - 2a(3x + a) = 0 \Rightarrow (3x + a)(8x - 2a) = 0$

$\Rightarrow x = \frac{a}{4}$ or $x = -\frac{a}{3}$. Since $x \neq -\frac{a}{3}$, we have $x = \frac{a}{4}$.

When $x = \frac{a}{4}$, we get $l = \frac{a}{2}$ [From (1)]

The other extreme value of l (*i.e.* 2a) is given by putting

$x = 0$ or $x = 2a$ in (1).

Hence the length of the simple equivalent lies between $\frac{a}{2}$ and 2a.

Example 22:

A sphere of radius a, is suspended by a fine wire from a fixed poit at a distance l from its centre. Show that the time of a small oscillation is given by

$2\pi\left(\frac{5l^2 + 2a^2}{5lg}\right)^{1/2}\left[1 + \frac{1}{4}\sin^2\left(\frac{\alpha}{2}\right)\right]$ *where α represents the amplitude of the vibration.*

Solution:

Suppose that the axis of rotation is passing, through O, where OC = l,

Moment of inertia of sphere of mass M about the axis of rotation is $M\left(\frac{2}{5}a^2 + l^2\right)$.

Equation of motion is $M\left(\frac{2}{5}a^2 + l^2\right)\ddot{\theta} = -Mgl\sin\theta$

$$\Rightarrow \ddot{\theta} = -\frac{5gl}{2a^2 + 5l^2}\sin\theta.$$

Integrating, we get $\dot{\theta}^2 = \frac{10gl}{2a^2 + 5l^2}\cos\theta + \lambda$ ...(1)

Let when q = a, $\dot{\theta} = 0$.

Hence (1) reduces to

$$\dot{\theta}^2 = \frac{10gl}{2a^2 + 5l^2}(\cos\theta - \cos\alpha)$$

$$\Rightarrow \quad \frac{d\theta}{dt} = -\sqrt{\left(\frac{10gl}{5a^2 + 5l^2}\right)}\sqrt{(\cos\theta - \cos\alpha)}$$

($\because$ Sphere is coming in the direction of θ decreasing)

$$= -\sqrt{\left(\frac{10gl}{2a^2+5l^2}\right)}\sqrt{\left(1-2\sin^2\frac{\theta}{2}-1+2\sin^2\frac{\alpha}{2}\right)}$$

$$= -\sqrt{\left(\frac{10gl}{2a^2+5l^2}\right)}\sqrt{2}\cdot\sqrt{\left(\sin^2\frac{\alpha}{2}-\sin^2\frac{\theta}{2}\right)}$$

If t be the time from one extreme to the lowest point, then

$$t = -\frac{1}{\sqrt{2}}\sqrt{\left(\frac{2a^2+5l^2}{10gl}\right)}\int_{\alpha}^{0}\frac{d\theta}{\sqrt{\{\sin^2(\alpha/2)-\sin^2(\theta/2)}}$$

$$= \frac{1}{\sqrt{2}}\sqrt{\left(\frac{2a^2+5l^2}{10gl}\right)}\int_{0}^{\alpha}\frac{d\theta}{\sqrt{\{\sin^2(\alpha/2)-\sin^2(\theta/2)}}$$

Putting sin (θ/2) = sin (α/2) sin ϕ,

i.e. $\frac{1}{2}\cos\frac{\theta}{2}d\theta = \sin\frac{1}{2}\alpha\cos\phi\, d\phi$, **we get**

$$t = \sqrt{\left(\frac{2a^2+5l^2}{5gl}\right)}\int_{0}^{\pi/2}\frac{d\phi}{\cos(\theta/2)}$$

$$= \sqrt{\left(\frac{2a^2+5l^2}{5gl}\right)}\int_{0}^{\pi/2}\frac{d\phi}{\sqrt{\left\{1-\sin^2\frac{\alpha}{2}\cdot\sin^2\phi\right\}}}$$

$$= \sqrt{\left(\frac{2a^2+5l^2}{5gl}\right)}\int_{0}^{\pi/2}\left[1+\frac{1}{2}\sin^2\frac{\alpha}{2}\sin^2\phi+\ldots\right]d\phi$$

$$\left[\because (1-x)^{-1/2} = 1+\frac{1}{2}x+\ldots\right]$$

$$= \sqrt{\left(\frac{2a^2+5l^2}{5gl}\right)}\left[\frac{\pi}{2}+\frac{1}{2}\sin^2\frac{\alpha}{2}\cdot\frac{\pi}{4}+\ldots\right]$$

$$\because \int_{0}^{\pi/2}\sin^2\phi\, d\phi = (\pi/4)$$

$$= (\pi/2)\sqrt{\left(\frac{2a^2+5l^2}{5gl}\right)}\left[1+\frac{1}{4}\sin^2\frac{\alpha}{2}\right]$$

neglecting higher powers of sin α/2, since a is small.

∴ Time for one small oscillation is

$$4t = 2\pi\sqrt{\left(\frac{2a^2+5l^2}{5gl}\right)}\left[1+\frac{1}{4}\sin^2\frac{\alpha}{2}\right].$$

Example 23:

Three equal particles are attached to a weightless rod at equal distances a apart. The system is suspended, and is free to turn about a point of the rod distant x from the middle particle. Find the time of a small oscillation and show that it is least when x= .82 a nearly.

Solution:

Let the three particles each of mass m, be attached to the rod at the points A, B and C such that AB = BC = a.

Again let the system rotate about ON such that OB = x. Then M.I. of the three particles about

$$\text{ON} = m(a-x)^2 + mx^2 + m(a+x)^2$$

$$\Rightarrow \quad 3mk^2 = m(a-x)^2 + mx^2 + m(a+x)^2$$

$$\Rightarrow \quad k^2 = \frac{3x^2+2a^2}{3},$$

where k is the radius of gyration of the system about ON. Now if l is the length of the equivalent simple pendulum then we have

$$l = \frac{k^2}{\text{Dist of C.G. of the system from O}}$$

$$= \frac{k^2}{x}$$

$$= \frac{3x^2+2a^2}{3x} = x + \frac{2a^2}{3x}.$$

$$\therefore \quad \frac{dl}{dx} = 1 - \frac{2a^2}{3x^2}$$

For max. or min. of l, we have $\frac{dl}{dx} = 0$

i.e. $1 - \frac{2a^2}{3x^2} = 0 \Rightarrow x = \frac{a}{3}\sqrt{6} = .816a = .82a$ nearly.

Further $\frac{d^2l}{dx^2} = \frac{4a^2}{3x^3}$, which is positive for x = .82a

Hence min, value of l is given by x = .82a.

Example 24:

Find the time of oscillation of a compound pendulum consisting of a rod of mass m and length a, carrying at one end a sphere of mass m1 and diameter 2b, the other end of the rod being fixed.

Solution:

Let OA = a be the rod of mass m, and a sphere of mass m1 be attached to it at A.

If h is the distance of the C.G. of the system from O, then

$$h = \frac{m \cdot \frac{a}{2} + m_1 (a + b)}{m + m_1} \qquad ...(1)$$

Also if k is the radius of gyration of the system about the axis through O, we have

$$(m + m1)k^2 = m \cdot \frac{a}{2} + m_1 \left[\frac{2}{5} b^2 + (a + b)^2\right]$$

$$\Rightarrow \qquad k^2 = \frac{m \frac{a^2}{3} + m_1 \left[\frac{2}{5} b^2 + (a + b)^2\right]}{m + m_1}$$

Hence length of equivalent simple pendulum.

$$= \frac{k^2}{h}$$

$$= \frac{m \frac{a^2}{2} + m_1 \left[\frac{2}{5} b^2 + (a + b)^2\right]}{m + m_1} \cdot \frac{m + m_1}{m \frac{a}{2} + m_1 (a + b)}$$

$$= \frac{m \frac{a^2}{3} + m_1 \left[\frac{2}{5} b^2 + (a + b)^2\right]}{m \frac{a}{2} + m_1 (a + b)}$$

and the time of complete oscillation is

$$= \left(\frac{k^2}{gh}\right)^{1/2} = \frac{2\pi}{\sqrt{g}} \left[\frac{m \frac{a^2}{3} + m_1 \left\{\frac{2}{5} b^2 + (a + b)^2\right\}}{m \frac{a}{2} + m_1 (a + b)}\right]^{1/2}$$

Example 25:

A simple circular pendulum is formed of a mass M suspended from a fixed ponit by a weightless wire of length l, if a mass m, very small compared with M, be knotted on to the wire at a distance a from the point of suspension, show that the time of a small vibration of the pendulum is approximately diminished by

$$\frac{m}{2M}\cdot\frac{a}{l}\left(1-\frac{a}{l}\right) \text{ of itself.}$$

Solution:

Let t be the period of simple pendulum before knotting the mass m, then t $= 2\pi\sqrt{\left(\frac{l}{g}\right)}$.

Let k be th radius of gyration when mass m is attached to the wire at a distance a from the point of suspension O.

Then $(m + M)\, k^2 = Ml^2 + ma^2$

or $k^2 = \frac{ml^2 + ma^2}{M + m}$

Distance of C.G. of the system from O is

$$h = \frac{Ml + ma}{M + m}$$

If t′ be period for the compound pendulum consisting of masses M and m, then

$$t' = 2\pi\sqrt{\left(\frac{k^2}{gh}\right)}$$

$$= 2\pi\left[\frac{1}{g}\left(\frac{ml^2 + ma^2}{M + m}\cdot\frac{M + m}{Ml + ma}\right)\right]^{1/2}$$

$$= 2\pi\left(\frac{Ml^2 + ma^2}{g(Ml + ma)}\right)^{1/2}$$

$$= 2\pi\sqrt{\left(\frac{l}{g}\right)}\left[1 + \frac{ma^2}{Ml^2}\right]\left[1 + \frac{ma}{Ml}\right]^{-1/2}$$

$$= 2\pi\sqrt{\left(\frac{l}{g}\right)}\left[1 + \frac{ma^2}{2Ml^2}\right]\left[1 - \frac{ma}{2Ml}\right],$$

neglecting higher powers of $\frac{m}{M}$.

$$= 2\pi\sqrt{\left(\frac{l}{g}\right)}\left[1-\frac{ma}{2Ml}\left(1-\frac{a}{l}\right)\right]$$

$$= t\left[1-\frac{ma}{2Ml}\left(1-\frac{a}{l}\right)\right]$$

$$\Rightarrow \qquad t - t' = \frac{ma}{2Ml}\left(1-\frac{a}{l}\right)t.$$

Example 26:

A weightless straight rod ABC of length 2a is movable about the end A which is fixed an carries two particles fo the same mass, one fastened to th middle ponit B and the other to the end C of the rod. If the rod be held in a horizontal position and then let go, show that its angular velocity when vertical is $\left(\frac{6g}{5a}\right)^{1/2}$ *and that* $\frac{5a}{3}$ *is the length of the simple equivalent pendulum.*

Solution:

Let v, v′ be the velocities of the masses at B and C when in vertical position. Let ω be the angular velocity of the rod in this position.

Then we have energy equation as

$$\frac{1}{2}mv^2 + \frac{1}{2}mv'^2 = mg.a + mg.2a$$

Also v = aω and v′ = 2aω

$$\therefore \qquad \frac{1}{2}m(a^2+4a^2)\,\omega^2 = mga + 2mga$$

$$\Rightarrow \qquad \omega = \left(\frac{6g}{5a}\right)^{1/2}$$

Again $(m + m)k^2 = ma^2 + m\,(2a)^2 \Rightarrow k^2 = \frac{5a^2}{2}$

Distance of C.G. from A

$$h = \frac{m.a + m.2a}{m+m} = \frac{3a}{2}$$

$$\therefore \qquad l = \frac{k^2}{h} = \frac{\frac{5a^2}{2}}{\frac{3a}{2}} = \frac{5a}{3}.$$

Example 27:

A rectangular plate swings in a vertical plane about one of its corners. If its period is one second, find the length of the diagonal.

Solution:

Let k be the radius of gyration of the plate about the axis, through A and perpendicular to its plane; then we have

$$mk^2 = m\frac{a^2 + b^2}{4.3} + mh^2 \qquad \text{[by parallel axis theorem]}$$

$$= \frac{mh^2}{3} + mh^2 = \frac{4mh^2}{3}$$

$$\Rightarrow k^2 = \frac{4h^2}{3}, \text{BG} = \text{GD}.$$

Further, distance of C.G. from

$$A = AG = h = \frac{1}{2}\sqrt{(a^2 + b^2)}$$

$$\therefore \qquad \text{period} = 2\pi\sqrt{\left(\frac{k^2}{hg}\right)}$$

$$= 2\pi\sqrt{\left(\frac{4h^2}{3gh}\right)} = 4\pi\sqrt{\left(\frac{h}{3g}\right)}$$

But period = 1

$$\Rightarrow \qquad 4\pi\sqrt{\left(\frac{h}{3g}\right)} = 1 \text{ or } h = \frac{3g}{16\pi^2}$$

$$\therefore \text{ Length of the diagonal} = 2h = \frac{3g}{8\pi^2}.$$

Example 28:

A pendulum is supported at O, and P is the centre o oscillation. Show that, if an additional weight is rigidly attached at P, the period of oscillation is unaltered.

Solution:

Let m be the mass of the body forming the compound pendulum and let h be the depth of its C.G. below the point o suspension O. Also let k be its radius of gyration about the horizontal axis through O; then we easily obtain.

$$OP = (k^2/h)$$

$$\Rightarrow \text{Period of Oscillation} = 2\pi\sqrt{\left(\frac{k^2/h}{g}\right)} = T\text{, say.}$$

Let an additional weight M be knotted at P, then if k′ is the radius of gyration about the horizontal axis through O, we immediately have

$$(M+m)\,k'^2 = mk'^2 + M.OP^2$$

$$= mk^2 + M.\left(\frac{k^2}{h}\right)^2$$

$$= k^2\left(m + M\frac{k^2}{h^2}\right) \qquad ...(2)$$

and by well known C.G. formula

$$(M+m)h' = mh + M.OP$$

$$= mh + M\cdot\frac{k^2}{h}$$

$$= h\left(m + M\cdot\frac{k^2}{h^2}\right) \qquad ...(3)$$

$$(1)\text{ and }(2) \Rightarrow \frac{k'^2}{h'} = \frac{k^2}{h} \Rightarrow T'$$

$$i.e.\ 2\pi\sqrt{\left(\frac{(k'^2/h')}{g}\right)} = 2\pi\sqrt{\left(\frac{(k^2/h)}{g}\right)} = T$$

$\Rightarrow$ Period of oscillation is unaltered.

Example 29:

Three motion rods AB, BC, CD each of length a, ar freely jointed at B and C and suspended from the points A and D which are in the same horizontal line and a distance a apart. Prove that when the rods move in a vertical plane, the length of simple equivalent pendulum is $\frac{5a}{6}$.

Solution:

The system form a compound pendulum swinging about the horizontal AD. The figure is self explanatory.

Let m be the mass of the each rod.

Let h be the depth of C.G. of the system from AD and k the radius of gyration of the system about the horizontal axis AD.

Then we easily obtain $3mk^2$ = sum of the moments of inertia of three rods about AD.

$$= m\frac{a^2}{3} + m\frac{a^2}{3} + ma^2 = \frac{5ma^2}{3} \Rightarrow k^2 = (5a^2/9)$$

and $$h = \frac{\left(m\frac{a}{2} + m\frac{a}{2} + ma\right)}{3m} = \frac{2ma}{3m} = \frac{2a}{3}$$

$$\Rightarrow \qquad (k^2/h) = (5a^2/9)/(2a/3) = \frac{5a}{6}$$

$\Rightarrow$ length of simple equivalent pendulum $= \dfrac{5a}{6}$.

Example 30:

A thin uniform rod has one end attached to a smooth hinge and allowed to fall fro m a horizontal position. Show that the horizontal strain on the hinge is greatest when the rod is inclined at an angle of 45° to the vertical, and that the vertical strain is then $\frac{11}{8}$ times the weight of the rod.

Solution:

Let OA = 2a, and let the rod make an angle q with the horizontal after time t. Equation of motion of G along and perpendicular to GO are

$$ma\dot{\theta}^2 = Y\sin\theta + X\cos\theta - mg\sin\theta \qquad ...(1)$$

$$ma\ddot{\theta} = -Y\cos\theta + X\sin\theta + mg\cos\theta \qquad ...(2)$$

Since $$k^2 = a^2 + \frac{a^2}{3} = \frac{4}{3}a^2,$$

$\therefore$ moment equation about O is

$$m\cdot\frac{4}{3}a^2\ddot{\theta} = mg.a\cos\theta$$

$$\Rightarrow \qquad \ddot{\theta} = \frac{3g}{4a}\cos\theta \qquad ...(3)$$

Integrating (3), we get

$$\dot{\theta}^2 = \frac{3g}{2a}\sin\theta + C$$

when $\theta = 0$, $\dot{\theta} = 0 \therefore C = 0, \therefore \dot{\theta}^2 = \frac{3g}{2a}\sin\theta$.

Putting this value of $\dot{\theta}^2$ in (1), we get

$$\frac{3}{2}\text{mg}\sin\theta = \text{Y}\sin\theta + \cos\theta - \text{mg}\sin\theta$$

$$\Rightarrow \quad \text{Y}\sin\theta + \text{X}\cos\theta = \frac{5}{2}\text{mg}\sin\theta \quad ...(4)$$

With the help of (3), the equation 92) becomes as

$$-\text{Y}\cos\theta + \text{X}\sin\theta + \text{mg}\cos\theta = \frac{3\text{mg}}{4}\cos\theta \quad ...(5)$$

Multiplying (4) by cos q and (5) by sin q and adding, we get

$$\text{X} = \left(\frac{5}{2} - \frac{1}{4}\right)\text{mg}\sin\theta\cos\theta$$

$$= \frac{9}{4}\text{mg}\sin\theta\cos\theta$$

$$= \frac{9}{8}\text{mg}\sin 2\theta.$$

Similarly, we have $\quad \text{Y} = \text{mg}\left(\frac{5}{2}\sin^2\theta + \frac{1}{4}\cos^2\theta\right).$

We observe that X is maximum when $\sin 2\theta = 1$

i.e., when $\quad 2\theta = \frac{\pi}{2}$ or $\theta = \frac{\pi}{4}.$

when $\theta = (\pi/4)$, we have

$$\text{Y} = \text{mg}\left[\frac{5}{2}\sin^2(\pi/4) + \frac{1}{4}\cos^2(\pi/4)\right]$$

$$= \text{mg}\left[\frac{5}{2}\cdot\frac{1}{2} + \frac{1}{4}\cdot\frac{1}{2}\right] = \frac{11}{8}\text{mg} = \frac{11}{8}$$

times the weight of the rod.

Example 31:

A heavy homogeneous cube of weight W, can swing about an edge which is horizontal, it starts from rest being displaced from its unstable position of equilibrium. When the perpendicular from the centre of gravity upon the edge has turned through an angle θ, show that the components of the action at the hinge along and at right angles to this perpendicular of the action at the hinge along and at right angles to this perpendicular are

$$\frac{1}{2}\text{W}(3 - 5\cos\theta) \text{ and } \frac{1}{4}\text{W}\sin\theta.$$

Solution:

Le G_0 be the initial position of C.G. and G be the position of C.G. when the edge has turned through an angle θ.

$$OG_0 = OG = \sqrt{(OL^2 + LG_0^2)}$$
$$= \sqrt{(a^2 + a^2)} = a\sqrt{2},$$

where 2a is the length of the edge.

Equation of motion of G along and perpendicular to GO are

$$Ma\sqrt{2\dot{\theta}^2} = mg \cos\theta - X \quad ...(1)$$

and $$ma\sqrt{2\ddot{\theta}} = mg \sin\theta - Y \quad ...(2)$$

where X, Y are the components of the reaction of the axis in this position.

Moment equation about O is $mk^2\ddot{\theta} = mga\sqrt{2}\sin\theta$

$$\Rightarrow \quad m\left(2a^2 + \frac{2}{3}a^2\right)\ddot{\theta} = \sqrt{2}amg \sin\theta$$

$$\Rightarrow \quad \ddot{\theta} = \frac{3}{8}\cdot\frac{\sqrt{2}}{a}g\sin\theta \quad ...(3)$$

Integrating, we get $\quad \dot{\theta}^2 = -\frac{3}{4a}\sqrt{2g\cos\theta} + C$

Initially $\quad \dot{\theta} = 0$, when $\theta = 0$

$$\therefore \quad \dot{\theta}^2 = \frac{3\sqrt{2}g}{4a}(1 - \cos\theta) \quad ...(4)$$

From (1) and (4), we have

$$\frac{3}{2}mg\,(1 - \cos\theta) = mg\cos\theta - X$$

$$\Rightarrow \quad X = mg\left(\frac{3}{2}\cos\theta + \cos\theta - \frac{3}{2}\right)$$

$$= \frac{mg}{2}(5\cos\theta - 3) = -\frac{mg}{2}(3 - 5\cos\theta)$$

$$= -\frac{1}{2}W(3 - 5\cos\theta) \quad [\because mg = W],$$

where negative sign of X shows its opposite direction.

From (2) and (3), we have

$$\frac{3}{4}mg\sin\theta = mg\sin\theta - Y$$

$$\Rightarrow \qquad Y = mg\sin\theta - \frac{3}{4}mg\sin\theta = \frac{1}{4}mg\sin\theta.$$

Example 32:

A circular area can turn freely about a horizontal axis which passes through a point O of its circumference and is perp. to its plane. If motion commences when the diameter through O is vertically above, show that when the diameter has turned through an angle q the components of the strain at O along and perp. to this diameter are respectively $\frac{1}{3}W(7\cos\theta - 4)$ *and* $\frac{1}{3}W\sin\theta$.

Solution:

Initially, when the diameter through O is vertically above O. M.I. of the disc about of the disc about an axis through O perp. to the disc

$$= M\frac{a^2}{2} + Ma^2 = \frac{3Ma^2}{2}.$$

If k is the radius of gyration, then

$$Mk^2 = \frac{3Ma^2}{2} \Rightarrow k^2 = \frac{3a^2}{2}$$

After time t, lt the diameter OA makes an angle q with the vertical. In this position we will have

$$Mk^2\frac{d^2\theta}{dt^2} = Mgh\sin\theta.$$

where h = distance of C.G. of the disc from O = a.

$$\therefore \qquad Mk^2\frac{d^2\theta}{dt^2} = Mga\sin\theta$$

$$\Rightarrow \qquad \frac{3a^2}{2}\frac{d^2\theta}{dt^2} = ga\sin\theta$$

$$\Rightarrow \qquad \frac{d^2\theta}{dt^2} = \sin\theta.$$

Multiplying by $2\dot{\theta}$ on both sides and integrating it, we get

$$(d\theta/dt)^2 = -\frac{4\dot{g}}{3a}\cos\theta + c$$

Initially $\theta = 0$, $(d\theta/dt) = 0$. $\therefore\ 0 = -\frac{4g}{3a} + a \Rightarrow c = \frac{4g}{3a}$

Hence $$\left(\frac{d\theta}{dt}\right)^2 = \frac{4g}{3a}(1-\cos\theta) \qquad ...(2)$$

Now considering the motion of C.G., we have

$$Ma\left(\frac{d\theta}{dt}\right)^2 = Mg\cos\theta - X \qquad ...(3)$$

and $$Ma\frac{d^2\theta}{dt^2} = Mg\sin\theta - Y \qquad ...(4)$$

where X, Y are the components of the reaction and perp. to GO.

Solving equation (3), we get

$$X = Mg\cos\theta - Ma\frac{4g}{3a}(1-\cos\theta)$$

$$\Rightarrow \quad X = \frac{Mg}{3}(7\cos\theta - 4)$$

$$= \frac{1}{3}W(7\cos\theta - 4) \qquad ...(5)$$

Similarly, solving equations (1) and (4), w get

$$Y = Mg\sin\theta - Ma\frac{2g}{3a}\sin\theta$$

$$= \frac{Mg}{3}\sin\theta = \frac{1}{3}W\sin\theta \qquad ...(6)$$

Example 33:

A circular disc of weight W can turn freely about a horizontal axis perp. to its plane which passes through a point O on its circumference. If it starts from rest with the diameter vertically above O, show that the resultant pressure on the axis when that diameter is horizontal and vertically below O are respectively $\frac{1}{3}\sqrt{(17)}\,W$ *and* $\frac{11}{3}W$*, further prove that the axis must be able to bear at least* $\frac{11}{3}$ *times the weight of the disc.*

Solution:

When the diameter is horizontal, viz $q = \frac{\pi}{2}$, *we have*

$$X = \frac{W}{3}(0-4) = -\frac{4W}{3},\ Y = \frac{W}{3} \qquad \left(\because \sin\frac{\pi}{2} = 1\right)$$

Hence resultant pressure in this case = $\sqrt{\left(\frac{16}{9}W^2 + \frac{W^2}{9}\right)} = \frac{W}{3}\sqrt{(17)}$

When the diameter is vertically below.

$$q = p, \therefore X = \frac{W}{3}(-7-4)$$

$$= -\frac{11W}{3}, Y = \frac{1}{3}W\sin\pi = 0$$

Resultant pressure in this case = $\left\{\left(\frac{11W}{3}\right)^2 + 0\right\}^{1/2} = \frac{11}{3}W.$

in general, we have

$$\sqrt{(X^2+Y^2)} = \left[\left\{\frac{W}{3}(7\cos\theta - 4)\right\}^2 + \left\{\frac{W}{3}\sin\theta\right\}^2\right]^{1/2}$$

$$= \left\{\frac{W^2}{9}(48\cos^2\theta - 56\cos\theta + 17\right\}^{1/2}$$

This is maximum when $\theta = \pi$ and its value is $\frac{11}{3}W$, which implies that the maximum pressure, that the axis must be able to bear is at least $\frac{11}{3}$ times the weight of the disc.

Example 34:

A right cone of angle 2a can turn freely about an axis passing through the centre of its base and perpendicular to the axis; if the cone starts from rest with its axis horizontal, show that the when axis is vertical, the thrust on the fixed axis is to the weight of the cone as $1 + \frac{1}{2}\cos^2\alpha : 1 - \frac{1}{3}\cos^2\alpha$.

Solution:

After any time t, let the cone take the position. If the height of the cone *i.e.* OV = h then OG = $\frac{1}{4}$h where G denotes the centre of gravity of the cone. Now since the C.G. of the cone *i.e.* point G is describing a circle or radius h/4, the equations of motion of G are

$$M \cdot \frac{1}{4}h\dot{\theta}^2 = X - Mg\sin\theta \quad ...(1)$$

$$M \cdot \frac{1}{4}h\ddot{\theta} = Mg\cos\theta - Y \quad ...(2)$$

where X and Y denote the components of reaction at O along and perp. to OX. Taking moments about O, we have

$$Mk^2\ddot{\theta} = Mg\frac{1}{4}h\cos\theta \quad ...(3)$$

Also Mk^2 = M.I. of the cone about AB $= M\cdot\frac{1}{20}(2h^2 + 3h^2 + \tan^2\alpha)$

$$\Rightarrow \quad k^2 = \frac{h^2}{20}(2+3\tan^2\alpha) \quad ...(4)$$

Substituting this value of k^2 in (3), we get

$$h\ddot{\theta} = \frac{5}{2+3\tan^2\alpha}g\cos\theta$$

Multiplying both sides by $2\dot{\theta}$ and integrating, we get

$$h\dot{\theta}^2 = \frac{10g}{2+3\tan^2\alpha}\sin\theta + C$$

Initially $\dot{\theta} = 0$, when $\theta = 0$, giving there by the constant $C = 0$.

Therefore, we have $h\dot{\theta}^2 = \dfrac{10g}{2+3\tan^2\alpha}\sin\theta$ ...(6)

Using (6) in (1), we get

$$M\cdot\frac{1}{4}\frac{10g}{2+3\tan^2\alpha}\sin\theta = X - Mg\sin\theta$$

$$\Rightarrow \quad X = Mg\sin\theta\left(\frac{9+6\tan^2\alpha}{4+6\tan^2\alpha}\right)$$

Also using (5) in (2), we get

$$Y = Mg\cos\theta\left[\frac{3+6\tan^2\alpha}{8+12\tan^2\alpha}\right]$$

When the axis is vertical *i.e.*, when $\theta = \pi/2$, we have

$$X = Mg\left(\frac{9+6\tan^2\alpha}{4+6\tan^2\alpha}\right), Y = 0$$

$$\therefore \quad \text{Resultant pressure} = \sqrt{(X^2+Y^2)} = X$$

$$= Mg\left(\frac{9+6\tan^2\alpha}{4+6\tan^2\alpha}\right)$$

$$= Mg\left(\frac{9\cos^2\alpha + 6\sin^2\alpha}{4\cos^2\alpha + 6\sin^2\alpha}\right)$$

$$\Rightarrow \qquad \frac{X}{Mg} = \frac{6 + 3\cos^2\alpha}{6 - 2\cos^2\alpha} = \frac{1 + \frac{1}{2}\cos^2\alpha}{1 - \frac{1}{3}\cos^2\alpha}$$

Note: If $2\alpha = \pi/2$ then in that case, we have

$$\frac{X}{Mg} = \frac{1 + \frac{1}{2}\cos^2(\pi/4)}{1 - \frac{1}{3}\cos^2(\pi/4)} = \frac{1 + \frac{1}{4}}{1 - \frac{1}{6}} = \frac{3}{2}.$$

Example 35:

A uniform semi-circular arc, of mass m and radius a, is fixed at its ends to two points in the same vertical line and is rotating with constant angular velocity ω. Show that the horizontal thrust on the upper end is $m\frac{g + \omega^2 a}{\pi}$.

Solution:

Let the uniform semi-circular arc with centre at O rotate about Ab with constant angular, then $OG = \frac{2a}{\pi}$. As the rotate, the point G will describe a circle of radius $\frac{2a}{\pi}$ about the point O.

Let X and Y be the horizontal an vertical components of reactions at the point and X′ and Y′ the horizontal and vertical reactions at the lower end B. Now since the arc is rotating with constant angular velocity w about AB, only effective force on it is $m\frac{2a}{\pi}\omega^2$ along GO.

Taking moments about the point B, we have

$$m\frac{2a}{\pi}\omega^2 a = -mg\frac{2a}{\pi} + X.2a$$

[∵ moment of the effective forces = moment of external forces]

$$\Rightarrow \qquad X = w\frac{(g + a\omega^2)}{\pi}.$$

Example 36:

A uniform rod OA of mass M and length 2a rests on a smooth table an is free to turn about a smooth pivot at its end O; in contact with it at distance b from O is an inelastic particle of mass m, a horizontal blow of impulse P, is given to the rod at a distance x from O in a direction perp. to the rod; find the resulting instantaneous angular velocity of the rod and the impulsive action at O and on the particle.

Solution:

Let OA be the rod of length 2a and let a horizontal blow of impulse P be given at a distance x from O. Further let S be the impulse of the action between the rod and inelastic particle of mass m. Then the moment equation about A is

$$M\frac{4}{3}a^2\omega = Px - Sb \qquad ...(1)$$

But $S = mb\,\omega$, (since velocity bw is generated in mass m by the impulse S).

$$\therefore \quad M\frac{4}{3}a^2\omega = Px - Mb^2\omega$$

$$\Rightarrow \quad \omega = \frac{Px}{\frac{4}{3}Ma^2 + Mb^2}$$

and $$S = \frac{mPbx}{\frac{4}{3}Ma^2 + mb^2}.$$

Now since the change in the motion of C.G. of the rod is the same as if all the impulsive forces were applied there, so $Ma\omega = P - S - X$, where X is the impulsive action at O.

$$\therefore \quad X = P - (Ma + mb)\,\omega$$

$$= P[1 - (mb + Ma)x] \Big/ \left(M\frac{4}{3}a^2 + mb^2\right).$$

Example 37:

A rod, of mass m and length 2a, which is capable of free motion about one and A falls from a vertical position and when it is horizontal strikes a fixed inelastic obstacle at a distance b from the end A. Show that the impulse of the blow is $m\frac{2}{b}\sqrt{(2ga/3)}$ *and that the impulse of the reaction at A is* $m\sqrt{(3ga/2}\left[1 - \frac{4a}{3b}\right]$ *vertically upwards.*

Solution:

If w is the angular velocity just before striking the obstacle then we have the energy equation as $\frac{1}{2}m\cdot\frac{4}{3}a^2\omega^2 - 0 = mga.$

[Change of K.E. = work done]. $\therefore \omega = \sqrt{(3g/2a)}$

Let the rod AB strike the inelastic obstacle at O such that AO = b and the impulse of the blow be P and the impulsive reaction at A be X.

Since the rod reduces to rest after striking the obstacle, therefore we get on taking moment about A

$$m\frac{4}{3}a^2(0-\omega) = -Pb$$

$$\Rightarrow \qquad P = \frac{4ma^2\omega}{3b} = \frac{2a}{b}m\cdot\sqrt{(2ga/3)}$$

Also for G, we have $m(0 - a\omega) = -P - X$

$$\Rightarrow \qquad X = m\sqrt{(3ga/2)}\left[1-\frac{4a}{3b}\right].$$

Example 38:

A uniform beam AB can turn about its end A is in equilibrium; find the point of its length where a blow must be applied to it so that the impulses at A may be in each case $\frac{1}{n}$ th of that of the blow.

Solution:

Let aB be the uniform rod of mass m and length 2a. Let an impulse P be applied at a distance x from A so as to produce an impulsive action $\frac{1}{n}P$ at A. If the angular velocity produced is w, then the equations of motion are

$$mk^2\omega = Px \Rightarrow m\frac{4}{3}a^3\omega = PX \qquad ...(1)$$

and

$$ma\omega = P + \frac{1}{n}p = \frac{n+1}{n}P \qquad ...(2)$$

Eliminating P from these two equations, we get $x = \frac{4}{3}\left(\frac{n+1}{n}\right)a$

Note. If the direction of the impulsive action is opposite to that as shown in Fig. then in that case we will have $x = \frac{4}{3}\left(\frac{n-1}{n}\right)a$.

Example 39:

A rod of mass nM is lying in a horizontal table and has one end fixed; a particle of mass M is in contact with it. The rod receives a horizontal blow at its free end; find the position of the particle so that it may start moving with the maximum velocity. In this case show that the kinetic energies communicated to the rod and mass are equal.

Solution:

Let AB be the rod, the end A of the which is fixed. Let an impulse P be applied to the rod at the end B so as to give an angular velocity ω, if the particle of mass M is at C where AC = x then the velocity V acquired by the particle will be V = xω. Thus we get the moment equation as

$$nM.\frac{4}{3}a^2\omega + Mx\omega.x = P.2a$$

$$\Rightarrow \qquad \omega = \frac{2aP}{M\frac{4}{3}(a^2n + x^2)}$$

$$\therefore \qquad V = x\omega = \frac{2aPx}{M\frac{4}{3}(na^2 + x^2)}$$

For maximum V, we must have $\frac{dV}{dx} = 0$

$$\Rightarrow \qquad \frac{2aP}{M}\left[\frac{\frac{4}{3}na^2 + x^2 - 2x^2}{\left(\frac{4}{3}na^2 + x^2\right)^2}\right] = 0$$

$$\Rightarrow \qquad \frac{4}{3}na^2 - x^2 = 0 \Rightarrow x = 2a\sqrt{(n/3)}$$

Also K.E. of the rod $= \frac{1}{2}nM \cdot \frac{4}{3}a^2\omega^2$

$$= \frac{2}{3}nMa^2\omega^2 \qquad ...(1)$$

and K.E. of the particle $= \frac{1}{2}Mx^2\omega^2 = \frac{1}{2}M\frac{4a^2n}{3}\omega^2$

$$= \frac{2}{3}Mna^2\omega^2. \qquad ...(2)$$

From (1) and (2), we observe that kinetic energies of the rod and mass are equal.

Example 40:

The door of a railway carriage stands upon at right angles to the length of the train when the latter starts to move with an acceleration f; the door being supposed to be smoothly hinged to the carriage and to be uniform and of *breadth 2a, show that its angular velocity when it has turned through an angle θ is $\sqrt{\left(\frac{3f}{2a}\sin\theta\right)}$.*

Solution:

Let ABCD be the door which an rotate about AB. If the train moves with acceleration f, then every element of the door will have the same acceleration f parallel to the rails. Now consider an elementary strip PQRS at a distance x from AB. Mass of the strip = $\frac{M}{2a}\delta x$, where M is the mass of the door. Hence moment equation about AB gives

$$M\frac{4}{3}a^2\ddot{\theta} = \int_0^{2a}\frac{m}{2a}dx\, f\cos\theta.x$$

$$= ma\, f\cos\theta$$

$$\Rightarrow \qquad \ddot{\theta} = \frac{3f}{4a}\cos\theta$$

Multiplying both sides by $2\dot{\theta}$ and integrating it, we get

$$\dot{\theta}^2 = \frac{3f}{2a}\sin\theta + \lambda$$

Initially $\dot{\theta} = 0$ when $\theta = 0$ $\qquad \therefore \lambda = 0$

Hence $\dot{\theta} = \sqrt{\left(\frac{3f}{2a}\sin\theta\right)}$.

Example 41:

Two wheels on spindles in fixed bearings suddenly engage so that their angular velocities become inversely proportional to their radii and in opposite directions. One wheel, of radius a and moment of inertia I_1 has angular velocity w initially, the other of radius b and moment of inertia I_2 is initially at rest. Show that their new angular velocities are

$$\frac{I_2b^2}{I_1b^2 + I_2a^2}\omega \text{ and } \frac{I_1ab\omega}{I_1b^2 + I_2a^2}.$$

Solution:

Let A and B be the two wheels. The wheel A is of radius a and moment of inertia I_1 whereas the wheel B is of radius b and moment of inertia I_2. Initially A was rotating with angular velocity ω and the wheel B was at rest. Now let ω_1

and ω_2 be the angular velocity of A and B after the impact. Since the velocity of the point of contact is the same for each wheel, we have

$$a\omega_1 = b\omega_2 \quad ...(1)$$

Also
$$I_1(\omega - \omega_1) = R \times a \text{ (for the wheel A)} \quad ...(2)$$

$$I_2(\omega - 0) = R \times b \text{ (for the wheel B)} \quad ...(3)$$

where R is the impulsive force.

From the last two equations, we get

$$I_1(\omega - \omega_1)\,b = I_2 a\omega_2 \quad ...(4)$$

Now substituting the value of ω_2 from (1) in (4), we get

$$\omega_1 = \frac{I_1 b^2}{I_1 b^2 + I_2 a^2}\,\omega$$

Substituting the value of ω_1 in (1), we have

$$\omega_2 = \frac{I_1 ab}{I_1 b^2 + I_2 a^2}\,\omega.$$

Example 42:

A pendulum is constructed of a solid sphere of mass M and radius a which is attached to the end of a rod of mass m and length b. Show that there will be no strain on the axis if the pendulum be struck at a distance

$$\left[M\left\{\frac{2}{5}a^2 + (a+b)^2\right\} + \frac{1}{3}mb^2\right] \div \left[M(a+b) + \frac{1}{2}mb\right] \text{ from the axis.}$$

Solution:

Let OA = b be the rod fixed at the point O. Let a sphere of radius a and mass M be attached to the other end A of the rod.

Distance of the C.G. of the pendulum from O

$$h = \frac{m(b/2) + M(b+a)}{m+M} \quad ...(1)$$

Let k be the radius of gyration of the pendulum about O, then we have

$$(m+M)\,k^2 = M\left[(b+a)^2 + \frac{2}{5}a^2\right] + \frac{4}{3}m\left(\frac{b}{2}\right)^2$$

$$\Rightarrow \quad k^2 = \frac{M}{m+M}\left[(b+a)^2 + \frac{2}{5}a^2\right] + \frac{4m}{3(m+M)}\left(\frac{k}{2}\right)^2$$

$\therefore$ Distance of centre of percussion from O $= \dfrac{k^2}{h}$

$$= \frac{M\left[\frac{2}{5}a^2 + (a+b)^2\right] + \frac{1}{3}mb^2}{\frac{1}{2}mb + M(a+b)}$$

EXERCISES

1. Two bodies can move freely and independently under the action of gyration about the same horizontal axis, their masses are m, m′ and the distance of their centres of gravity from the axis are h and h′. If the lengths of their equivalent simple pendulum be l, l′, Prove that when fastened together the length of the equivalent simple pendulum will be

$$\frac{mhl + m'h'l}{mh + m'h'}.$$

2. Find the length of the equivalent cases, the axis being horizontal:

   (i) Circular disc; axis a tangent to it.

   (ii) Hemisphere; axis a diameter of the base.

   (a) A diagonal of one face, (b) an edge.

3. A uniform string of length 20 feet and mass 40 lbs. hangs in equal length over a circular pulley, of mass 10 lbs, and small radius, the axis of the pulley being horizontal, masses of 40 and 34 lbs. are attached to the ends of the string and motion takes place. Show that the time taken by the smaller mass to reach the pulley is $\frac{1}{4}\sqrt{(15)}\ \log_e(9 + 4\sqrt{5})$ seconds.

4. A uniform wire, in the form of an arc of a circle of given radius; is swinging about a horizontal axis through the middle point of the arc perpendicular to the plane of the arc. Show that the time of a small oscillation is independent of the length of the arc, and length of an equivalent simple pendulum is equal to the diameter of the circle.

5. Find the length of the simple equivalent pendulum for an elliptic lamina when the axis is a latus rectum..

5

HAMILTONIAN FORMULATION AND VARIATIONAL PRINCIPLES

HAMILTON'S FORM OF THE EQUATIONS OF MOTION

Here we shall obtain the differential equations of motion of a conservative holonomic dynamical system in a form which constitutes the basis of most of the advanced theory of dynamics. Let $(q_1, q_2, \ldots\ldots, q_n)$ be the generalised co-ordinates and let $L(q_1, q_2, \ldots q_n; \dot{q}_1, \dot{q}_2, \ldots \dot{q}_n; t)$, the kinetic potential of the system, so that the equations of motion in the Lagrangian form are

$$\frac{d}{dt}(\partial L/\partial \dot{q}_i) - (\partial L/\partial q_i) = 0; (i = 1, 2, \ldots, n) \qquad \ldots(1)$$

writing $p_i = (\partial L/\partial \dot{q}_i)$ we get $\dot{p}_i = (\partial L/\partial q_i)$ $(i = 1, 2, \ldots, n)$ ...(2)

hence from the former of these sets of equations we can regard either of the sets of quantities $(q_1, q_2, \ldots a_n)$ or $(p_1, p_2, \ldots, p_n)$ as functions of the other set.

Now, let δ denote the increment in any function of the variables $(q_1, q_2, \ldots, q_n; p_1, p_2, \ldots, p_n)$ or $(\dot{q}_1, q_2, \ldots, q_n; \dot{q}_1, \dot{q}_2, \ldots, \dot{q}_n)$; then we get

$$dL = \sum_{i=1}^{n}\left(\frac{\partial L}{\partial q_i}dq_i + \frac{\partial L}{\partial \dot{q}_i}d\dot{q}_i\right) + \frac{\partial L}{\partial t}\text{(when L contains t explicitly)}$$

$$dL = \sum_{i=1}^{n}\left((\dot{p}_i dq_i + \dot{d}q_i)\frac{\partial L}{\partial t}\right)dt$$

$$= d\left(\sum_{i=1}^{n} p_i\dot{q}_i\right) + \sum_{i=1}^{n}(\dot{q}_i dq_i - p_i dp_i) + \frac{\partial L}{\partial t}dt$$

$$\Rightarrow d\left[\sum_{i=1}^{n}(p_i\dot{q}_i) - L\right] = \sum_{i=1}^{n}(\dot{q}_i dp_i - p_i dq_i) - (\partial L/\partial t)dt.$$

Thus if the quantity $\sum_{i=1}^{n}(p_i\dot{q}_i = L)$ when expressed in terms of $(q_1, q_2 \ldots q_n; p_1, p_2, \ldots, p_n; t)$ be denoted by H, we have

$$dH = \sum_{i=1}^{n} (q_i dp_i - \dot{p}_i dq_i) - \frac{\partial L}{\partial t} dt$$

$$\Rightarrow \sum_{i=1}^{n} \frac{\partial H}{\partial q_i} dq_i + \sum_{i=1}^{n} \frac{\partial H}{\partial p_i} dp_i + \frac{\partial H}{\partial t} dt = \sum_{i=1}^{n} (\dot{q}_i dp_i - \dot{p}_i dq_i) - \frac{\partial L}{\partial t} dt$$

$$\Rightarrow \dot{p}t = -\frac{\partial H}{\partial pi}, \ddot{p}i = -\frac{\partial H}{\partial qi}, \frac{\partial H}{\partial t} = -\frac{\partial L}{\partial t}$$

If H does not contain t explicity (*i.e.* does not contain t explicity) we have $\dot{p}i = -(\partial H/\partial qi)$ and $\dot{q}i = (\partial H/\partial pi)$. ...(4)

These equations are called as Hamilton's equations, or Hamilton's canonical equations and the function H is called Hamiltonian.

The total order of Hamilton's equations is the same as the total order of Lagrange's equations, namely 2n. But whereas Lagrange's equations present us with n equations each of the second order. Hamilton's equation are 2n equations, each of the first order. Hamilton's equations can also be written as

$$\frac{dpi}{-(\partial H/\partial qi)} = \frac{dqi}{(\partial H/\partial pi)} = dt.$$

VARIATIONAL METHODS

Techniques of Calculus of Variations

The calculus of variations arose out of the quest for the mathematical requirements in the solution of problems like the study of:

(i) The path followed by a body falling freely under gravity, (brachistochrone) first studied by Newton,

(ii) The equilibrium shape of a freely hanging homogeneous flexible cord between two horizontal points (catenary), first studied by Bernoulli. Presently the technique of calculus of variations, serves as a mathematical preliminary (in the form of Euler-Lagrange's equation) in the study of a wide range of physical problems such a geodesics and minimal surface in Riemannian and differential geometrics and the various *variational (minimal)* principles in the different branches of physics, The technique is co-ordinates invariant and there in lies its great power. First we develop here this technique in a purely mathematical form.

Suppose A and B are fixed points (x_1, y_1), (x_2, y_2) in a cartesian plane.

Also suppose that (x, y, y') is known functional form of the variables x, y, y' {= dy/dx)}. Then if C is a curve joining A and B and having equation y = y (x), Then the integral

$$I=\int_{x_1}^{x_2} f[x,y,y']\,dx \qquad ...(1)$$

has a definite value whenever the function y (x) is prescribed. The value of I will change as we vary the from of the curve C through A, B. Consequently we may consider that in general there will be some curve

C through these fixed points such that the value of I *taken along it is stationary (in general a* maximum or minimum) compared with the value along neighbouring paths C. Calculus of variations, the branch of mathematics of concerned amongst other things with finding the form of y (x) from which this stationary property holds. Let the path $\overline{C}$ have the equation $y = \overline{y}$ (x) and let the equation of a neighbouring curve C by $y = \overline{y}(x) + \varepsilon\eta(x)$, and $\overline{P}X = \overline{y}(x) \Rightarrow P\overline{P} = \varepsilon\eta(x)$.

Hence the values of I taken along is thus a function of ε of the form

$$I(\varepsilon) = \int_{x_1}^{x_2} f[x,\overline{y}+\varepsilon\eta,\overline{y}'+\varepsilon\eta']\,dx = \int_{x_1}^{x_2} f[x,y,y']\,dx \qquad ...(2)$$

where $y=\overline{y}+\varepsilon\eta$ and $y'=\overline{y'}+\varepsilon\eta'$

But the curve $\overline{C}$, for which ε = 0, makes I stationary, so we must have I′ stationary, so we must have I′ (0) = 0. Now differentiating (2) w.r.t. ε, we get

$$I'(\varepsilon) = \int_{x_1}^{x_2}\left[\frac{\partial f}{\partial x}\frac{\partial x}{\partial \varepsilon}+\frac{\partial f}{\partial y}\frac{\partial y}{\partial \varepsilon}+\frac{\partial f}{\partial y'}\frac{\partial y'}{\partial \varepsilon}\right]dx \qquad [\because f=f[x,y,y']] \quad ...(3)$$

$$\Rightarrow I'(\varepsilon) = \int_{x_1}^{x_2}\left[\frac{\partial f}{\partial y}\eta(x)+\frac{\partial f}{\partial y'}\eta'(x)\right]dx \qquad [\because y=\overline{y}+\varepsilon\eta(x)]$$

$$=\int_{x_1}^{x_2}[\eta f_y.\eta(x)+f_{y'}.\eta'(x)]\,dx$$

$$I'(\varepsilon) = \int_{x_1}^{x_2}[\eta f_y(x,\overline{y}+\varepsilon\eta,\overline{y'}+\varepsilon\eta')] + \eta' f_{y'}(x,\overline{y}+\varepsilon\eta,\overline{y}+\varepsilon\eta')]dx \qquad ...(4)$$

where $f_{y'}(x,\overline{y}+\varepsilon\eta,\overline{y}+\varepsilon\eta')]dx$

$$=(\partial/\partial y)\, f\,(x,y,y') \text{ when } y=\overline{y}+\varepsilon\eta,\ y'=\overline{y'}+\varepsilon\eta,$$

with a similar meaning for $f_{y'}(x,\overline{y}+\varepsilon\eta,\overline{y'}+\varepsilon\eta')$. Hence the stationary condition give I′ (0) = 0.

$$\Rightarrow \int_{x_1}^{x_2} [\eta f_{y'}(x,\bar{y},\bar{y}') + \eta' f_{y'}(x,\bar{y},\bar{y}')\, dx = 0 \qquad ...(5)$$

Now $\int_{x_1}^{x_2} \eta' f_{y'}(x,\bar{y},\bar{y}')\, dx$

$$= \left[\eta f_{y'}(x,\bar{y},\bar{y}')\right]_{x_1}^{x_2} - \int_{x_1}^{x_2} n \frac{d}{dx} f_{y'}(x,\bar{y},\bar{y}')\, dx$$

$$= -\int_{x_1}^{x_2} n \frac{d}{dx} f_{y'}(x,\bar{y},\bar{y}')\, dx \;(\because \eta(x_1) = \eta(x_2) = 0) \qquad ...(6)$$

Using (6), equation (5) implies

$$\int_{x_1}^{x_2} \eta(x)\left[f_y(x,\bar{y},\bar{y}') - \frac{d}{dx} f_{y'}(x,\bar{y},\bar{y}')\right] dx = 0 \qquad ...(7)$$

But η (x) is arbitrary, subject to its being differentiable and vanishing at A, B; (7) implies that

$$f_y(x,\bar{y},\bar{y}') - (d/dx)\, f_{y'}(x,\bar{y},\bar{y}') = 0 \qquad ...(8)$$

or $$(\partial f/\partial y) - (d/dx)(\partial f/\partial y') = 0. \qquad ...(9)$$

This is called *Euler's Lagrange's equation.* Equation (9) can be proved from (7) by using the following lemma.

Lemma: If x_1 and x_2 ($>x_1$) *are fixed constants and* ϕ *(x) is a particular continuous function for* $x_1 \le \phi \le x_2$ and if

$$\int_{x_1}^{x_2} \eta(x)\phi(x)\, dx = 0 \qquad ...(10)$$

for every choice of continuously dijjerentiable function h(x) for which $\eta(x_1) = \eta(x_2) = 0$ *then* $f(x) = 0$ *indentically in* $x_1 \le x \le x_2$.

Proof:

Let the lemma be not true for all x in $x_1 \le x \le x_2$. Let x′ be a point where ϕ (x′) $\neq 0$ and > 0. But ϕ (x) is continuous in $x_1 \le x \le x_2$ and in particular is continuous at x = x′. Hence there exist an interval $x'_1 \le x \le x'_0$ around x′ where ϕ (x) > 0. For the other x's ϕ (x) any both vanish; then the equation $\int_{x_1}^{x_2} \eta(x)\phi(x)dx = 0$ could be written as $\int_{x_1}^{x_2'} \eta(x)\phi(x)dx = 0$.

But $\eta(x)$ is at our disposal; we could choose it as greater than zero for $x_1' \le x \le x_2'$ and $\eta(x) = 0$ for other values of x. Thus $\eta(x)\ \phi\ (x) > 0$ for $x_1' \le x \le x_2'$; consequently integrand cannot be zero. Thus we arrive at the contradiction. Hence $\phi(x) = 0$ in $x_1 \le x \le x_2$.

Certain Remarks About Euler-Lagrange's Equation

(A) We have $(\partial f/\partial y) - (d/dx)(\partial f/\partial y') = 0$

where $f = f\,(x, y, y')$

which can be re-written as

$(\partial f/\partial y) - (dp/dx) = 0$ where $p = (\partial f/\partial y')$ ...(11)

But $\left(\dfrac{dp}{dx}\right) = \left(\dfrac{\partial p}{\partial x}\right) + \left(\dfrac{\partial p}{\partial y}\right)\left(\dfrac{dy}{dx}\right) + \left(\dfrac{\partial p}{\partial y'}\right)\left(\dfrac{dy'}{dx}\right) = \left(\dfrac{\partial^2 f}{\partial x \partial y'}\right) +$

$(\partial^2 f/\partial y \partial y')(dy/dx) + (\partial^2 f/\partial y'^2)(d^2y/dx^2)$. Hence (9) give

$(\partial f/\partial y) - [(\partial/\partial x)(\partial f/\partial y') + (\partial/\partial y)((\partial f/\partial y')(dy/dx)$

$+\ (\partial^2 f/\partial y'^2)(d^2y/dx^2)] = 0$

or $(\partial^2 f/\partial y'^2)(d^2y/dx^2) + (\partial^2 f/\partial y \partial y')(dy/dx) - (\partial f/\partial y) + (\partial^2 f/\partial x\, \partial y') = 0$

...(12)

This is a second order differential equation for determining y as a function of x. The solution will contain two arbitrary constants which could be determined from the conditions:

$y = y_1$ at $x = x_1$ and $y = y_2$ at $x = x_2$ ...(13)

(B) Consider $\dfrac{d}{dx}\left[f - y'\dfrac{\partial f}{\partial y'}\right] = \dfrac{\partial f}{\partial y'}$

i.e. $\dfrac{dQ}{dx} = \dfrac{\partial f}{\partial x}$ which $Q = f - y'\ \dfrac{\partial f}{\partial y'}$ and f is a function of x, y, y¢

$$\Rightarrow \frac{\partial f}{\partial x}\left[f - y'\frac{\partial f}{\partial y'}\right] + \frac{\partial}{\partial y}\left[f - y'\frac{\partial f}{dy'}\right]\frac{dy}{dx} + \frac{\partial}{\partial y'}\left[f - y'\frac{\partial f}{\partial y'}\right]\frac{d^2y}{dx^2} = \frac{\partial f}{\partial x}$$

$$\Rightarrow -y'\frac{\partial^2 f}{\partial x \partial y'} + \frac{\partial f}{\partial y}\frac{dy}{dx} - y'\frac{\partial^2 f}{\partial y \partial y'}\frac{dy}{dx} + \frac{\partial f}{\partial y'}\frac{d^2y}{dx^2}\frac{\partial f}{\partial y'}\frac{\partial^2 y}{\partial x^2} - y'\frac{\partial^2 f}{\partial y'^2}\frac{d^2y}{dx^2} = 0$$

$$\Rightarrow y'\left[\frac{\partial f}{\partial y} - \frac{\partial^2 f}{\partial x \partial y'} - y'\frac{\partial^2 y}{\partial y \partial y'} - y''\frac{\partial^2 f}{\partial y'^2}\right] = 0$$

$\Rightarrow f_y - f_{xy'} - y' fyy' - y'' f_{yy'} = 0$ (if $y' \neq 0$) ...(15)

which is same as (12) and shows that if Euler's equation is satisfied equation (14) is also satisfied but if (14) is satisfied, Euler's equation may not be true.

(C) If f does not contain x explicity, i.e. $I = \int_{x_1}^{x_2} f(y, y')dx$,

then from (14), we have

$(d/dx)\{f - y'(\partial f/\partial y')\} = 0$ $\{\because (df/x) = 0\}$

$\Rightarrow f - y'(\partial f/\partial y') = \text{constant} = C$ (say.) ...(16)

Obviously (14) is a first order differential equation.

(D) If f does not contain y explicity, then we have $I = \int_{x_1}^{x_2} f(x, y')dx$.

$\therefore$ from the equation

$(\partial f/\partial y) - (d/dx)(\partial f/\partial y') = 0$ we obtain $(d/dx)(\partial f/\partial y') = 0$

$\Rightarrow (\partial f/\partial y') = C$ (say). ...(17)

(E) If we assume that the end points are not fixed.

i.e. $\eta(x_1) \neq 0$ and $\eta(x_2) \neq 0$.

Euler's equation still holds in this case, if $(\partial f/\partial y') = 0$ when $x = x_1$, x_2 This becomes the boundary condition of the problem.

(F) Euler's equation gives only a necessary condition; even if it is satisfied, there may be no extremum.

(G) The conditions to be imposed on f are such that its partial derivative are continuous and differentiable.

(H) The conditions to be imposed on the curves are that they should be continuous curves.

Brachistochrone Problem

Given two points A and B in a vertical plane, to find for the moveable particle M, the path A MB, descending along which by its own gravity and beginning to be urged from the point A, it may in the shortest time reach the point B. It is a tacit in the statement that the particle descends without friction.

Let A be the origin, then velocity of the particle of mass M at any time t is given by

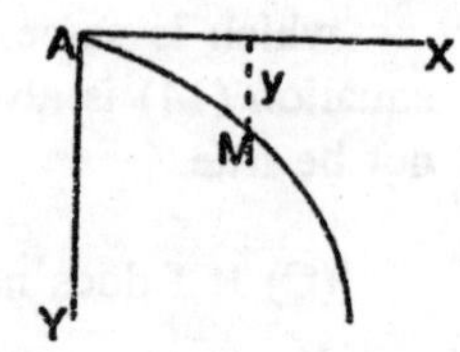

Fig. 5.1

$$v = (ds/dt) = \sqrt{(2gy)}$$

$$\Rightarrow dt = (ds/\sqrt{2gy})$$

$$\Rightarrow t = \int_A^B \frac{ds}{\sqrt{(2gy)}} = \int_A^B \frac{\sqrt{(1+y'^2}}{\sqrt{(2gy)}} dx$$

$$\frac{1}{\sqrt{(2g)}} \int_A^B \frac{\sqrt{1+y'^2}}{\sqrt{2}} dx = \frac{1}{\sqrt{(2g)}} \int_A^B f(y, y')dx,$$

where $f(y, y') = \dfrac{\sqrt{(1+y'^2)}}{\sqrt{y}}$

As x is absent in f, so we have $f - y'(\partial f/\partial y') A$

$$\Rightarrow \frac{\sqrt{(1+y'^2)}}{\sqrt{y}} - y' \frac{y'}{\sqrt{\{y(1+y'^2\}}} = A$$

$$\Rightarrow \frac{1}{\sqrt{\{y(1+y'^2)\}}} = \text{constant} \Rightarrow y(1+y'^2) = \text{constant} = 2c, \text{ (say)}$$

But $\quad (dy/dx) = \tan\psi \Rightarrow y' = \tan\psi$

$$\therefore y \sec^2\psi = 2c \text{ or } y = 2c\cos^2\psi = c(1+\cos^2\psi)$$

Also $\quad dx = \cot\psi\, dy = -2c \sin 2\psi \cot\psi\, d\psi$
$= -4c \cos^2\psi\, d\psi = -2c\,(1 + \cos^2\psi)\, d\psi$

$$\Rightarrow x = a - 2c\left(\psi + \frac{\sin^2\psi}{2}\right) = a - 2c(\psi + \sin\psi\cos\psi)$$

Hence the required path is

$x = a - c\,(2\psi + \sin 2\psi)$, $y = c\,(1 + \cos^2\psi)$ (cycloid)

Extension of the Variational Method

Suppose the n-co-ordinates $q_1, q_2, \ldots q_n$ are each functions of an independent variable t and that we required the solution of the variational problem

$$I = \int_{t_1}^{t_2} f(q_1, q_2, \ldots, q_n; \dot{q}_1\, \dot{q}_2, \ldots, \dot{q}_n; t)dt$$

$$= \int_{t_1}^{t_2} f(q, \dot{q}, t)\; dt = \text{stationary value}$$

where f is of known functional from, t_1 and t_2 are fixed and each q_i is to be determined.

Let $q_i = q_i(t)$ give the stationary value to I and let $q_i = q_i(t) + \varepsilon_i \eta_i(t)$ be the neighbouring path.

$$\Rightarrow I(\varepsilon_1, \varepsilon_2, ..., \varepsilon_n) = \int_{t_1}^{t_2} f\{q_i(t) + \varepsilon_i \eta_i(t); \dot{q}_i(t) + \varepsilon_i \dot{\eta}_i(t), t\}\, dt$$

$$= \int_{t_1}^{t_2} f(q_i \dot{q}_i; t) dt + \Sigma\varepsilon_i \int_{t_1}^{t_2} \left\{ \dot{\eta}_i(t) \frac{\partial f}{\partial \dot{q}_i} + \dot{\eta}_i(t) \frac{\partial f}{\partial \dot{q}_i} \right\} dt + o(\varepsilon_i^2)$$

First variation $\delta I = \Sigma\varepsilon_i \int_{t_1}^{t_2} \left\{ \dot{\eta}_i(t) \frac{\partial f}{\partial \dot{q}_i} + \dot{\eta}_i(t) \frac{\partial f}{\partial \dot{q}_i} \right\} dt$

$$= \Sigma\varepsilon_i\, \dot{\eta}_i(t) \frac{\partial f}{\partial \dot{q}_i} dt + \Sigma\varepsilon_i \int_{t_1}^{t_2} \dot{\eta}_i(t) \frac{\partial f}{\partial \dot{q}_i} dt$$

$$= \Sigma\varepsilon_i \int_{t_1}^{t_2} \dot{\eta}_i(t) \frac{\partial f}{\partial q_i} dt + \Sigma e_i \left[\left\{ n_i(t) \frac{\partial f}{\partial \dot{q}_i} \right\}_{t_1}^{t_2} - \int_{t_1}^{t_2} \dot{\eta}_i(t) \frac{d}{dt}\left(\frac{\partial f}{\partial \dot{q}_i} \right) dt \right]$$

$$= \Sigma\varepsilon_i \int_{t_1}^{t_2} \dot{\eta}_i(t)_i \left[\frac{\partial f}{\partial q_i} - \frac{d}{dt}\left(\frac{\partial f}{\partial \dot{q}_i} \right) \right] \qquad \{\because 0 = \eta_i(t_1) = \eta_i(t_2)\}.$$

As η_i's are arbitrary and I is stationary, so we have

$$(\partial f / \partial q_i) - (d/dt)(\partial f / \partial \dot{q}_i) \qquad (i = 1, 2, ..., n)$$

Hamilton's Variational Principle ***(Proof Based on Calculus of Variation)***

Variational (minimal) principles has been the greatest fascination of old generation physicists and in this pursuit several and varied variational principles have been put forth in the various branches of physics, such as, in optics, the Fermat's principles of *'lest time'*, in mechanics, the Gauss's principles of *'least consiraint'*, the Hertz's principle of *'lest curvature'* and most important of all the Hamilton's *variational principle'* which will be our main centre of attraction here in mechanics. The great value of these variational principles; lies in their extreme economy of expression.

Let T, V be the kinetic and potential energies of a. Conservative holonomic dynamical system defined by n generalised co-ordinates $q_1, q_2, ..., q_n$ at time t, writing L = T – V, we know that Lagrange's equations for the motion of the system are:

$$(\partial L / \partial q_i') - (d/dt)(\partial L / \partial \dot{q}_i) \qquad (i = 1, 2, ...,n)$$

Now applying previous article we can say that these are the n Euler-Lagrange's equation arising from the variational problem.

$$\int_{t_1}^{t_1} L(q_1, q_2, ..., q_n; \dot{q}_1, \dot{q}_2, ..., \dot{q}_n; t)\ dt = \text{stationary (i.e. stat)}$$

where t_1, t_2 are fixed. Thus we have established that

During the motion of a 'conservative holonomic dynamical system over a fixed time interval, the time integral over that interval of the difference between the kinetic and potential energies is stationary. This is Hamilton's principle.

Derivation of Hamilton Equations from the Variational Principle

Hamilton's principle implies

$$\delta I = \delta \int_{t_1}^{t_2} L dt = 0 \text{ or } \delta\ \delta \int_{t_1}^{t_2} [\Sigma_i p_i \dot{q}_1 - H(q, p, t)]\ dt = 0$$

$$[\because L = \Sigma_i p_i \dot{q}_i - H(q, p, t)]$$

This implies $\delta \Sigma_i \int_{q_1}^{q_2} p_1 d\ q_1 - \delta \int_{t_1}^{t_2} H\ dt = 0.$ ...(1)

Equation (1) is called the modified Hamilton's principle.

Now $\delta I = \frac{\partial I}{\partial \alpha} d\alpha = d\alpha \frac{\partial}{\partial \alpha} \int_{t_1}^{t_2} (\Sigma_i p_i \dot{q}_i - H(q, p, t) dt = 0$

where $\delta = d\alpha(\partial / \partial_\alpha)$

$$\Rightarrow d\alpha \int_{t_1}^{t_2} \frac{\partial}{\partial \alpha} [\Sigma p_i, \dot{q}_i - H(q, p, t) dt = 0$$

[$\because$ the times t_1, t_2 are not varied not so they are not functions of α, thus the differentiation can be interchanged].

$$\Rightarrow d\alpha \int_{t_1}^{t_2} \Sigma_i \left[\frac{\partial p_i}{\partial \alpha} \dot{q}_i + \frac{\partial \dot{q}_i}{\partial \alpha_i} p_i - \frac{\partial H}{\partial q_i} \frac{\partial q_i}{\partial \alpha} - \frac{\partial H}{\partial p_i} \frac{\partial p_i}{\partial \alpha} \right] dt = 0 \quad ...(2)$$

Further, we have $\int_{t_1}^{t_2} \frac{\partial \dot{q}_i}{\partial \alpha} p_i dt = \int_{t_1}^{t_2} p_i \frac{d}{dt} \left(\frac{\partial q_i}{\partial \alpha} \right) dt = p_i \left[\frac{\partial p_i}{\partial \alpha} \right]_{t_1}^{t_2} - \int_{t_1}^{t_2} \dot{p}_i \frac{\partial q_i}{\partial \alpha} dt.$

But all the varied paths have the same end points. Hence $\frac{\partial \dot{q}_i}{\partial \alpha}$ vanishes

for t_1 and t_2. $\Rightarrow \int_{t_1}^{t_2} \frac{\partial q_i}{\partial \alpha} p_i dt = - \int_{t_1}^{t_2} \dot{p}_i \frac{\partial q_i}{\partial \alpha} dt = \int_{t_2}^{t_1} p_i \frac{\partial q_i}{\partial \alpha} dt.$

Making this substitution in equations (2), we have

$$d\alpha\int_{t_1}^{t_2}\Sigma\left[\frac{\partial q_i}{\partial\alpha}\dot{q}_i-\frac{\partial H}{\partial q_i}\frac{\partial q_i}{\partial\alpha}-\frac{\partial H}{\partial p_i}\frac{\partial p_i}{\partial\alpha}-\frac{\partial q_i}{\partial\alpha}\right]dt=0 \qquad ...(2)$$

$$\Rightarrow\int_{t_1}^{t_2}\Sigma\dot{q}_i\frac{\partial\dot{q}_i}{\partial\alpha}q\alpha-\frac{\partial H}{\partial q_i}\frac{\partial q_i}{\partial\alpha}q\alpha-\frac{\partial H}{\partial p_i}\frac{\partial p_i}{\partial\alpha}d\alpha-p_i\frac{\partial q_i}{\partial\alpha}d\alpha\,dt=0 \qquad ...(3)$$

But $\delta p_i = d\alpha.(\partial p_i/\partial\alpha)$ and $\delta q_i = (\partial q_i/\partial\alpha)d\alpha$

$$\therefore (3)\Rightarrow\int_{t_1}^{t_2}\Sigma\left[\delta p_i\left(\dot{q}_i-\frac{\partial H}{\partial p_i}\right)+\delta q_i\left(\frac{\partial H}{\partial q_i}-\dot{p}_i\right)\right]dt=0.$$

The variation δq_i and δp_i are independent to each other, hence equation (4) holds good only when the coefficients of δp_i and δq_i vanish separately.

The (4) $\Rightarrow \dot{q}_i = (\partial H/\partial p_i), \dot{p}_i = -(\partial H/\partial q_i)$. These are Hamilton's equations.

Principal of Least Action

Principle of least action states that if T is kinetic energy, at time t, of a conservative, holonomic dynamical system specified by the generalised co-ordinates, then the integral $I=\int_{t_1}^{t_2}2T\,dt$

has necessary an extreme value, minimum or maximum, on actual path as compared with varied path as the systems passes from one configuration at time t_0 to another configuration at time t_r.

We know that L = T – V, *i.e.* Lagrangian = K.E. – P.E. and T + V = E (const), since system is conservative.

But by Hamilton's principle, we know that

$$\int_{t_0}^{t_1}\delta L\,dt=0\Rightarrow\int_{t_0}^{t_1}\delta(T-V)dt=0\int_{t_0}^{t_1}\delta(2T-E)dt=0$$

$$\Rightarrow\int_{t_0}^{t_2}\delta(2T)\,dt=0\Rightarrow\delta\int_{t_0}^{t_1}(2T)\,dt=0. \qquad ...(1)$$

[$\because$ $\delta E = 0$ as E, the total energy is const.]

Result (1), is known as *Principle of least action.*

Equation (1) can also be written as $\delta A = 0$, where $A=\int_{t_0}^{t_1}2T\,dt$ and is defined by action as follows:

This implies that principal of least action states that the action in the actual path is minimum compared with the varied path, as the system passes from one configuration to another.

Distinction Between Hamilton's Principle and Principle of Least Action

In Hamilton's principle, the time of description $t_1 - t_0$ is prescribed (fixed) as the body moves from one configuration to another configuration, while in the principle of least action there is no such restriction on the time $t_1 - t_0$ but the total energy between the end points A and B is prescribed.

Deduction of Largrange's Equation from Hamilton's Principle

By Hamilton's principle, we have $\int_{t_0}^{t_1} \delta L dt = 0$

$$\therefore (1) \Rightarrow \int_{t_0}^{t_1} \sum_{i=1}^{n} \left(\frac{L}{\partial q_i} \delta q_i + \frac{L}{\partial \dot{q}_i} \delta \dot{q}_i \right) dt = 0$$

$$\Rightarrow \int_{t_0}^{t_1} \sum_{i=1}^{n} \frac{\partial L}{\partial q_i} \delta q_i \, dt + \int_{t_0}^{t_1} \sum_{i=1}^{n} \frac{\partial L}{\partial \dot{q}_i} \frac{d}{dt} (\delta q_i) \, dt = 0$$

Now integrating by parts, we have

$$\int_{t_0}^{t_1} \sum_{i=1}^{n} \frac{\partial L}{\partial q_i} \delta q_i \, dt + \left\{ \sum_{i=1}^{n} \frac{\partial L}{\partial \dot{q}_i} \delta q_i \right\}_{t_0}^{t_1} - \int_{t_0} \left\{ \sum_{i=1}^{n} \frac{d}{dt} \left(\frac{\partial L}{\partial \dot{q}_i} \right) \delta q_i \right\} dt = 0$$

$$\Rightarrow \int_{t_0}^{t_1} \left[\sum_{i=1}^{n} \right] \left\{ \frac{d}{dt} \left(\frac{\partial L}{\partial \dot{q}_i} \right) - \frac{\partial L}{\partial q_i} \delta q_i \right\} dt = 0$$

[$\because$ middle term vanishes as all $\delta q_i = 0$ at t_0 and t_1]

$$\Rightarrow \sum_{i=1}^{n} \left\{ \frac{d}{dt} \left(\frac{\partial L}{\partial \dot{q}_i} \right) - \frac{\partial L}{\partial q_i} \right\} \delta q_i = 0.$$

Here δq_i's are arbitrary and independent to each other, so equating to zero their coefficients, we readily obtain

$$\frac{d}{dt} \left(\frac{\partial L}{\partial \dot{q}_i} \right) - \frac{\partial L}{\partial q_i} = 0$$

Deduction of Hamilton's Principle

(Proof based on D'Alembert's principle).

Assume that the conservative holonomic dynamical system moves from A to C, where A and C, are the initial and final configurations of the system at time t_1 and t_2 respectively. Let ABC be the actual path and AB'C. AB"C the two neighbouring paths out of infinite number of possibilities. *In order to deduce the principle, the following two conditions must be satisfied.*

1. δt must be equal to zero at A and B *i.e.* at t_1 the particle must be at A, at t_2 the particle must be at C.
2. δr must be equal to zero at A and C $\Rightarrow$ that the points A, and C are fixed in space.

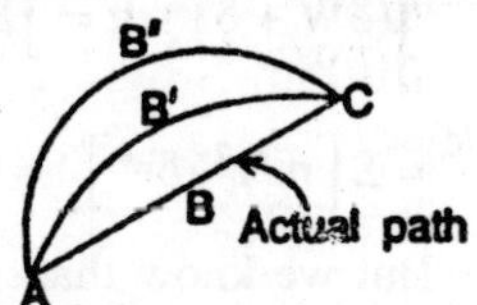

Fig. 5.2

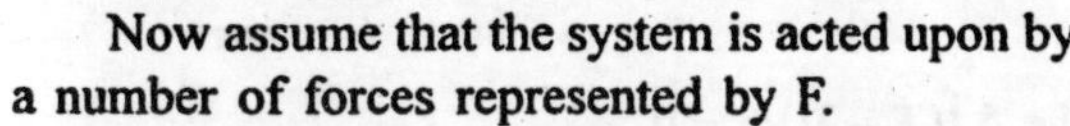
Now assume that the system is acted upon by a number of forces represented by F.

Let the ith particle of system be acted upon by a force $F_i = m_i \ddot{r}_i$ is acceleration vector.

Again by D'A Alembert's principle, we have

$$\sum_i (F_i - m\ddot{r}_i)\cdot\delta r_i = 0, \quad i.e. \quad \sum_i F_i \cdot \delta \dot{r}_i - \Sigma m_i \ddot{r}_i \cdot \delta r_i = 0 \qquad ...(1)$$

If there is a little variation along the actual and neighbouring paths, then

$$\delta r_i = r_i - r_i \quad \text{(say)}.$$

$$\Rightarrow (d/dt)(\delta r_i) = (d/dt)(r_i - r_i) = (dr_i'/dt) - (dr_i/dt)$$

$$= \delta\ (dr_i/dt) = \delta(d\dot{r}_i) \qquad ...(2)$$

where dashes have been used for neighbouring paths.

But $\ddot{r}_i \cdot \delta_i = (d/dt)\ddot{r}_i \cdot \delta r_i) - \dot{r}_i \cdot (d/dt)(\delta r_i)$. ...(3)

Using (2), (3) $\Rightarrow \ddot{r}_i \cdot \delta r_i = (d/dt)(\dot{r}_i \cdot \delta r_i) - \dot{r}_i \delta(\dot{r}_i)$ ...(4)

$$\therefore (1) \Rightarrow \sum_i F_i \cdot \delta r_i - \sum_i m_i\,[(d/dt)(r_i \cdot \delta r_i) - \dot{r}_i \cdot \delta \dot{r}_i] = 0$$

$$\text{or} \quad \sum_i F_i \cdot \delta r_i - \sum_i m_i\,[(d/dt)(r_i \cdot \delta r_i) - \frac{1}{2}\delta(\dot{r}_i^2 = 0$$

$$\text{or} \quad \sum_i F_i \cdot \delta r_i + \sum_i \frac{1}{2} m_i \delta(\dot{r}_i^2 = \sum_i (d/dt)(m_i \ddot{r}_i \cdot \delta r_i)$$

$$\text{or} \quad \sum_i F_i \cdot \delta r_i + \delta\left(\sum_i \frac{1}{2} m_i \dot{r}_i^2\right) = \sum_i (d/dt)(m_i r_i \cdot \delta r_i) \qquad ...(5)$$

But $\sum_i \frac{1}{2} m_i \dot{r}_i^2$ = kinetic energy of the system = T

and $\sum_i F_i \cdot \delta r_i$ = work done by the forces F_i during displacement δr_i δW (say).

$\therefore$ equation (5) $\Rightarrow \delta W + \delta T = \sum_i (d/dt)(m_i \dot{r}_i \cdot \delta r_i)$ ...(6)

Integrating (6) between the limits t_1 and t_2, we get

$$\int_{t_1}^{t_2}(\delta W+\delta T)\,dt=\int_{t_1}^{t_2}\sum_i \frac{d}{dt}(m_i\dot{r}_i\cdot\delta r_i)\,dt=\Sigma\int_{t_1}^{t_2}d\,(m_i\dot{r}_i\cdot\delta r_i)$$

$$=\Sigma\left[m^2 r_i^2\cdot\delta r^2\right]_A^C=0\ [\text{since } \delta r^2=0 \text{ at the end points A anc C.}$$

But we know that, for a conservative system, $\delta W = -\,\delta V$ where V is potential energy

$$\Rightarrow \int_{t_1}^{t_2}(-\,\delta V+\delta T)dt=0,\text{i.e. } \delta\int_{t_1}^{t_2}(T-V)dt=0$$

$$i.e.\quad \int_{t_1}^{t_2}(T-V)\,dt=0 \quad\text{or}\quad \delta\int_{t_1}^{t_2}L\,dt=0$$

or $\delta\int_{t_1}^{t_2}L\,dt$ = stat = extremum. This is Hamilton's principle.

Extension of Hamilton's Principle to Non-conservative and Non-holonomic System

We can generalise Hamilton's principle to include non-conservative forces as well, so that an alternative form of the Lagrange's equation can be obtained. The extension of the Hamilton's principle is

$$\delta I=\delta\int_1^2(T+W)\,dt=0 \qquad ...(1)$$

where $$W=\Sigma F_i\cdot r_i \qquad ...(2)$$

We know that the variations δq_i or δr_i are identical with virtual displacements of the co-ordinates as there is no variation of time. Thus we can consider the varied path in configuration space as built up by a succession of virtual displacements from the actual path of motion C.

Again each virtual displacements takes place at some definite time and at that time the forces acting on the body have definite values. δW represents the amount of work done by the forces on the system during the period of virtual displacement from the actual to the varied path. Thus the Hamilton's principle given by (1) can be said as *the integral of the variation of kinetic energy together with the amount of virtual work involved in the variation must be zero.*

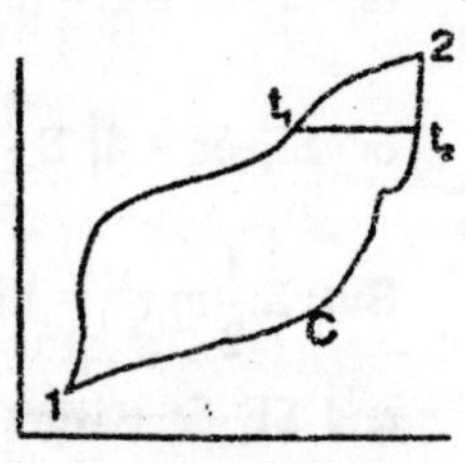

Fig. 5.3

We can evaluate the variations δr_i in terms of δq_i by making use of the equations of transformation between r and q, where each q depends on the path chosen through a parameter say α:

$$r_i = r\{q_k(\alpha,t)t\}$$

We can abbreviated the process by using the equivalence of δr_i with a virtual displacement. We know that

$$\sum_i F_i \cdot \delta r_i = \sum_k Q_k \delta q_k .$$

thus (1) may be put as $\delta \int_t^2 T\,dt + \int_1^2 \sum_k Q_k \delta q_k dt = 0.$ ...(3)

Now it can be shown easily that (3) reduces to ordinary from of Hamilton's principle, in case Q_k's are derivable form the generalised potential. Therefore the integral of virtual work, under these conditions becomes,

$$\int_t^2 \sum_k Q_k \delta q_k\, \delta q_k\, dt = -\int_1^2 \sum_k \delta q_k \left(\frac{\partial V}{\partial q_k} - \frac{d}{dt}\frac{\partial V}{\partial \dot{q}_k} \right) dt$$

Now reversing by integration-paths procedure; the above integral can be put as

$$-\int_t^2 \sum_k \left(\frac{\partial V}{\partial q_k}\delta q_k + \frac{\partial V}{\partial \dot{q}_k}\delta q_k \right) dt = -\delta \int_1^2 V\,dt$$

Thus (3) reduces to

$$\delta \int_1^2 T\,dt = \int_1^2 V\,dt = \delta \int_1^2 (T - V)\,dt\; \delta \int_1^2 L dt = 0,$$

which is Hamilton's principle.

For more general problem, the variation of the first integral in (3) can be written at once, as T like L for conservative systems is a function of q_k and $\dot{q}_k$

$$\therefore \delta \int_1^2 T\,dt = \int_1^2 \sum_b \left(\frac{\partial T}{\partial q_k} - \frac{d}{dt}\frac{\partial T}{\partial \dot{q}_k} \right) \delta q_k dt \qquad ...(4)$$

$$\Rightarrow \int_1^2 \sum_k \left(\frac{\partial T}{\partial q_k} - \frac{d}{dt}\frac{\partial T}{\partial \dot{q}_k} + Q_k \right) \delta q_k dt = 0 \qquad ...(5)$$

Further it is assumed that the constraints are holonomic, so the integral (5) can vanish if and only if the separate coefficients vanish, *i.e.*

$$\frac{d}{dt}\frac{\partial T}{\partial \dot{q}_k} - \frac{\partial T}{\partial q_k} = Q_k$$

so that (1) represents the proper extension of Hamilton's principle, which yields that from of Lagrange's equation, in case the forces are not derived from a potential.

We can also extend the Hamilton's principle to cover certain categories of non-holonomic systems as well. While deriving Lagrange's equations from Hamilton's or D'Alembert's principle, application of holonomic constraints is made only in last step when the variation q_k are considered as independent of each other.

While in non-holonomic system the generalized co-ordinates are not independent to each other so they cannot be reduced further by means of equations of constraints of the form

$f\,[q_1, q_2,...q_n;t] = 0$ Thus q_k's can not be as all independent.

We can further treat non-holonomic system, provided the equations of constraint can be putting the from

$$\sum_j q_{ij} da_j + a_{ij} dt = 0 \;\; [j = 1,2, - ...m] \qquad ...(7)$$

which is a relation connecting the differentials of q's since in variation process used in Hamilton's principle, the time for each point on the path is taken constant, therefore the virtual displacements occurring in the variation must satisfy the equations of constraint of the form

$$\sum_j q_{ij} \delta q_j = 0, (j = 1,2,...m) \qquad ...(8)$$

The equations (8) can very well be used to reduce the number of virtual displacement to independent ones. The method used for eliminating these extra virtual displacements is that of Lagrange's *undetermined multipliers.*

Also from (8), we get

$$\lambda_l \sum_j a_{ij} \delta q_j = 0, (j = 1,2,...m) \qquad ...(9)$$

where λ_l are some undetermined constants, which in general, are functions of time.

Now first of all summing the equations (9) over l and then integrating the resulting equation from 1 to 2, we get

$$\int_1^2 \sum_{ji} \lambda_l a_{ij} \delta q_j dt = 0 \qquad ...(10)$$

Again the equations corresponding to (5) in the case of conservative system are given as

$$\int_1^2 dt \sum_j \left(\frac{\partial L}{\partial q_j} - \frac{d}{dt} \frac{\partial L}{\partial \dot{q}_j} \right) \delta q_j = 0 \qquad ...(11)$$

Combining the equations (10) with (11), we get

$$\int_1^2 dt \sum_j \left(\frac{\partial L}{\partial q_j} - \frac{d}{dt}\frac{\partial L}{\partial \dot{q}_j} + \sum_l \lambda_l a_{ij} \right) \delta q_j = 0 \quad ...(12)$$

It is to be noted here that δq_j's are still not independent. They are connected by the m relations given by (8.) This is, while the first n – m of these equations may be chosen independently, the last m are then fixed by the equations (8). Since the values of λ_l's are at our disposal, we choose them to be such that

$$\frac{\partial L}{\partial q_j} - \frac{d}{dt}\frac{\partial L}{\partial \dot{q}_j} + \sum_l \lambda_l a_{ij} = 0, (j = n - m + 1, ... n) \quad ...(13)$$

which are in the nature of equations of motion for the last m of the q_j variable.

Using the value of λ_l obtained from (13) in (12), we get

$$\int_1^2 dt \sum_{j=1}^{n-m} \left(\frac{\partial L}{\partial q_j} - \frac{d}{dt}\frac{\partial L}{\partial \dot{q}_j} + \sum_l \lambda_l a_{ij} \right) \delta q_j = 0 \quad ...(14)$$

Since δq_j's involved here are independent ones, therefore we have

$$\frac{\partial L}{\partial q_j} - \frac{d}{dt}\frac{\partial L}{\partial \dot{q}_j} + \sum_l \lambda_l a_{lj} = 0, (j = 1, 2, ... n - m) \quad ...(15)$$

Now combining (13) with (15), we get

$$\frac{d}{dt}\frac{\partial L}{\partial \dot{q}_j x} - \frac{\partial L}{\partial q_j} = \sum_l \lambda_l a_{lj}, (j = 1, 2, ... n) \quad ...(16)$$

which are known as Lagrange's equations for non holonomic systems. We now observe that (16) gives us a total of only n equations, where as the unknowns involved are (n + m) in number, namely then n co-ordinates q_l and the m, λ_l 's. The additional equationals required are exactly the equations of constraint *i.e.*

$$\sum_j a_{ij}\dot{q}_j + a_{ij} + 0 \quad ...(17)$$

The equations (16) together with (17) constitute (n + m) equations for n + m unknowns.

It is to be noted here that equation (7) is not the most general type of non-holonomic constraint. For example, it does not include equations of constraints in the form of inequalities. More over it includes holonomic constraints. An equation of the form

$$f(q_1, q_2, q_3, ... q_n ; t) = 0 \qquad ...(18)$$

it is of the same form as the equation 97) with the coefficients

$$a_{lj} = \frac{\partial f}{\partial q_j} \text{ and } a_{ji} = \frac{\partial f}{\partial t} \qquad ...(19)$$

It means that method of Lagrange's undetermined multipliers can be used also for holonomic constraints, when it is not easy to reduce all the q's to independent co-ordinates.

PHYSICAL SIGNIFICANCE OF THE HAMILTONIAN

If the Hamiltonian H is independent of t explicity, prove that it is (a) constant and (b) equal to the total energy of the system.

Proof:

(a) we have $\frac{dH}{dt} = \sum_{i=1}^{n} \frac{\partial H}{\partial qi}\frac{dqi}{dt} + \sum_{i=1}^{n} \frac{\partial H}{\partial pi}\frac{dpi}{dt}$

$$= \sum_{i=1}^{n} -(\dot{p}_i)\dot{q}_i + \sum_{i=1}^{n} \dot{q}_i \dot{p}_i \left(\because \dot{p}_i = -\frac{\partial H}{\partial qi} \text{ and } \dot{q}_i = \frac{\partial H}{\partial pi} \right) = 0$$

$\Rightarrow$ H = constant, say E.

(b) By Euler's theorem on homogeneous function, we have

$\Sigma \dot{q}_i \frac{\partial T}{\partial \dot{q}_i} = 2T$, where T is the K.E. of the system.

But $L = T - V$, $\therefore \frac{\partial L}{\partial \dot{q}_i} = \frac{\partial (T-V)}{\dot{q}_i} = \frac{\partial T}{\partial \dot{q}_i}$ (V does not depend on $\dot{q}_i$)

or $\Sigma \dot{q}_i \frac{\partial L}{\partial \dot{q}_i} = 2T \Rightarrow \Sigma \dot{q}_i \, \dot{p}_i = 2T \left(\because p_i = \frac{\partial L}{\partial \dot{q}_i} \right)$

$\therefore H = \Sigma p_i \dot{q}_i - L = 2T - (T - V) = T + V = E.$

PASSAGE FROM THE HAMILTONIAN TO THE LAGRANGIAN

Suppose that we are given a function *H (q, p, t) and are told that the motion of the system satisfies the canonical equations

$$\dot{p}_i = -(\partial H / \partial qw_i) \text{ and } \dot{q}_i = (\partial H / \partial qw_i) \qquad ...(1)$$

Then we want to find a function

L (p$_1$, p$_2$, ..., p$_n$; q$_1$, q$_2$, ..., q$_n$; t), *i.e.* L (p, q, t)

Such that the motion also satisfies the equations

$(d/dt)\ (\partial L/\partial \dot{q}_i) - (\partial L/q_i) = 0.$ ...(2)

Solve the first set of equations in (1) for the p's in terms of the q's, the $\dot{q}$'s and t.

Then write $L = \sum_{i=1}^{n} \dot{q}_i p_i - H$ and express L as a function of the q's, the $\dot{q}$'s and t. This is the required Lagrangian.

$$\therefore (\partial L/\partial q_i) = p_i \left(\text{using } L = \sum_{i=1}^{n} p_i \dot{q}_i - H \right)$$

$$\Rightarrow (d/dt)(\partial L/\partial \dot{q}_i) = \dot{p}_i \text{ and } (\partial L/\partial q_i) = -(\partial H/\partial q_i)$$

$$\Rightarrow \frac{d}{dt}(dL/\partial \dot{q}_i) - (\partial L/\partial q_i) = \dot{p}_i + (\partial H/\partial q_i) = 0$$

i.e. L satisfies (2) assuming (1).

SOLVED EXAMPLES

Example 1:

A sphere rolls down a rough included plane; if x be the distance of the point of contact of the sphere from a fixed point on the plane, find the acceleration.

Solution:

We have $T = \frac{1}{2}m(\dot{x}^2 + k^2\dot{\theta}^2) = \frac{1}{2}m\left(\dot{x}^2 + \frac{2}{5}a^2\dot{\theta}^2\right)\left(\because k^2 = \frac{2}{5}a^2\right)$

$$= \frac{1}{2}m\left(\dot{x}^2 \frac{2}{5}\dot{x}^2\right) = \frac{7}{10}m\dot{x}^2; \quad ...(1)$$

$$V = -\ mgx \sin\alpha \quad ...(2)$$

$$\therefore L = T - V = \frac{7}{10}m\dot{x}^2 + mgx \sin\alpha \quad ...(3)$$

Now $p_x = (\partial L/\partial \dot{x}) = \frac{7}{10}m\dot{x} \Rightarrow \dot{x} = (5p_x/7m)$

Thus $H = -L + p_x\dot{x} = -\frac{7}{10}m\dot{x} - mgx \sin\alpha + p_x.(5p_x/7m)$

$$= \frac{5}{14}(p_x^2/m) - mgx \sin\alpha$$

$\therefore$ One of Hamilton's equations gives

$$p_x = -(\partial H/\partial x) = mg \sin\alpha \Rightarrow \frac{7}{5}m\ddot{x} = mg \sin\alpha \Rightarrow \ddot{x} = \frac{5}{7}g \sin\alpha$$

Example 2:

A particle of mass ma moves in a force field of potential V.

(a) Write the Hamiltonian and

(b) Hamilton's equations in artesian co-ordinates.

Solution:

(a) we have

$T = \frac{1}{2}m(\dot{x}^2 + \dot{y}^2 + \dot{z}^2)$

$\Rightarrow L = \frac{1}{2}m(\dot{x}^2 + \dot{y}^2 + \dot{z}^2) - V(x,y,z)$ ...(1)

$\Rightarrow \dot{x} = (p_x / m),\ \dot{y} = (p_y / m), \dot{z} = (p_z / m).$

Thus $H = \Sigma p_x \dot{q}_z - \dot{p}_x x + \dot{p}_y y + \dot{p}_z z - \frac{1}{2}m(\dot{x}^2 + \dot{y}^2 + \dot{z}^2) + V(x,y,z)$

$= p_x\ (p_x/m) + p_y\ (p_y/m) + (p_z\ (p_z/m)$

$- \frac{1}{2}m[p_x^2 / m^2) + (p_y^2 / m^2) + (p_z^2 / m^2)] + V(x,y,z)$

$= (p_x^2 / 2m) + (p_y^2 / 2m) + (p_z^2 / 2m) + V(x,y,z)$

= total energy of the system.

(b) Hamilton's equations are:

$\dot{p}_x = -(\partial H / \partial x); \dot{p}_y = -(\partial H / \partial y); \dot{p}_z = -(\partial H / \partial z)$ and

$\dot{x} = (\dot{p}_x = -(\partial H / \partial x); \dot{p}_y\ \dot{x} = (\partial H / \partial p_x); \dot{y} = (\partial H / \partial p_y); \dot{z} = (\partial H / \partial p_z).$

$\Rightarrow \dot{p}_x = -(\partial V / \partial x), \dot{p}_y = -(\partial V / \partial y), \dot{p}_z = -(\partial V / \partial z)$

$\dot{x} = (p_x / m), \dot{y} = (p_y / m), \dot{z} = (p_z / m).$

Example 3:

If the Hamiltonian H is independent of time explicity, prove that it is

(a) a constant, and

(b) equal to the total energy of the system.

Solution:

(a) $(dH/dt) = \sum_{i=1}^{n} (\partial H / \partial p_i)\dot{p}_i + \sum_{i=1}^{n} (\partial H / \partial q_i)\dot{q}_i$

$\sum_{i=1}^{n} \dot{q}_i\, \dot{p}_i + (-\dot{p}_i)\, \dot{q}_i = 0$ $[\because (\partial H / \partial p_i) = \dot{q}_i, (\partial H / \partial q_i) = -\dot{p}_i]$

$\Rightarrow$ H = constant = E say.

(b) By Euler's theorem on homogeneous functions, we have

$$\sum_{i=1}^{n} \dot{q}_i \, (\partial T / \partial \dot{q}_i) = 2T. \qquad ...(2)$$

Put

$$p_i = (\partial L / \partial \dot{q}_i) = \{\partial(T - V) / \partial \dot{q}_i\} = (\partial T / \partial \dot{q}_i) - (\partial V / \partial \dot{q}_i) = (\partial T / \partial \dot{q}_i)$$

$$\{\because (\partial V / \partial \dot{q}_i) = 0 \text{ as V is independent of } \dot{q}_i\}$$

$$\therefore (2) \Rightarrow \sum_{i=1}^{n} \dot{q}_i p_i = 2T$$

Thus $H = \sum_{i=1}^{n} p_i \dot{q}_i - L = 2T - L = 2T - (T - V) = T + V = E.$

Example 4:

Write the Hamiltonian and equation of motion for a simple pendulum.

Solution:

We have $T = \frac{1}{4} ml^2\dot{\theta}^2$ and $V = mgl\,(1 - \cos\theta)$,

$$\therefore L = T - V = \frac{1}{2} ml^2\dot{\theta}^2 - mgl(1 - \cos\theta) \qquad ...(1)$$

$$\Rightarrow H = \Sigma p_i \dot{q}_i - L = p_\theta \dot{\theta} - L = ml^2\dot{\theta}^2 - \left\{\frac{1}{2} ml^2\theta^2 - mgl(1 - \cos\theta)\right\}$$

$$= \frac{1}{2} ml^2\dot{\theta}^2 + mgl\,(1 - \cos\theta) = T + V = \text{total energy.}$$

Now $p_\theta = (\partial L / \partial \dot{\theta}) = ml^2\dot{\theta}^2 = (p_\theta / ml^2)$

$$\therefore H = \frac{1}{2} ml^2 (p_\theta / ml^2)^2 + mgl(1 - \cos\theta) = (p_\theta^2 / 2ml^2) + mgl(1 - \cos\theta)$$

$$\Rightarrow (\partial H / \partial p_\theta), \dot{p}_\theta = -(\partial H / \partial \theta) \Rightarrow \dot{\theta} = (p_\theta / ml^2) \text{ and } \dot{p}_\theta = -mgl\sin\theta,$$

These represent Hamilton's equations for a simple pendulum.

From above, we have $p_\theta = ml^2\dot{\theta}$, i.e. $p_e = ml^2\ddot{\theta}$

$$\therefore ml^2\ddot{\theta}, = -mgl\sin\theta \Rightarrow \ddot{\theta} + (g/l)\sin\theta = 0$$

This gives the equation of motion of the simple pendulum.

Example 5:

Write the Hamiltonian function and equation of motion for a compound pendulum.

Solution:

We have $L = \frac{1}{2} I\dot{\theta}^2 + mgh\cos\theta \Rightarrow p_\theta = (\partial L / \partial\theta) = I\theta.$

where I mk^2

$\therefore H = \Sigma p_i \dot{q}_i - L = p_\theta \dot{\theta} - L = I\dot{\theta}\dot{\theta} - \frac{1}{2} I\dot{\theta}^2 - mgh\cos\theta$

$= \frac{1}{2} I\dot{\theta}^2 - mgh\cos\theta$

$\Rightarrow \frac{1}{2} H = (p_\theta / I)^2 - mgh\cos\theta = (p_\theta^2 / 2I)\, 2\, mgh\cos\theta \{\because \dot{\theta} = (p_\theta / I)\}$

$\therefore (\partial H / \partial p_\theta) = (p_\theta / I), (\partial H / \partial\theta) = mgh\sin\theta$

Thus the Hamilton's equations for $\dot{\theta}$ and $\dot{p}_\theta$ are given by

$\dot{\theta} = (\partial H / \partial p_\theta), \dot{p}_\theta = -(\partial H / \partial\theta)$

i.e. $\dot{\theta} = (p_\theta / I)$ and $\dot{p}_\theta = -mgh\sin\theta$. But. $p_\theta = I\theta \Rightarrow \dot{p}_\theta = I\ddot{\theta}.$

$\therefore I\ddot{\theta} = -mgh\sin\theta \Rightarrow \ddot{\theta} + \frac{mgh}{I}\sin\theta = 0.$

This is exactly the same as obtained previously using Lagrange's equations.

Example 6:

Obtain Euler's equations from Hamilton's equations.

Solution:

We know that $2T = (A\omega_1^2 + B\omega_2^2 + C\omega_3^2),$

$\Rightarrow L = T - V = \frac{1}{2}(A\omega_1^2 + B_2^2 + C\omega_3^2) - V$

Also Euler's geometrical relations give

$\omega_1 = \dot{\theta}\sin\psi\sin\theta\cos\psi;$

$\omega_2 = \dot{\theta}\cos\psi + \dot{\phi}\sin\theta\sin\psi;$ and

$\omega_3 = \psi + \phi\cos\theta.$

Now H = T + V $= \frac{1}{2}(A\omega_1^2 + B\omega_2^2 + C_3^2) + V$

$$P_\phi = \frac{\partial L}{\partial\dot{\theta}} = \frac{\partial L}{\partial\omega_1}\frac{\partial\omega_1}{\partial\dot{\theta}} + \frac{\partial L}{\partial\omega_2}\frac{\partial\omega_2}{\partial\dot{\theta}} + \frac{\partial L}{\partial\omega_3}\frac{\partial\omega_3}{\partial\dot{\theta}}.$$

$A\omega_1 \sin\psi + B\omega_2 \cos\psi + C\omega_3 . 0$

$$p_\theta = \frac{\partial L}{\partial \dot{\phi}} = -A\omega_1 \sin\theta\cos\psi + B\omega_2 \sin\theta\sin\psi + C\omega_3 \cos\theta \quad ...(2)$$

and $p_\psi = (\partial L/\partial\dot{\psi}) = C\omega_3$

Solving the three equations for ω_2 , ω_2, ω_3 we have

$$\omega_1 = \frac{1}{A}\left[p_\theta \sin\psi + (p_\psi\cos\theta - p_\phi)\frac{\cos\psi}{\sin\theta}\right]$$

$$\omega_2 = \frac{1}{A}\left[p_\theta \cos\psi - (p_\psi\cos\theta - p_\phi)\frac{\sin\psi}{\sin\theta}\right]; \text{ and } \omega_3 = \frac{1}{C}.p_\psi$$

Also, Hamilton's equations are $\dot{p}_\psi = -\frac{\partial H}{\partial\psi}$ and $\dot{\psi} = \frac{\partial H}{\partial p_\psi}$

Now $\dot{p}_\psi = -\frac{\partial H}{\partial\psi}$

$$\Rightarrow C\dot{\omega}_3 = -\left[\frac{\partial H}{\partial\omega_1}\frac{\partial\omega_1}{\partial\psi} + \frac{\partial H}{\partial\omega_2}\frac{\partial\omega_2}{\partial\psi} + \frac{\partial H}{\partial\omega_3}\frac{\partial\omega_3}{\partial\psi}\right] - \frac{\partial V}{\partial\psi}$$

$$= -\left[A\omega_1.\frac{1}{A}B\omega_2 + B\omega_2\left(\frac{A}{B}\omega_1\right) + C\omega_3.0\right] - \frac{\partial V}{\partial\psi}$$

$$= (A - B)\omega_1\omega_2 - \frac{\partial V}{\partial\psi}$$

$$\Rightarrow C\frac{d\omega_1}{dt} - (A - B)\omega_1\omega_2 = N\left(\because -\frac{\partial V}{\partial\phi} = N\right)$$

This is Euler's third familiar dynamical equation

Also, $\dot{\psi} = (\partial H/\partial p_\psi) = \frac{\partial H}{\partial\omega_1}\frac{\partial\omega_1}{\partial p_\psi} + \frac{\partial H}{\partial\omega_2}\frac{\partial\omega_2}{\partial p_\psi} + \frac{\partial H}{\partial\omega_3}\frac{\partial\omega_3}{\partial p_\psi}$

$= (\omega_1 \cos\psi - \omega_2 \sin\psi)\cot\theta + \omega_3 = -\dot{\phi}\sin\theta\cot\theta + \omega_3$

i.e. $\dot{\psi} = -\dot{\phi}\cos\theta + \omega_3 \Rightarrow \omega_3 = \dot{\psi} + \dot{\phi}\cos\theta$

This is Euler's third geometrical equation.

One the same lines, we can deduce Euler's other equations (dynamical and geometrical).

Example 7:

Prove that

$\left(\frac{\partial H}{dt}\right) = \left(\frac{\partial H}{dt}\right)$ *where H is the Hamilton's function.*

Solution:

Let $q_1, q_2 ..., q_n$ be the generalised co-ordinates then Hamilton's equation are given by

$$\dot{p}_i = -\frac{\partial H}{dq_i} \text{ and } \dot{q}_i = \frac{\partial H}{dp_i}(i = 1,2,...,n) \quad ...(1)$$

But Hamiltonian H is a function of q's and ps'

$$\therefore \frac{\partial H}{dt} = \frac{\partial H}{\partial t} + \sum_{i=1}^{n} \frac{\partial H}{\partial q_i}\dot{q}_i + \sum_{i=1}^{n} \frac{\partial H}{\partial p_i}\dot{p}_i$$

$$= \frac{\partial H}{\partial t} + \sum_{i=1}^{n} \frac{\partial H}{\partial q_i}(-\dot{p}_i)\,\dot{q}_i + \sum_{i=1}^{n} \dot{q}_i\dot{p}_i = \frac{\partial H}{\partial t} \quad \text{[using (1)]}$$

Example 8:

Use Hamilton's equations to find the equations of motion of a projectile in space.

Solution:

Let (x,y,z) be the co-ordinates of the projectile in space at time t, then we have

$$T = \frac{1}{2}m(\dot{x}^2 + \dot{y}^2 + \dot{z}^2),\ V = mgz$$

$$\therefore L = T - V = \frac{1}{2}m\,(\dot{x}^2 + \dot{y}^2 + \dot{z}^2) - mgz$$

$$\Rightarrow p_x = \frac{\partial L}{\partial \dot{x}} = m\dot{x},\ p_y = \frac{\partial L}{\partial \dot{y}} = m\dot{y}, p_z = \frac{\partial L}{\partial \dot{z}} = m\dot{z}$$

But L does not involve t explicity therefore Hamiltonian H is given by

$$H = T + V = \frac{1}{2}(\dot{x}^2 + \dot{y}^2 + \dot{z}^2) + mgz$$

$$= \frac{1}{2}m\left(\frac{p_x^2}{m^2} + \frac{p_y^2}{m^2} + \frac{p_z^2}{m^2}\right) + mgz = \frac{1}{2m}(p_x^2 + p_y^2 + p_z^2) + mgz$$

Now Hamilton's equations are given by

$$\dot{p}_x = -\frac{\partial H}{\partial x} = 0 \quad ...(1)$$

$$\dot{x} = \frac{\partial H}{\partial p_x} = \frac{p_x}{m} \quad ...(2)$$

$$\dot{p}_y = -\frac{\partial H}{\partial_y} = 0 \quad ...(3)$$

$$\dot{y} = \frac{\partial H}{\partial p_y} = \frac{p_y}{m} \quad \text{...(4)}$$

$$\dot{p}_z = -\frac{\partial H}{\partial_z} = -mg \quad \text{...(5)}$$

$$\dot{z} = \frac{\partial H}{\partial p_z} = \frac{p_z}{m} \quad \text{...(6)}$$

Using (1) and (2), we have $\ddot{x} = 0$ ...(7)

Using (3) and (4), we have $\ddot{y} = 0$ ...(8)

Again making use of (6) and (5), we have

$m\ddot{z} = \dot{p}_z \mp 0\, mg$ or $\ddot{z} = -g$. ...(9)

These (7, 8, 9) are the equations of motion of the projectile in space.

Example 9:

Using cylindrical coordinates (ρ, φ, z) *write the Hamiltonian and Hamilton's equations for a particle of mass m moving in a force field of potential V* (ρ, φ, z).

Solution:

In cylindrical coordinates, co-ordinates of any points are

$$x = \rho\cos\phi, y = \rho\sin\phi, z = z \quad \text{...(1)}$$

$$\therefore T = \frac{1}{2}m(\dot{x}^2 + \dot{y}^2 + \dot{z}^2) = \frac{1}{2}m(\dot{\rho}^2 + \rho^2\dot{\phi}^2 + \dot{z}^2) \quad \text{...(2)}$$

$$\Rightarrow L = T - V = \frac{1}{2}m(\dot{\rho}^2 + \rho^2\dot{\phi}^2 + \dot{z}^r) - V(\rho,\phi,z) \quad \text{...(3)}$$

$$\Rightarrow p_\rho = \frac{\partial L}{\partial\dot{\rho}} = m\dot{\rho}, p_\phi = \frac{\partial L}{\partial\dot{\phi}} = mp^2\dot{\phi} \text{ and } p_z = \frac{\partial L}{\partial\dot{z}} = m\dot{z}$$

Evidently, L does not involve t explicity, therefore Hamiltonian H is given by

$$h = T + V\frac{1}{2}m(\dot{\rho}^2 + \rho^2\dot{\phi}^2 + z^2) + V$$

$$= \frac{1}{2}\left[\frac{p_\rho^2}{m^2} + \frac{p_\phi^2}{m^2\rho^2} + \frac{p_z^2}{m^2}\right] + V = \frac{1}{2m}\left[p_\rho^2 + \frac{p_\phi^2}{\rho^2} + p_z^2\right] + V$$

Hence, Hamilton's are given by:

$$\dot{p}_\rho = -\frac{\partial H}{\partial\rho} = \frac{p_\phi^2}{m\rho^2} - \frac{\partial V}{\partial\rho}; \dot{\rho} = \frac{\partial H}{\partial p_\rho} = \frac{p_\rho}{m_\phi}$$

$$\dot{p}_\phi = -\frac{\partial H}{\partial \phi} = -\frac{\partial V}{\partial \phi}; \dot{\phi} = \frac{\partial H}{\partial p_\phi} = \frac{p_\phi}{m\rho^2}$$

$$\dot{p}_z = -\frac{\partial H}{\partial z} = -\frac{\partial V}{\partial z}; \dot{z} = \frac{\partial H}{\partial p_z} = \frac{p_z}{m}$$

Example 10:

Using cylindrical coordinates, write the Hamiltonian and Hamilton's equations for a particle of mass moving on the inside of a frictionless cone $x^2 + y^2 = z^2 \tan^2 \alpha$

Solution:

Like previous example, we have

$$T = \frac{1}{2}m(\dot{x}^2 + \dot{y}^2 + \dot{z}^2) = \frac{1}{2}m(\dot{\rho}^2 + \rho^2\dot{\phi}^2 + \rho^2 \cot^2 \alpha)$$

$$[\because x = \rho\cos\phi, y = \rho\sin\phi, z = \rho\cot\alpha]$$

$$= \frac{1}{2}m(\dot{\rho}^2 \operatorname{cosec}^2\alpha + \dot{\rho}^2\dot{\phi}^2) \qquad \text{...(1)}$$

and $V = -W = -mgz = mg\rho\cot\alpha,$

[$\because$ the particle is above the vertex (origin)

$$\Rightarrow L = T - V \frac{1}{2}m(\rho^2 \operatorname{cosec}^2\alpha + \rho^2\dot{\phi}^2) - mg\rho\cot\alpha \qquad \text{...(2)}$$

This gives, $p_\rho = \frac{\partial L}{\partial \dot{\rho}} = m\rho \operatorname{cosec}^2\alpha, p_\phi = \frac{\partial L}{\partial \dot{\phi}} = m\rho^2\dot{\phi}$ ...(3)

Again, L does not involve t explicitly, therefore Hemiltonian H is given by,

$$H = T + V \frac{1}{2} m(\dot{\rho}^2 \operatorname{cosec}^2\alpha + \rho^2\dot{\phi}^2) + mg\rho\cot\alpha$$

$$= \frac{1}{2}m\left[\frac{p_\rho^2}{m^2 \operatorname{cosec}^2\alpha} + \frac{p_\phi^2}{m^2\rho^2}\right] + mg\,\rho\,\text{co}\,\alpha + \frac{1}{2m}\left[\frac{p_\rho^2}{\operatorname{cosec}^2\alpha} + \frac{p_\phi^2}{\rho^2}\right] + mg\,\rho\cot\alpha$$

Thus Hamilton's equations are given by:

$$\dot{p}_\rho = -\frac{\partial H}{\partial \phi} = \frac{p_\phi^2}{m\rho^2} - mg\cot\alpha; \dot{\rho} = \frac{\partial H}{\partial p_\rho} = \frac{p_\rho}{m \operatorname{cosec}^2\alpha}.$$

$$\dot{p}_\phi = -\frac{\partial H}{\partial \phi} = 0 \qquad \dot{\phi} = \frac{\partial H}{\partial p_\phi} = \frac{p_\phi}{m\rho^2}.$$

Example 11:

Use the variational method to show that the shortest curve joining two fixed is a straight line

Solution:

We have

$$\frac{ds}{dx} = \sqrt{\left\{1 + \left(\frac{dy}{dx}\right)^2\right\}}$$ for any curve, joining two fixed points say

$A \equiv (x_1, y_1)$ and $B \equiv (x_2, y_2)$.

$$\Rightarrow s = \int_{x_1}^{x_2} \sqrt{(1 + y'^2)}\ dx = \text{length of the curve joining A to B.}$$

$$= \int_{x_1}^{x_2} f(y')\,dx \text{ where } f(y') = \sqrt{(1 + y'^2)} \qquad ...(1)$$

In equation (1), y is absent from f, therefore for s to be stationary (here minimum), we have from Euler-Lagrange's equation

$$\frac{\partial f}{\partial y'} = (\text{constant}) \Rightarrow \frac{\partial}{\partial y'}[(\sqrt{1 + y'^2})] = \text{cpmst.} \ \because f = (1 + y'^2)^{1/2}$$

$$\Rightarrow \frac{y'}{\sqrt{(1 + y'^2)}} = (\text{constant}) \ i.e. \ y' = b \text{ where b is constant.}$$

$$\Rightarrow \frac{dy}{dx} = b \text{ or } y = a + b\,x \text{ where a is a constant.} \qquad ...(2)$$

$\Rightarrow$ the shortest path joining A to B is the curve whose equation is y = a + bx and this is evidently a line.

Example 12:

Show that the area of the surface of revolution of a curve y = y (x) is

$$2\pi \int_{x_1}^{x_2} y\sqrt{(1 + y'^2)}dx.$$

Hence show that for this to be a minimum,, the curve must be a catenary.

Solution:

Consider any curve, and let $A \equiv (x_1, y_1)$ and $B \equiv (x_2, y_2)$ be its extremities, then it this curve revolves about x-axis the surface of revolution is given by

$$S=\int 2\pi y\,ds=\pi\int y\frac{ds}{dx}dx=2\pi\int_{x_1}^{x_2} y\sqrt{(1+y'^2)}dx$$

$$\Rightarrow S=2\pi\int_{x_1}^{x_2} f(y,y')\,dx,\ \text{ where } f=f(y,y')=y\sqrt{(1+y'^2)}$$

Evidently, x is absent from f, so for S to be stationary (here a minimum) we have:

$$f-y'\frac{\partial f}{\partial y'}=\text{(constant) } \textit{i.e. } y\sqrt{(1+y'^2)}-y'\frac{yy'}{\sqrt{(1+y')}}=\text{const.}$$

$$\Rightarrow \frac{y}{\sqrt{(1+y'^2)}}=c \text{ where c is constant } \textit{i.e. } y=c\sqrt{(1+\tan^2\psi}$$

$$[\because y'=\tan\psi]$$

$\therefore$ **y = c sec y and this represents catenary.**

Example 13:

A particle of unit mass is projected so that its total energy is h in a field of force of which the potential energy is ϕ (r) at a distance r from the origin.

Deduce from the principle of energy and least action that the differential equation of the path is

$$c^2\left[r^2+\left(\frac{dr}{d\theta}\right)^2\right]=r^4[h-\phi(r)].$$

Solution:

Let T and V be the kinetic are potential energies, then we have T + V = h $\Rightarrow$ T = h – V

$$=h-\phi(r),\ \because V=\phi(r) \text{ given}$$

$$\Rightarrow \frac{1}{2}v^2=h-\phi(r) \text{ where v is velocity } \left(\because T=\frac{1}{2}mv^2=\frac{1}{2}v^2\right)$$

$$\Rightarrow v=\sqrt{2}\{h-\phi(r)\}^{1/2}$$

Whence, the action $A=\int_{t_0}^{t_1} 2T\,dt$, **by definition given earlier**

$$=\int_{t_0}^{t_1} 2.\frac{1}{2}v^2dt=\int_{t_c}^{t_1} v\,ds \text{ since } v=(ds/dt)=\sqrt{2}\int_{t_0}^{t_1}\{h-\phi(r)\}^{1/2}ds$$

$$=\sqrt{2}\int_{t_0}^{t_1}\{h-\phi(r)\}^{1/2}\left\{1+r^2\left(\frac{d\theta}{dr}\right)^2\right\}^{1/2}dr\quad \frac{ds}{dr}=\left\{1+r^2\left(\frac{d\theta}{dr}\right)^2\right\}^{1/2}$$

$$= \sqrt{2}\int_{t_0}^{t_1}[\{h-\phi(r)\}^{1/2}\{1+r^2\theta'^2\}^{1/2}]\ dr \text{ where } \theta' = \frac{d\theta}{dr}$$

$$= \sqrt{2}\int_{t_0}^{t_1} f(\theta', r)dr, \text{ where } f(\theta', r) = \{h-\phi(r)\}^{1/2}\{1+r^2\theta'^2\}^{1/2}$$

Evidently, θ is absent from f, therefore we must have

$$\frac{\partial f}{\partial \theta'} = c \text{ (const.)} \Rightarrow \frac{\partial f}{\partial \theta'}[\{h-\phi(r)\}^{1/2}\{1+r^2\theta'^2\}^{1/2]} = c$$

$$\Rightarrow \{h-\phi(r)\}^{1/2}\frac{r^2}{\left\{r^2+\left(\frac{dr}{d\theta}\right)^2\right\}^{1/2}} = c$$

$$\Rightarrow c^2\left\{r^2+\left(\frac{dr}{d\theta}\right)^2\right\} = r^4\{h-\phi(r)\}.$$

This is the required equation.

Example 14:

A projectile is launched in a vertical plane with a velocity whose horizontal and vertical components are v_x and v_y respectively. Calculate the value of the integral $\int_0^{t_0} l\, dt$, *where* $t_0 = \frac{n\pi}{\omega}$.

Evaluate this integral for the varied path given by the equations

$$x = v_x t, y = V_y t - \frac{1}{2}gt^2 + \varepsilon \sin \omega t,$$

where ε is a small constant quantity.

Show that the integral $\int_0^{t_0} L\ dt$ *is greater for the varied path than for the actual path, but the result is in agreement with Hamilton's principle.*

Solution:

The path of the projectile is given by

$$x = V_x t, y = V_y t - \frac{1}{2}gt^2.$$

Also V = mgy, where V denotes the potential,

whence $L = T - V = \frac{1}{2}m(\dot{x}^2 + \dot{y}^2) - mgy$

$$=\frac{1}{2}m\,(y_x^2+(v_y-gt)^2]-mg\left(v_y t-\frac{1}{2}gt^2\right)$$

$$=\frac{1}{2}m[v_x^2+v_y^2)-4gtv_y+2g^2t^2] \qquad ...(1)$$

$$\Rightarrow \int_0^{t_0} L dt=\int_0^{t_0}(T-V)dt=\frac{1}{2}m\int_0^{t_0}[(v_x^2+v_y^2)-4gtv_y+2g^2t^2]dt$$

$$=\frac{1}{2}m\left[(v_x^2+v_y^2)t_0-2t_0^2v_y+\frac{2}{3}g^2t_0^3\right] \qquad ...(1)$$

Also the varied path is given by : $x=v_x t,\ y=v_y t-\frac{1}{2}gt^2+\varepsilon\sin\omega t$

Now after obtaining $\dot{x},\dot{y}$; we have

$$T=\frac{1}{2}m[v_x^2+(y_v-gt+\varepsilon\omega\cos\omega t)^2] \text{ and}$$

$$V=mg\left(v_y t-\frac{1}{2}gt^2+\varepsilon\sin\omega t\right)\Rightarrow \int_0^{t_0=n\pi/\omega} L dt=\int_0^{t_0}(T-V)dt$$

$$\int_0^{t_0}\left[\frac{1}{2}m\{v_x^2+v_y-gt+\varepsilon\omega\cos\omega t)^2\}-mg(v_y t-\frac{1}{2}gt^2+\varepsilon\sin\omega t\right]dt$$

$$=\frac{1}{2}m\left[(v_x^2+v_y^2)t_0-2t_0^2gv_y+\frac{2}{3}g^2t_0^3+\frac{1}{2}\varepsilon^2\omega^2t_0\right]$$

[$\because$ other integrals vanish)

$$=\frac{1}{2}m[(v_x^2+v_y^2)t_0-2t_0^2gv_y+\frac{2}{3}g^2t_0^3]+m\pi n\omega\varepsilon^2 \qquad ...(2)$$

From equations (1) and (2), we see that the integral $\int_0^{t_0} L\,dt$ is greater for the varied path then for the actual path and is minimum when $\varepsilon=0$. Evidently, the minimum value in this case, the varied *path coincides with actual path.*

Example 15:

A particle moves in a straight line with central acceleration ω^2x between two fixed points x_0 and x_1 in the prescribed time t_1-t_0. Show that Hamilton's principal function S is

$$\frac{\omega}{2\sin\omega(t_1-t_0)}\left[(x_1^2+x_0^2)\cos\omega\,(t_1-t_0-2x_1x_0\right]$$

Solution:

Equation of motion is, $\ddot{x}=\omega^2x \qquad ...(1)$

Solving (1), the path is x = A cos ωt + B sin ωt ...(2)

Now, $\dot{x} = \omega[-A\sin\omega t + B\cos\omega t] \Rightarrow T = \frac{1}{2}\dot{x}^2$.

Also, we have potential V = work done against the force

$$= \int_0^{t_0} \omega^2 x dx = \frac{1}{2}\omega^2 x^2 \quad ...(3)$$

Again, we also have

$A\cos\omega t_0 + B\sin\omega t_0 - x_0 = 0$ $(t = t_0 ; x = x_0)$

and $A\cos\omega t_1 + B\sin\omega t_1 - x_1 = 0$ $(t = t_1 ; x = x_1)$

Saving these

$$A = \frac{x_0 \sin\omega t_1\ 0\ x_1 \sin\omega t_0}{\sin\omega(t_1 - t_0)}, B = \frac{x_1\cos\omega t_0 - x_0\cos\omega t_1}{\sin\omega(t_1 - t_0)}$$

$$\Rightarrow B^2 - A^2 = [x_1^2\cos 2\omega t_0 + x_0^2\cos 2\omega t_1\ 2x_1x_0$$

$$-\cos\omega(t_1 + t_0)]\frac{1}{\sin^2\omega(t_1 - t_0)} \quad ...(4)$$

∴ S = Hamilton's principal function

$$= \int_{t_0}^{t_1} L dt = \int_{t_0}^{t_1}(T - V)dt \quad (\because L = T - V)$$

$$= \int_{t_0}^{t_1}\left(\frac{1}{2}\dot{x}^2 - \frac{1}{2}\omega^2x^2\right)dt \quad \text{[from above]}$$

$$= \frac{1}{2}\omega^2\int_{t_0}^{t_1}[(-A\sin\omega t + B\cos\omega t)^2 - (A\cos\omega t + B\sin\omega t)^2]dt$$

$$= \frac{1}{2}\omega\left[(B - A)^2\sin 2\omega t + 2AB\cos 2\omega t\right]_{t_0}^{t_1}$$

$$= \frac{1}{2}\omega\left[(B^2 - A^2)\cos\omega(t_1 + t_0)\sin\omega(t_1 - t_0) - 2AB\sin\omega(t_1 - t_0\sin\omega(t_1 - t_0)\right]$$

Substituting for $B^2 - A^2$ and 2AB, we obtain

$$S = \frac{\omega}{2\sin\omega(t_1 - t_0)}[(x_1^2\cos 2\omega t_0 + x_0^2\cos 2\omega t_1 - 2x_1x_0$$

$$\cos w(t_1 + t_0)\}\cos w(t_1 + t_0) +$$

$$\{x_1^2\sin 2\omega t_0 + x_0^2\sin 2\omega t_1 - 2x_1x_0\sin\omega(t_1 + t_0)\}\sin\omega(t_1 + t_0)]$$

$$= \frac{\omega}{2\sin\omega(t_1 - t_0)}[x_1^2\cos\omega(t_1 - t_0) + x_0^2\cos\omega(t_1 - t_0) - 2x_1x_0]$$

$$= \frac{\omega}{2\sin\omega(t_1 - t_0)}[x_1^2 + x_0^2 \cos\omega(t_1 - t_0) - 2x_1x_0]$$

This is the required result.

Example 16:

A particle moves in a plane curve, under the central acceleration $\omega^2 r$, between two fixed points (x_0, y_0) and (x_1, y_1) in the prescribed time $t_1 - t_0$; prove that Hamilton's principle function S is

$$= \frac{\omega}{2\sin\omega(t_1 - t_0)}[(x_1^2 + y_1^2 + x_0^2 + y_0^2)\cos\omega(t_1 - t_0) - 2(x_1x_0 + y_1y_0)]$$

Solution:

Equations of motion of the particle are given by

$$\dot{x} = -\omega^2 x \text{ and } \ddot{y} = -\omega^2 y \qquad ...(1)$$

$$x = A\cos\omega t + B\sin\omega t;\ y = C\cos\omega t + D\sin\omega t$$

Now, kinetic energy $T = \frac{1}{2}gw^2(\dot{x}^2 + \dot{y}^2)$

$$= \frac{1}{2}\omega^2 [(-A\sin\omega t + B\cos\omega t)^2 + (-C\sin\omega t + D\cos\omega t)^2]$$

Potential $V = \frac{1}{2}\omega^2 r^2 = \frac{1}{2}\omega^2(x^2 + y^2)$

Hence Hamilton's principal function S is given by

$$S = \int_{t_0}^{t_1} L\,dt = \int_{t_0}^{t_1} (T - V)\ dt \text{ since } L = T - V$$

$$= \int_{t_0}^{t_1} \left[\frac{1}{2}(\dot{x}^2 + \dot{y}^2) - \frac{1}{2}\omega^2(x^2 + y^2)\right] dt \qquad ...(2)$$

But $\int_{t_0}^{t_1} \left(\frac{1}{2}\dot{x}^2 - \frac{1}{2}\omega^2 x^2\right) dt = \frac{\omega}{2\sin\omega(t_1 - t_0)}[(x_1^2 - x_0^2)\cos\omega(t_1 - t_0) - 2x_1x_0]$

and $\int_{t_0}^{t_1} \left(\frac{1}{2}\dot{y}^2 - \frac{1}{2}\omega^2 \dot{y}^2\right) dt = \frac{\omega}{2\sin\omega(t_1 - t_0)}$

$$\times [(y_1^2 - y_0^2)\cos\omega(t_1 - t_0) - 2y_1y_0]$$

$$\therefore S = \frac{\omega}{2\sin\omega(t_1 - t_0)}$$

$$[(x_1^2 - x_0^2 + y_1^0 + y_0^2)\cos\omega(t_1 - t_0) - 2(x_1x_0 + y_1y_0)]$$

Example 17:

Use Hamilton's principle to find the equation of motion of one - dimensional harmonic oscillator.

Solution:

The kinetic energy of harmonic oscillator is given by $T = m\dot{x}^2$ and the potential energy of the harmonic oscillator is given by

$$V = -\int F dx = \int kx dx = \frac{1}{2}kx^2.$$

$\therefore$ The Lagrangian of the system $L = T - V \;\; V = \frac{1}{2}m\dot{x}^2 - \frac{1}{2}kx^2.$

Using Hamilton's Principle, we have $\delta \int_{t_1}^{t_2} L\, dt = 0.$

$$\Rightarrow \delta \int_{t_1}^{t_2} \left(\frac{1}{2}m\dot{x}^2 - \frac{1}{2}kx^2\right) dt = 0 \Rightarrow \int_{t_1}^{t_2} \delta\left(\frac{1}{2}m\dot{x}^2 - \frac{1}{2}kx^2\right) dt = 0$$

$$\Rightarrow \delta \int_{t_1}^{t_2} (m\dot{x}\delta\dot{x} - kx\delta x) dt = 0 \;\; \text{But } \delta\dot{x} = (d/dt)(\delta x). \quad ...(1)$$

$$\therefore (1) \Rightarrow \int_{t_1}^{t_2} m\dot{x}\frac{d}{dt}(\delta\dot{x})\, dt - \int_{t_1}^{t_2} kx\, \delta x\, dt = 0$$

$$\text{i.e.,} [m\dot{x}\, \delta x]_{t_1}^{t_2} - \int_{t_1}^{t_2} m\frac{d}{dt}(\dot{x})\, dt - \int_{t_1}^{t_2} kx\, \delta x\, dt = 0 \quad ...(2)$$

But $[m\dot{x}\, \delta x]_{t_1}^{t_2} = 0$ [$\because$ $\delta x = 0$ at fixed points, i.e, at instants t_1 and t_2]

$$\therefore (2) \Rightarrow \int_{t_1}^{t_2} m\frac{d}{dt}(\dot{x})\, \delta x\, dt - \int_{t_1}^{t_2} kx\, \delta x\, dt = 0 \Rightarrow \int_{t_1}^{t_2} (m\dot{\dot{x}} + kx)\delta\, dt = 0$$

But δx is arbitrary, hence the above equation is only satisfied if $m\dot{x} + kx = 0$. This is the equation of motion for one dimensional harmonic oscillator.

Example 18(a):

A particle moves in the xy-plane under the influence of a central force depending only on its distance from the origin.

(a) Set up the Hamiltonian for the system.

(b) Write Hamilton's equations of motion.

Solution:

(a) Let the p potential due to the central force be V(r). Then, we have

$$T = \frac{1}{2}mv^2 = \frac{1}{2}m\,[(\text{radial velocity})^2 + (\text{transverse velocity}^2)]$$

$$= \frac{1}{2}m(\dot{r}^2 + r^2\dot{\theta}^2),$$

$$L = T - V = \frac{1}{2}m(\dot{r}^2 + r^2\dot{\theta}^2) - V(r).$$

$$\therefore p_r = (\partial L/\partial\dot{r}) = m\dot{r}, p_\theta = (\partial L/\partial\dot{r}) = mr^2\dot{\theta}$$

$$\Rightarrow \dot{r} = (p_r/m), \dot{\theta} = (p_\theta/mr^2)$$

Thus $H = \Sigma p_i\dot{q}_i - L = p_r\dot{q}_r + p_\theta\dot{q}_\theta - L$

$$= p_r.\dot{r} + p_\theta\dot{\theta} - \frac{1}{2}m(\dot{r}^2 + r^2\dot{\theta}^2) + V(r)$$

$$= p_r(p_r/m) + p_\theta(p_\theta/mr^2)$$

$$-\frac{1}{2}m\{p_r^2/m^2) + r^2.(p_\theta^2/m^2r^4)\} - V(r)\}$$

$= (p_r^2/2m) + (p_\theta^2/2m_r^2) + V(r) =$ total energy of the system.

(b) Hamilton's equations are

$$\dot{p}_i = -(\partial H/\partial q_i), \dot{q}_i = (\partial H/\partial p_i)$$

$$\Rightarrow \dot{r} = (\partial H/\partial p_r) = (p_r/m), \dot{\theta} = (\partial H/\partial p_\theta) = (p_\theta/mr^2)$$

$$\dot{p}_1 = -(\partial H/\partial r) = (p_\theta^2/mr^3) - V(r), \dot{p}_\theta = -(\partial H/\partial\theta) = 0.$$

Example 18(b):

A particle of mass m moves in a force field of potential V. Write

(a) *The Hamiltonian and*

(b) *Hamilton's equations in spherical polar co-ordinates.*

Solution:

K.E. is given by

$$T = \frac{1}{2}m(\dot{r}^2 + r^2\dot{\theta}^2 + r^2\sin^2\theta\dot{\phi}^2) \qquad \text{...(1)}$$

$$\therefore L = T - V = \frac{1}{2}m(\dot{r}^2 + r^2\dot{\theta}^2 + r^2\sin^2\theta\dot{\phi}^2 - V \qquad \text{...(2)}$$

We have $p_r = (\partial L/\partial\dot{r}) = m\dot{r}, p_\theta = (\partial L/\partial\dot{\theta}) = mr^2\dot{\theta},$

$p_\phi = (\partial L/\partial\dot{\phi}) = mr^2 \sin^2\theta\dot{\phi}$

$\Rightarrow \dot{r} = (p_r/m), \dot{\theta} = (p_\theta/mr^2), \dot{\phi} = p\phi/(mr^2\sin^2\theta).$ ...(3)

Now Hamiltonian is given by

$h = \Sigma p_i \dot{q}_i - L = p_r\dot{r} + p_\theta\dot{\theta} + p\phi\dot{\phi} - L$

$= \dfrac{p_r^2}{2m} + \dfrac{p_\theta^2}{2mr^2} + \dfrac{p_\theta^2}{2mr^2\sin^2\theta} + V(r,\theta,\phi)$

= total energy of the system.

(b) Hamilton's equations are given by

$\dot{q}_i = (\partial H/\partial p_i), \dot{p}_i = -(\partial H/\partial q_i)$

i.e. $\dot{r} = \dfrac{\partial H}{\partial p_r} = \dfrac{p_r}{m}$ $\quad \dot{p}r = -\dfrac{\partial H}{\partial r} = \dfrac{p_\theta^2}{mr^3} + \dfrac{p_\phi^2}{mr^3\sin^2\theta} - \dfrac{\partial V}{\partial r}$

$\dot{\theta} = \dfrac{\partial H}{\partial p_\theta} = \dfrac{p_\theta}{mr^2}$ $\quad \dot{p}\theta = -\dfrac{\partial H}{\partial \theta} = \dfrac{p_\phi^2\cos\theta}{mr^2\sin^3\theta} - \dfrac{\partial V}{\partial \theta}$

$\dot{\phi} = \dfrac{\partial H}{\partial p_\phi} = \dfrac{p_\phi}{mr^2\sin^r\theta}$ $\quad \dot{p}\phi = -\dfrac{\partial H}{\partial \phi} = -\dfrac{\partial V}{\partial \phi}$.

Example 19:

If H is the Hamiltonian prove that if f is any function depending (df/dt) = $((\partial f/\partial t) + [H.f]$

Solution:

We have

$(df/dt) = (\partial f/\partial t) + \{\partial f/\partial q_i)(dq_i/dt) + (\partial f/\partial p_i)(dp_i/dt)\}$

$\Rightarrow (df/dt) = (\partial f/\partial t) + \Sigma\{\partial f/\partial q_i)(\partial H/\partial q_i) - (\partial f/\partial p_i)(\partial H/\partial qi)\}$

$\{\because$ By Hamilton's equations $\dot{q}i = \partial H/\partial p_i, \dot{p}_i = -(\partial H/\partial q_i)\}$

$\Rightarrow (df/dt)(\partial f/\partial t) + [H,f]$ where [H, f] is the Poisson Bracket)

EXERCISES

1. Write the Hamiltonian for the motion of a spherical pendulum and obtain Hamilton's equations. Solve them to show that Hamiltonian is a constant.
2. Derive the Euler's dynamical equations from Hamilton's equations.

3. If H is the Hamiltonian, prove that if f is any function depending on position, momentum and time, then

   $(df/dt) = (\partial f/\partial t) + [H, f]$ where [H,f] is the poisson's Bracket.

4. A heavy bead of mass **m** freely movable on a smooth circular wire of radius a which is made to rotate about a vertical diameter with spin ω, prove that the action,

$$A = ma^2 \int_{\theta_1}^{\theta_2} \left[\frac{2H}{ma^2} + \frac{2g}{a}\cos\theta + \omega^2 \sin^2\theta\right]^{1/2} d\theta$$

   where **H** is the Hamiltonian and θ is the angle the radius through the bead makes with the downward vertical.

5. A particle of unit mass is projected so that its total energy is k, in a field of a force a of which the potential energy is $\phi(r)$ at a distance r from the origin. Find the differential equation of the path.
6. State the variational principle of Hamilton.
7. State & prove the principle of least action.
8. State & prove the principle of least action for a conservative holonomic system, is the action really least in all cases.
9. Prove that for function f (y, y′, x)

$$\frac{\partial f}{\partial y} - \frac{d}{dx}\left(\frac{\partial f}{\partial y'}\right) = 0, \text{ where } y' = \frac{dy}{dx}$$

10. Obtain Hamilton's canonical equations of motion for rigid body.
11. Define Hamiltonian function and derive Hamilton's equations of motion.
12. Apply the technique of calculus of variation to obtain Euler Lagrange's equations.

6

EULER'S EQUATIONS OF MOTION

MOVING AXES AND THE FIXED AXES

Let a body turn about some fixed point O and let OA, OB, OC be the principal axes fixed in the body (which move with the body). Further let Ox, Oy, Oz the axes fixed in the space. After a time t, let the components of the angular velocity of the body; about Ox, Oy, Oz be θ_x, θ_y and θ_z; about OA, B and OC be ω_1, ω_2 and ω_3. Again let h_1, h_2, h_3 be the components of any vector h (say, angular momentum) along OA, OB, OC; h_x, h_y, h_z be the components of the same vector h along Ox, Oy, Oz then if α, β, γ, are the inclinations of OA, OB, OC to the axis Ox, we readily obtain

$$h_x = h_1 \cos\alpha + h_2 \cos\beta + h_3 \cos\gamma$$

$$\Rightarrow h_1 = \dot{h}_1 \cos\alpha + \dot{h}_2 \cos\beta + \dot{h}_3 \cos\gamma \text{ Op6}$$

$$+ h_1(-\sin\alpha.\dot{\alpha}) + h_2(-\sin\beta.\dot{\beta}) + h_3(-\sin\gamma\dot{\gamma}) \quad ...(1)$$

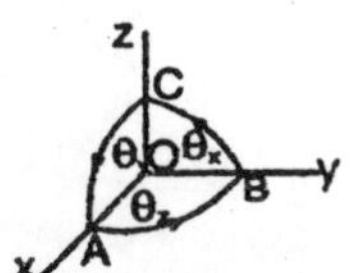

Fig. 6.1

Let the axes fixed in the body coincide with the axes fixed in space at time t, then we have

$$\alpha = 0, \beta = \frac{\pi}{2} = \gamma \Rightarrow \dot{h}_1 - h_2\dot{\beta} - h_3\dot{\gamma}$$

Again we know that β is the angle which the line OB makes with Ox, therefore β becomes the rate at which OB is receding from Ox, also the same rate is θζ ιμπλψινγ that $\dot{\beta} = \theta_z$ (they are in the same sense) ...(3)

Again γ denotes the rate at which OC is receding from Ox, also the same rate is denoted by θψ βυτ in opposite sense and hence $\dot{\gamma} = -\theta_y$.

Making these substitutions in the above result, we get

$$\dot{h}_x = \dot{h}_1 - h_2\theta_z + h_3\theta_y \quad ...(4)$$

By symmetry, we immediately get

$$\dot{h}_y = \dot{h}_2 - h_3\theta_x + h_1\theta_z \quad ...(5)$$

$$\dot{h}_z = \dot{h}_3 - h_1\theta_y + h_2\theta_x \quad ...(6)$$

when OA, OB, OC coincide with Ox, Oy, Oz, then we also have

$$\theta_x = \omega_1, \theta_y = \omega_2, \theta_z = \omega_3$$

$$\left.\begin{aligned} \Rightarrow \dot{h}_x &= \dot{h}_1 - h_2\omega_3 + h_3\omega_2 \\ \dot{h}_y &= \dot{h}_2 - h_3\omega_1 + h_1\omega_3 \\ \dot{h}_z &= \dot{h}_3 - h_1\omega_2 + h_2\omega_1 \end{aligned}\right] \quad ...(a)$$

This establishes the law, how the component of a vector along an axis fixed in space can be expressed in terms of the components of the same vector along the principal axes and the angular velocities $\omega_1, \omega_2, \omega_2$ about them.

To find the velocity of a point when the rigid body turns about O.

Let Ox, Oy, Oz the axes fixed in space. Consider a point P (x,y,z) in the body. Let $\omega_x, \omega_y, \omega_z$ be the components of the angular velocity of P about Ox, Oy and Oz respectively. First of all, we consider the rotation of P about Oy.

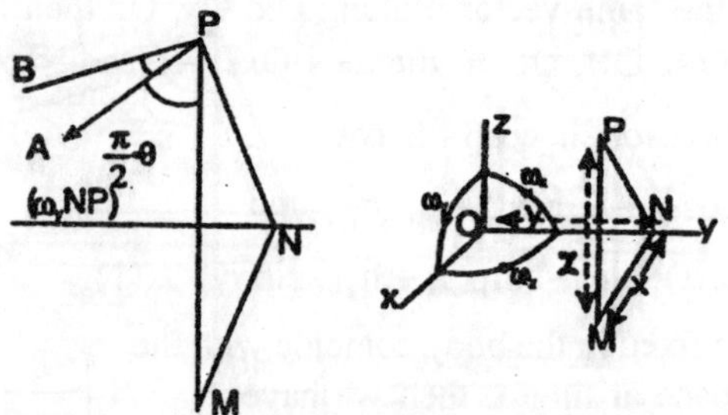

Fig. 6.2

Due to this rotation, velocity of P becomes ωψ NΠ ιν the direct ; in PA (to NP) . This lies in the plane PMN and hence parallel to the plane zOx. Draw a line PB parallel to OX and let it make an angle θ with the line PA. Again PN is perpendicular to PA and PM Now components of the velocity wy NP are.

$\omega_y NP\cos\theta$ alongPB *i.e.* || to O x *i.e.*

$\omega_y KP(PM/PN)$ || to Ox *i.e.* || to Ox

and $\omega_y NP\sin\theta$ along PM *i.e.* || to –z axis

i.e. $-\omega_y NP.(MN/NP)$ || ro Oz

$i.e. -\omega_y x \parallel$ to Oz

Similarly due to rot action about Oz we have the velocity components as:

$$\omega_z x \parallel Oy$$

and $\quad - \quad \omega_z x \parallel$ to Ox

Finally, due to rotation about Ox, we have the velocity components as :

$$\omega_x y \parallel Oz \text{ and } -\omega_x z \parallel \text{to } Oy$$

Hence due to three rotation, components of velocity of P are

$$(\omega_x y - \omega_z z) \parallel Ox, (\omega_z x - \omega_x z) \parallel \text{to } Oy$$

and $\quad (\omega_x y - \omega_y x) \parallel$ to Oz

and $\quad \dot{z} = (\omega_x y - \omega_y x)$

$$\Rightarrow u + (\omega_y z - \omega_z y), \dot{y} = v + (\omega_z x - \omega_y z)\dot{z} = w + (\omega_x y - \omega_y x).$$

where $(\dot{x}, \dot{y}, \dot{z})$ are the components of the velocity at P parallel to the axes respectively.

Note. If the point O is not at rest but itself moving with a velocity whose components are u,v,w, (|| to the axes), then components of velocity at P will be

$$\dot{x} = u + (\omega_y z - \omega_z y), \dot{y} = v + (\omega_z x - \omega_y z), \dot{z} = w + (\omega_x y - \omega_y x).$$

INVARIABLE LINE

Let the rigid turn about O under no forces. Suppose OA, OB OC are the principal axes of the body at O : $\omega_1, \omega_2, \omega_3$ the angular velocities about OA, OB, and OC respectively then component angular momentums about these axes are $A\omega_1, B\omega_2, C\omega_3$ where A, B, C are the moments of inertias of the body about the principal axes. *The resultant line of the angular momentum is known as invariable line and the resultant angular momentum is given by* $H = (A^2\omega_1^2 + B^2\omega_2^2 + C^2\omega_3^2)$. But here the body moves under no forces, therefore the sum of the moments of the external forces about O is zero implying there by that the angular momentum about any straight line through O is constant throughout the me motion *i.e.* H = constant or $A^2\omega_1^2 + B^2\omega_2^2 + C^2\omega_3^2$ = constant.

The direction ratios of the invariable line are therefore $A\,\omega_1$, $B\omega_2$, $C\omega_3$. *This also shows that the direction ratios of the invariable line change w.r.t. the principal axes OA, OB, OC because* ω_1, ω_2, ω_3 *change as t changes.*

LOCUS OF THE INVARIABLE LINE

Let the rigid body turn about O under no forces. Suppose OA, OB, OC are the principal axes of the body at O; $\omega_1, \omega_2, \omega_3$ the angular velocities about OA, OB and OC respectively then the component angular momentum about these axes are A ω_1, Bω_2, Xω_3 where A, B, C are the m, i's of the body about the principal axes.

$$\therefore [(A^2\omega_1^2 + B^2\omega_2^2 + C^2\omega_3^2)/(A^2\omega_1^2 + B\omega_2^2 + C\omega_3^2)] = (H^2/2T)$$

$$\Rightarrow A^2\omega_1^2\left(1-\frac{H^2}{2AT}\right) + B\omega_2^2\left(1-\frac{H^2}{2BT}\right) + C^2\omega_3^2\left(1-\frac{H^2}{2CT}\right) = 0. \quad ...(3)$$

Further, the equations of the invartiable line are

$(x/A\omega_1) = (y/B\omega_2) = (z/C\omega_3) = r$ (say)

[$\because$ Invariable line passes through O and has direction ratios Aω_1, Bω_r, Cω_1].

Substituting in the previous equation, we get

$$(x^2/r^2)\left(1-\frac{H^2}{2AT}\right) + (y^2/r^2)\left(1-\frac{H^2}{2BT}\right) + (z^2/r^2)\left(1-\frac{H^2}{2CT}\right) = 0$$

$$\Rightarrow x^2\left(1-\frac{H^2}{2AT}\right) + y^2\left(1-\frac{H^2}{2BT}\right) + z^2\left(1-\frac{H^2}{2CT}\right) = 0 \; (\because r \neq 0) \quad ...(4)$$

Equation (4) evidently represents a cone with vertex at the origin. The quantities H, A, B, C, T involved in equation (4) are constants, hence the above cone fixed in the body and is known as Invariable cone.

DEDUCTION OF EULER'S EQUATIONS FROM LAGRANGE'S EQUATIONS

Let the rigid body turn about some fixed point O under no forces. Suppose OA, OB, OC are the principal axes of the body at O; ω_1, ω_2, ω_3, the angular velocities about OA, OB OC respectively then the kinetic energy T is given by

$$T = \frac{1}{2}(a\omega_1^2 + B\omega_2^2 + C\omega_3^2)$$

where A, B, C are the moments of inertias of the body about OA, OB, OC respectively and Euler geometrical relations are

$$\omega_1 = \dot{\theta}\sin\phi - \dot{\phi}\sin\theta\cos\psi, \omega_2 = \dot{\theta}\cos\psi + \dot{\phi}\sin\theta\sin\psi,$$

$$\omega_3 = \dot{\phi}\cos\theta + \dot{\psi}.$$

Hence T can be thought to be the function of the generalised co - ordinates

θ, ϕ, ψ and the generalised velocities $\dot{\theta}, \dot{\phi}, \dot{\psi}$,

$$\because \frac{\partial T}{\partial \dot{\psi}} = \frac{\partial T}{\partial \omega_1}\frac{\partial \omega_1}{\partial \dot{\psi}} + \frac{\partial T}{\partial \omega_2}\frac{\partial \omega_2}{\partial \dot{\psi}} + \frac{\partial T}{\partial \omega_3}\frac{\partial \omega_3}{\partial \dot{\psi}}$$

$$= \frac{\partial T}{\partial \omega_3}\frac{\partial \omega_3}{\partial \dot{\psi}} \; (\because \omega_1, \omega_2 \text{ do not involve } \dot{\psi})$$

and $\dfrac{\partial T}{\partial \psi} = \dfrac{\partial T}{\partial \omega_1}\dfrac{\partial \omega_1}{\partial \psi} + \dfrac{\partial T}{\partial \omega_2}\dfrac{\partial \omega}{\partial \psi} + \dfrac{\partial T}{\partial \omega_3}\dfrac{\partial \omega_3}{\partial \psi}$

$$= A\omega_1 \frac{\partial \omega_1}{\partial \psi} + B\omega_2 \frac{\partial \omega_2}{\partial \psi} C\omega_3.0 \qquad \text{[using above results]}$$

$$= A\omega_1 \; (\dot{\theta}\cos\psi + \dot{\phi}\sin\theta\sin\psi) + B\omega_2(-\dot{\theta}\sin\psi + \dot{\phi}\sin\theta\cos\psi)$$

$= A\ \omega_1\omega_2 - B\omega_1\omega_2$ (using above results $= (A - B)\ \omega_1\omega_2$

Further, let W be the work function of the system and N the moment of the external forces about axis OC, then we readily obtain.

$$\frac{\partial W}{\partial \psi} = N$$

Now, Lagrange's ψ-equation gives

$$\frac{d}{dt}\left(\frac{\partial T}{\partial \dot{\psi}}\right) - \frac{\partial T}{\partial \psi} = \frac{\partial W}{\partial \psi} \text{ i.e. } \frac{d}{dt}(C\dot{\omega}_3) - (A - B)\omega_1\omega_2 = N$$

$$\Rightarrow C\frac{d\omega_3}{dt} - (A - B)\omega_1\omega_2 = N$$

This is Euler's third equations; and similarly other two equations can also be deduced.

EULER'S DYNAMICAL EQUATIONS

Let a rigid body turn about some fixed point O under the action of external sources such that L,M,N be the moments of the external forces, inertia about the principal axes fixed in the body then to obtain the equations of motion.

Let the body turn about some fixed point O and let OA, OB, OC be the principal axes fixed in the body (which move with the body).

Further, let Ox, Oy, Oz be the axes fixed in apace. After a time t, let the components of the angular velocity of the body, about Ox, Oy, and Oz by θ_1, θ_2, θ_3; about OA, OB and OC be $\omega_1, \omega_2, \omega_3$ .Again let h_1, h_2, h_3 be the components of the vector h, (angular momentum) along OA, OB, OC, h_x, h_y, h_z be the components of the same vector h along Ox, Oy, Oz. then we have

$$\dot{h}_x = \dot{h}_1 - h_2\theta_z + h_3\theta_y, \dot{h}_y = \dot{h}_2 - h_3\theta_x + h_1\theta_z, \text{ and}$$

$$\dot{h}_z = \dot{h}_3 - h_1\theta_y + h_2\theta_x,$$

$$\left.\begin{array}{l} \dot{h}_x = \dot{h}_1 - h_2\omega_3 + h_3\omega_2 \\ \Rightarrow \dot{h}_y = \dot{h}_2 - h_3\omega_1 + h_1\omega_3 \\ \dot{h}_z = \dot{h}_3 - h_1\omega_2 + h_2\omega_1 \end{array}\right]$$

(when OA, OB, OC concide with Ox, Oy, Oz) ...(1)

Again, if x,y,z are the co-ordinates of a particle m of the rigid body, relative to OA, OB, OC then relative to these axes, we have

$$\dot{x} = z\omega_2 - y\omega_3, \dot{y} = x\omega_3 - z\omega_3, \dot{z} = y\omega_1 - x\omega_2.$$

Now h_1 = components of angular momentum (h) about OA

= angular momentum about OA

$$= \Sigma m(y\dot{z} - z\dot{y}) = \Sigma m[y(y\omega_1 - x\omega_2) - z(x\omega_3 - z\omega_1)]$$

$$= \omega_1 \Sigma m(y^2 + z^2) - \omega_2 \Sigma mxy - \omega_3 \Sigma mzx = A\omega_1 - F\omega_2 - E\omega_3 \quad ...(2)$$

By symmetry, we then have

$h_2 = B\omega_2 - D\omega_3 - F\omega_1$ ...(3) and $h_3 = C\omega_3 - E\omega_1 - D\omega_2$ ...(4)

where A, B, C are the moments and D,E, F are the products of inertia about OA, OB, OC.

Here OA, OB, OC are the principal axes; therefore we have D = E = F = 0.

Now from above we have

$h_1 = A\omega_1$, $h_2 = B\omega_2$ and $h_3 = C\omega_3$

$\Rightarrow \dot{h}_1 = A\dot{\omega}_1, \dot{h}_2 = B\dot{\omega}_2$ and $\dot{h}_3 = c\dot{\omega}_3$

$$\left.\begin{array}{l} \dot{h}_x = A\dot{\omega}_1 - B\omega_2\omega_3 + C\omega_2\omega_3 \\ \text{whence } h_y = B\dot{\omega}_2 - C\omega_3\omega_1 + A\omega_1\omega_3 \\ \dot{h}_z = C\dot{\omega}_3 - A\omega_1\omega_2 + B\omega_2\omega_1 \end{array}\right] \quad ..(A)$$

[when OA, OP, OC coincide with Ox, Oy, Oz]

But $\dot{h}_x$ = angular momentum about OA

= moment of momentum about OA = L (given)

[when OA coincides with Ox]

and similarly $\dot{h}_y = M, \dot{h}_2 = N$

$\therefore A\dot{\omega}_1 - (B-C)\omega_2\omega_3 = L; B\dot{\omega}_2 - (C-A)\omega_3\omega_1 = M;$

$\therefore C\dot{\omega}_3 - (A-B)\omega_1\omega_2 = N.$ ...(B)

These are called as *Euler's dynamical equations.*

Special Case. *When the body moves under on forces.*

then we have L = 0 = M = N

$$\begin{cases} \therefore (B) \Rightarrow A\dot{\omega}_1 - (B-C)\omega_2\omega_3 = 0 & ...(X) \\ B\dot{\omega}_2 - (C-A)\omega_3\omega_1 = 0 & ...(Y) \\ C\dot{\omega}_3 - (A-B)\omega_1\omega_2 = 0 & ...(Z) \end{cases}$$

Euler's dynamical equations under no forces.

The special case of motion about O under no forces is of importance. In this case multiplying the three equations (X), (Y), (Z) by the ω_1, ω_2, ω_3 and adding, we get

$$A\omega_1\dot{\omega}_1 + B\omega_2\dot{\omega}_2 + C\omega_3\dot{\omega}_3 = 0 \Rightarrow A\omega_1^2 + B\omega_2^2 + C\omega_3^2 = \text{const.}$$

But it is proved in the forthcoming.

$$K.E. = T = \frac{1}{2}(A\omega_1^2 + B\omega_2^2 + C\omega_3^2)$$

$\therefore$ Above result shows that the kinetic energy remains constant during the motion. It is obvious since no work is being done on the body, there being on external forces. Another integral of equations (X), (Y), (Z) can be obtained then by multiplying these by $A\omega_1$, $B\omega_2$, $C\omega_3$ and adding to give

$$A^2\omega_1\dot{\omega}_1 + B^2\dot{\omega}_2\omega_2 + C^2\omega_3\dot{\omega}_3 = 0 \Rightarrow A^2\omega_1^2 + B^2\omega_2^2 + C^2\omega_3^2 = \text{const.}$$

But we know that $h_1 = A\omega_1, h_2 = B\omega_2, h_3 = C\omega_3$.

i.e. $h = (A\omega_1, B\omega_2, C\omega_3)$ and $/h/ = \sqrt{(A^2\omega_1^2 + B^2\omega_2^2 + C^2\omega_3^2}$

Hence the above equation implies the constancy of the magnitude of the angular momentum h during the motion. Physically this is attributable to the zero moment of forces about O.

KINETIC ENERGY

Suppose a rigid body terms about some fixed point. O. If ω_1, ω_2, ω_3 are the angular velocities and A,B, C the moments of inertia about the principal axes OA, OB, OC; then the kinetic energy of the body is

$$T=\frac{1}{2}(A\omega_1^2+B\omega_2^2+C\omega_3^2).$$

Proof:

A time t, let (x,y,z) be the co-ordinates, of a particle m of the body, referred to the principal axes OA, OB, OC; and ω_1, ω_2, ω_3 the angular velocities about these axes. Then the components of velocity of a particle of mass m of the body are given by

$$\dot{x}=(\omega_2 z-\omega_3 y),\ \dot{y}=(\omega_3 x-\omega_1 z),\ \dot{z}=(\omega_1 y-\omega_2 x)$$

∴ Kinetic energy of the body

$$T=\frac{1}{2}\Sigma m(\dot{x}^2+\dot{y}^2+\dot{z}^2)$$

$$=\frac{1}{2}\Sigma m[(\omega_2 z-\omega_3 y)^2+(\omega_3 x-\omega_3 z)^2+(\omega_1 y-\omega_2 x)^2]$$

$$=\frac{1}{2}\Sigma m[(\omega_1^2(z^2+y^2)+\omega_2^2(z^2+x^2)+\omega_3^2(x^2+y^2)$$

$$-2\omega_2\omega_3 yz-2\omega_3\omega_1 zx-2\omega_1\omega_2 xy]$$

$$=\frac{1}{2}[A\omega_1^2+B\omega_2^2+C\omega_3^2-2D\omega_2\omega_3-2E\omega_3\omega_1-2F\omega_1\omega^2],$$

where A, B, C are the moments and D, E, F are the product of inertias about OA, OB, OC.

But D = E = F = 0 [∵ OA, OB, OC are the principal axes]

$$\therefore T=\frac{1}{2}(a\omega_1^2+B\omega_2^2+C\omega_3^2).$$

EULER'S EQUATIONS (*for Impulsive Forces*)

Let the rigid body turn about a fixed point O and let OA, OB, OC (axes fixed in the body) be the principal axes which move along with the body. Let the body be given an impulse so that L, M, N are the moments of the impulse about OA, OB, OC respectively. Further, let ω_1, ω_2 ω_3 and ω_1', ω_2' ω_3' be the component angular velocities just before and just after the action of the impulse. Then we have, Change in angular momentum about OA

= moment of the impulse about OA

⇒ (angular momentum after the action of impulse

– angular momentum before the action of impulse) about OA = L

⇒ $A\omega_1' - A\omega_1 = L(\because h_1 = A\omega_1) \Rightarrow A(\omega_1' - \omega_1) = L$

and similarly $B(\omega_2' - \omega_2) = M$; $C(\omega_3' - \omega_3) = N$.

These are Euler's Equations of motion under impulsive forces.

EULERIAN ANGLES

Ir order to describe the rotation of a rigid body about a point (say O) we use three angular co-ordinates θ, ϕ ψ which are called *Euler's angles* described below. Let a rigid body turn about the point O. Let OA, OB, OC (axes fixed in the body) be the principal axes of the body at the point O which move along with the body. Initially; OA, OB, OC coincide with Ox, Oy, Oz. Construct a spherical surface of radius unity with centre at O.

Let the axes OX, Oy, Oz (fixed in space) meet the spherical surface in points (x, y, z). After a time t, when the rigid body is rotating let the axes OA, OB, OC (fixed in the body) meet the spherical surface in points A, B, C. Let ∠COz = θ, angle between the plane zOC and zOx = ϕ and angle between the planes zPC and COA = ψ then these angles are known as Eulerian angles. To obtain the values of ϕ and ψ more precisely we proceed as follows:

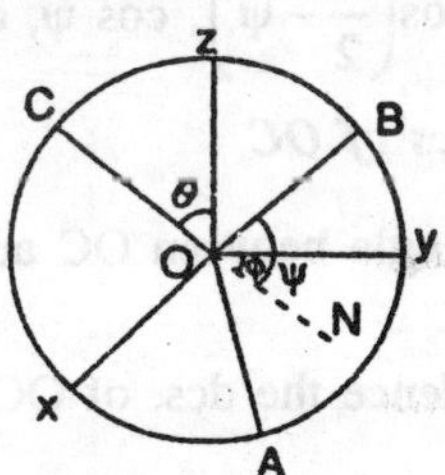

Fig. 6.3

Draw a line ON perpendicular to the plane zOC and obviously the normals to the planes COA and zOx are the lines OB and Oy respectively. But angles between two planes = angle between their normals; so we have

ϕ = angle between the planes zOC and zOx = angle between the normals ON OY and ψ = angle between the planes zOC and COA = angle between the normals ON and OB.

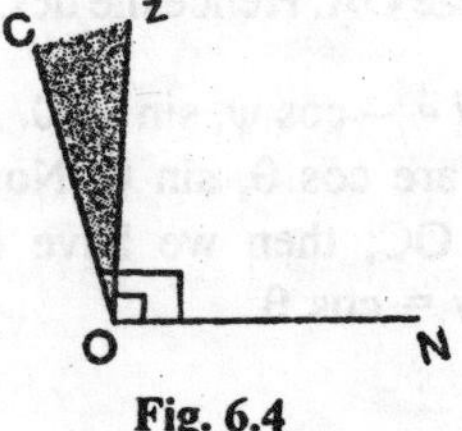

Fig. 6.4

Euler's Geometrical Equations

Let ω_1, ω_2, ω_3 be the component angular velocities about the principal axes OA, OB, OC. Obviously ∠zOC = θ and ON is normal to this plane so the angular velocity θ is about this line. Further the line ON being perpendicular to both Oz and OC lies in the xOy plane and as well as in AOB plane. Angle ϕ is in xOy plane, therefore angular velocity ϕ is about Oz since oz is ⊥ to this plane. Similarly the angle ψ is in the plane AOB, therefore angular velocity $\dot{\psi}$ is about

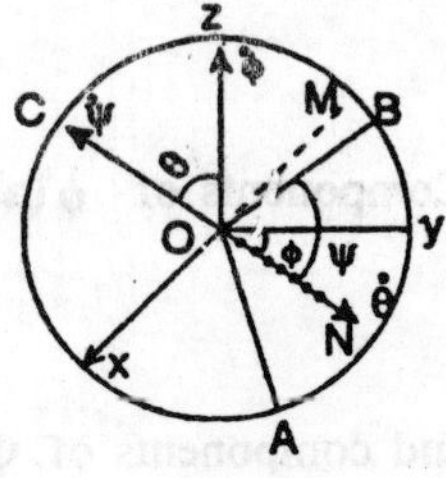

Fig. 6.5

OC which is normal to this plane. Now, we proceed to determine the d.cs of the lines ON, OC, OZ w.r.t. the principal axes OA, OB, OC.

(1) Dcs of ON

The line ON ($\perp$ to OC) lies in the plane A OB, therefore it makes an angle $\frac{\pi}{2}-\psi$ with the line OA and ψ with the line OB. The angle between ON and OC $=\frac{\pi}{2}$. Hence the d.c.s. of the line ON are

$$\cos\left(\frac{\pi}{2}-\psi\right),\ \cos\psi,\ \cos\frac{\pi}{2}\ \ \text{i.e.}\ \sin\psi,\ \cos\psi,\ 0$$

(2) Dcs of OC

Angle between OC and OA $=\frac{\pi}{2}$, angle between OC and OB $=\frac{\pi}{2}$

Hence the dcs. of OC are cos $=\frac{\pi}{2}$, $=\frac{\pi}{2}$ cos 0 *i.e.* 0,0, 1.

(3) Dcs of Oz

Draw a line OM perpendicular to OC (in the plane zOC). Since the line OM lies in zOC plane, it is normal to the ON further the line OM is normal to OC so it also lies in the plane AOB such that $\angle MON=(\pi/2)$. the line ON makes angle ψ with OB, therefore the line OM will make an angle y with the line OA. Hence the dcs. of the line OM are cos (p – ψ), $\cos\left(\frac{\pi}{2}-\psi\right)$, $\cos\frac{\pi}{2}$

i.e. – cos ψ, sin ψ, 0. Also the dcs of Oz w.r.t the coplanar lines OC and OM are cos θ, sin θ. Now let the line Oz make angles α, β, γ with OA, OB, OC; then we have cos α = – sin θ, cos ψ, cos β = sin θ sin ψ, cos γ = cos θ.

Hence, components of $\dot{\theta}$ (about ON) are $\begin{cases}\dot{\theta}\sin\psi \text{ about OA}\\ \dot{\theta}\cos\psi \text{ about OB}\\ \dot{\theta}\times 0 \text{ about OC}\end{cases}$

Components of $\dot{\phi}$ (about Oz) are $\begin{cases}-\dot{\phi}\sin\theta\cos\psi \text{ OA}\\ \dot{\phi}\cos\theta\sin\psi \text{ about OB}\\ \dot{\phi}\times\theta \text{ about OC}\end{cases}$

and components of ψ (about OC) are $\begin{cases}\psi.0 \text{ i.e. } 0 \text{ about OC}\\ \psi.0 \text{ i.e. } 0 \text{ about OA}\\ \psi.1 \text{ i.e. } \psi \text{ about OB}\end{cases}$

Now : let $\omega_1, \omega_2, \omega_3$ be the angular velocities about OA,OB, and OC respectively. Then we have

$$\left.\begin{aligned} \omega_1 &= \dot{\theta}\sin\psi - \phi\sin\theta\cos\psi && (1) \\ \omega_2 &= \dot{\theta}\sin\psi + \phi\sin\theta\sin\psi && (2) \\ \omega_3 &= \dot{\phi}\theta + \psi && (3) \end{aligned}\right\}$$

These are called Euler geometrical equations.

INSTANTANEOUS AXIS OF ROTATION

Let the rigid body turn about the fixed point O and at time t, let $\omega_1, \omega_2, \omega_3$ be the component angular velocity about the principal axes OA,OB,OC (fixed in the body), then d.cs of the resultant axes of rotation are $(\omega_1/\omega), (\omega_2/\omega), (\omega_3/\omega)$ where $\omega = \sqrt{(\omega_1^2 + \omega_2^2 + \omega_3^2)}$. But $\omega_1, \omega_2, \omega_3$ have been expressed (in the previous art) in terms of Eulerian angles θ, ϕ, ψ (which change from time to time). Consequently, the resultant axis of rotation also changes implying that at different instants, there are different axis of rotation. is known as instantaneous axis of rotation or simple the instantaneous axis of rotation or simple the instantaneous axis.

SOLVED EXAMPLES

Example 1:

A rectangular lamina ABCD in which BC = $\sqrt{2}$AB can turn freely about the middle point O of AD. Initially it is rotating with angular velocity Ω about a line through O perpendicular to AD and making an angle 30° with the plane of the rectangle. Show that after time t, the components of the angular velocity of the rectangle about the principal axes at O are

$$\frac{\sqrt{3}}{2}\operatorname{sech}\left(\frac{1}{2}\Omega t\right), \frac{\sqrt{3}}{2}\Omega\tanh\left(\frac{1}{2}\Omega\tanh\right)\frac{1}{2}\Omega\operatorname{sech}\left(\frac{1}{2}\Omega t\right)$$

Solution:

If G is the C, G. of the lamina ABCD, and OP, the line normal to its plane then OG, OA, OP form a set of principal axes at O. Since it is rotating about the line OR which is perpendicular to OA, therefore OR lies in the plane GOP.

Since $\angle GOR = 30°$,

$$\angle POR = 60°$$

and $\angle AOR = 90^\circ$

Direction cosines of OR are

$$\cos 30^\circ, \cos 90^\circ, \cos 60^\circ \text{ } i.e. \text{ } \frac{\sqrt{3}}{2}, 1, \frac{1}{2}.$$

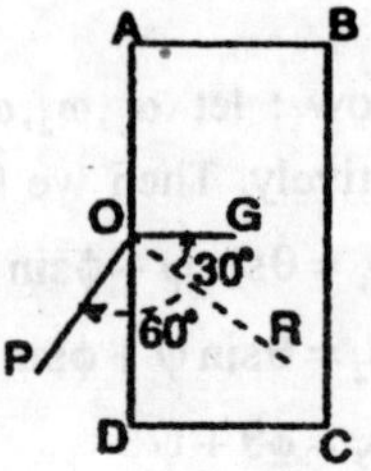

Now if we take AB = 2a then BC = $2\sqrt{2a}$.

A = moment of inertia about

$$OG = \frac{1}{2}M\left(\frac{1}{2}BC\right)^2 = \frac{2Ma^2}{3}.$$

Fig. 6.6

B = moment of inertia about

$$OA = \frac{1}{3}M\left[\left(\frac{1}{2}AB\right)^2 + \left(\frac{1}{3}AB\right)^2 \frac{2Ma^2}{3}\right] = \frac{4Ma^2}{3}$$

C = moment of inertia about OP

$$= \frac{1}{3}M\left\{\frac{1}{2}AB)^2 + \left(\frac{1}{2}BC\right)^2\right\} + MOG^2 = \frac{1}{3}M(3a^2) + Ma^2 = 2Ma^2$$

Euler's equations of motion under no forces are

$$A\dot{\omega}_1 - (B - C)\omega_2\omega_3 = 0;$$

$$B\dot{\omega}_2 - (C - A)\omega_3\omega_1 = 0; \qquad \text{...(1)}$$

$$C\dot{\omega}_2 - (A - B)\omega_1\omega_2 = 0.$$

Substituting the values A, B, C in (1), we get

$$\frac{2Ma^2}{3}\dot{\omega}_1 + \frac{2Ma^2}{3}\omega_2\omega_3 = 0 \Rightarrow \dot{\omega}_1 = -\omega_2\omega_3 \qquad \text{...(2)}$$

$$\frac{4Ma^2}{3}\dot{\omega}_2 = \frac{4Ma^2}{3}\omega_3\omega_1 = 0 \Rightarrow \dot{\omega}_2 = \omega_3\omega_1 \qquad \text{...(3)}$$

$$2Ma^2\dot{\omega}_3 + \frac{2Ma^2}{3}\omega_1\omega_2 = 0 \Rightarrow \dot{\omega}_3 = -\frac{1}{3}\omega_1\omega_2. \qquad \text{...(4)}$$

Solving (2) and (3), we get $\omega_1\omega_1 = \omega_2\dot{\omega}_2 = 0 \Rightarrow \omega_1^2 + \omega_2^2 = a$,

where a is a constant of integration.

But initially $\omega_1 = \frac{\sqrt{3}}{2}\Omega, \omega_2 = 0$

and $\omega_3 = \frac{1}{3}\Omega, \therefore a = \frac{3}{4}\Omega^2$.

$$\text{Hence } \omega_1^2 + \omega_2^2 = \frac{3}{4}\Omega^2. \qquad \text{...(5)}$$

Again solving (2) and (4), we get

$$\omega_1\dot{\omega}_1 - 3\omega_3\dot{\omega}_3 = 0 \Rightarrow \omega_1^2 - 3\omega_3^2 = b.$$

where b is constant of integration.

Initially $\omega_1 = \frac{1}{3}\sqrt{3\Omega}$ and $\omega_3 = \frac{1}{2}\Omega$ $\therefore$ b = 0.

Hence $\omega_1^2 - 3\omega_3^2 = 0 \Rightarrow \omega_1\sqrt{3\omega_3}$. ...(6)

Substituting the value for ω_3 from (6) in (2), we have

$$\dot{\omega}_2 = \frac{1}{\sqrt{3}}\omega_1 = \frac{1}{\sqrt{3}}\left(\frac{3}{4}\Omega^2 - \omega_2^2\right) \quad \text{[using (5)]}$$

i.e. $= \frac{d\omega_2}{dt} = \frac{1}{\sqrt{3}}\left(\frac{3}{4}\Omega^2 - \omega_2^2\right) \Rightarrow dt = \sqrt{3}.\frac{d\omega_2}{\frac{1}{4}\Omega^2 - \omega_2^2}$

$\Rightarrow t = \sqrt{3}.\frac{2}{\sqrt{3\Omega}}\tanh^{-1}\left(\frac{2\omega_2}{\sqrt{3\Omega}}\right) + C$, where C is constant.

Now t = 0, $\omega_2 = 0$, $\therefore$ C = 0.

Hence $t = \frac{2}{\Omega}\tanh^{-1}\frac{2\dot{\omega}_2}{\sqrt{3\Omega}} \Rightarrow \omega_2 = \frac{\sqrt{3}}{2}\Omega\tanh\left(\frac{1}{2}\Omega t\right)$

Putting this value of ω_2 in (5), we get $\omega_1 = \frac{\sqrt{3}}{2}\Omega\,\text{sech}\left(\frac{1}{2}\Omega t\right)$

And from (6), we get $\omega_2 = \frac{1}{2}\text{sech}\left(\frac{1}{2}\Omega t\right)$.

Thus angular velocities at time t are evaluated.

Example 2:

A uniform right circular cone of vertical angle 2α, moves under no forces except at its vertex, which is fixed. It is set rotating about a generator. Show that its axis describes in a space a right cone of angle 2β where

$$\tan\beta = \frac{1}{2}\tan\alpha + 2\cos\alpha$$

Solution:

Let OP be the generator and OZ the axis of the cone, whose semi-vertical angle is α. Let. OX and. OY be any two perpendicular lines perpendicular to OZ. Then OX, OY, OZ form a set of principal axes at O. The direction cosines of OP are cos (90 – α), cos 90, cos α *i.e.* sin α, 0, cos α.

If the initial angular velocity is ω, then initially, we have

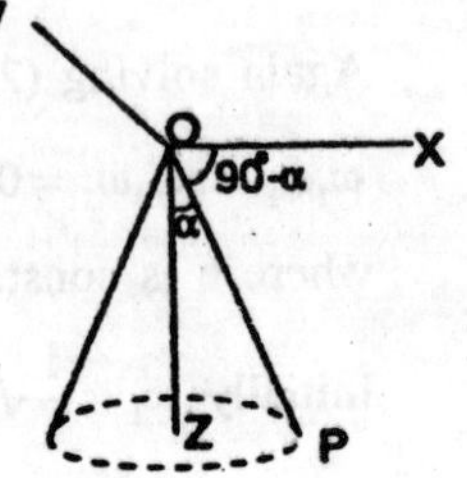

Fig. 6.7

$$\omega_1 = \omega \sin\alpha, \omega_2 = 0, \omega_3 = \omega \cos\alpha$$

Eular's equations of the motion under no forces are

$$A\dot{\omega}_1 - (B - C)\omega_2\omega_3 = 0;$$

$$B\dot{\omega}_2 - (C - A)\omega_3\omega_1 = 0;$$

$$C\dot{\omega}_3 - (A - B)\omega_1\omega_2 = 0. \qquad ...(1)$$

But here A = B, therefore (1) becomes

$$A\dot{\omega}_1 = (A - C)\omega_2\omega_3 \Rightarrow \dot{\omega}_1 = \frac{(A - C}{A}\omega_2\omega_3 \qquad ...(2)$$

$$A\dot{\omega}_2 = -(A - C)\omega_3\omega_1 = 0 \Rightarrow \omega_2 = -\frac{(A - C}{A}\omega_3\omega_1 \qquad ...(3)$$

$$C\dot{\omega}_3 = 0 \Rightarrow \dot{\omega}_3 = \text{const} = \omega\cos\alpha \qquad ...(4)$$

$$\text{Hence } \omega_2^2 + \omega_2^2 = \omega^2 \sin^2\alpha \qquad ...(5)$$

Now the direction cosines of the invariable line are proportional to $A\omega_1, B\omega_2, C\omega_3$.

If the invariable line makes axis (OZ) of the with the figure, an angle θ then $\cos\theta = \frac{C\omega_3}{\sqrt{(A^2\omega_1^2 + B^2\omega_2^2 + C^2\omega_3^2)}}$

But in this case B = A

$$\therefore \cos\theta = \frac{C\omega_3}{\sqrt{(A^2\omega_1^2 + \omega_2^2) + C^2\omega_3^2]}} = \frac{C\omega\cos\alpha}{\sqrt{[A^2\omega^2\sin^2\alpha + C^2\omega^2\cos^2\alpha]}}$$

$$= \frac{C}{\sqrt{[a^2\tan^2\alpha\, C^2]}} \text{ [multiplying num. and denom. by sec } \alpha]$$

$$\Rightarrow \tan\theta = \frac{A\tan\alpha}{C}$$

$$\text{Now A = B } = \frac{3M}{80}(4a^2 + h^2) + M\left(\frac{3h}{4}\right)^2 = \frac{3M}{20}(a^2 + 4h^2)\,[h = a\cot\alpha]$$

Substituting these values of A and C, we get

$$\tan\theta = \frac{1}{2a^2}(a^2 + 4h^2) \quad \tan\alpha = \frac{1}{2}\left(1 + 4\frac{h^2}{a^2}\right)\tan\alpha$$

$$=\frac{1}{2}(1+4\cot^2\alpha)\tan\alpha=\frac{1}{2}\tan\alpha+2\cot\alpha$$

It shows that value of tan θ is constant, implying thereby that θ remains constant throughout the motion. So the axis of the cone of semi vertical angle β such that

$$\tan\beta=\frac{1}{2}\tan\alpha+2\cot\alpha \quad \text{as } \theta = \beta.$$

Example 3:

A uniaxial body is supported at its centre of mass and is rotating initially with angular velocity ω about an axis perpendicular to the axis of symmetry. Prove that if a couple of constant moment N is applied about the axis of symmetry, the instantaneous axis will describe a cone whose equation referred to axis fixed in the body, of which that of z-axis coincide with the axis of symmetry, is

$$2AN\,(x^2 + y^2)^2 \tan^{-1}(y/x) = C\,(C - A)\omega^2 z^2$$

Solution:

Euler's equations of motion in general form are given by

$$A\frac{d\omega_1}{dt}-(B-C)\omega_2\omega_3=L;$$

$$B\frac{d\omega_2}{dt}-(C-A)\omega_3\omega_1=M;$$

$$C\frac{d\omega_3}{dt}-(A-B)\omega_1\omega_2=N.$$

Here, we have L = 0, M = 0, N = N and B = A.

$$\Rightarrow A\frac{d\omega_1}{dt}-(A-C)\omega_1\omega_2=0, \text{ or } \dot{\omega}_1=\lambda\omega_2\omega_3, \quad \text{...(1)}$$

$$\left[\text{Putting } \lambda=\frac{A-C}{A}\right]$$

$$\Rightarrow A\frac{d\omega_2}{dt}-(C-A)\omega_3\omega_1=0 \text{ or } \dot{\omega}_2=0\,\lambda\omega_3\omega_1, \quad \text{...(2)}$$

$$\text{and} \Rightarrow C\frac{d\omega_3}{dt}=N, \text{ or } C\dot{\omega}_3=N. \quad \text{...(3)}$$

Dividing (1) by (2), we obtain $\frac{\dot{\omega}_1}{\dot{\omega}_2}=-\frac{\omega_2}{\omega_1}$, or $\omega_1\dot{\omega}_1+\omega_2\dot{\omega}_2=0$

$\Rightarrow \omega_1^2+\omega_2^2=a$, where a is constant.

Initially $\omega_1 = \omega$, $\omega_2 = 0$,

$\therefore a = \omega^2 \Rightarrow \omega_1^2 + \omega_2^2$ ...(4)

Equation (3) $\Rightarrow C\omega_3 = N$.

$\Rightarrow Cw_3 = Nt + b$ where b is constant

Initially $t = 0$, $w_3 = 0$, $\Rightarrow b = 0$.

$\therefore C\omega_3 = N\,t \Rightarrow \omega_3 = (N/C)\,t$. ...(5)

Then $\therefore$ (1) and (2) reduce to $\dot{\omega}_1 = \frac{N}{C}\lambda t\,\omega_3$ and $\dot{\omega}_2 = -\frac{N}{C}\lambda t\omega_3$

Write $u = \omega_1 + i\omega_2$

Whence differentiating,

$\frac{du}{dt} = \dot{\omega}_1 + i\dot{\omega}_2 = \frac{N}{C}\lambda t(\omega_2 - i\omega_1)$, by the above results.

$= -i\frac{N}{C}\lambda t(\omega_1 + i\omega_2) = -i\frac{N}{C}\lambda tu$, by the above results.

Now integrating, $\log\, u = -i\frac{N\lambda}{C}\frac{t^2}{2} + k$ where k is constant.

But at $t = 0$, $u = \omega_1 + i\omega_2 = \omega$, $\therefore k = \log\omega$

$\Rightarrow \log\frac{u}{\omega} = -i\frac{\lambda N}{2C}t^2 \Rightarrow u = we^{-i\lambda Nt^2/2C}$

$\Rightarrow \omega_1 + i\omega_2 = \omega\left[\cos\left(\frac{\lambda N}{2C}\right)t^2 - i\sin\left(\frac{\lambda N}{2C}\right)t^2\right]$

Whence equating real and imaginary parts, we obtain

$\omega_1 = \omega\cos\left(\frac{\lambda N}{2C}\right)t^2$, $\omega_2 = -\omega\sin\left(\frac{\lambda N}{2C}\right)t^2$,

Putting $\lambda = [(A - C)/A]$, we get

$\omega_1 = \omega\cos\frac{(C-A)}{2AC}Nt^2$ and $\omega_2 = \omega\sin\frac{(C-A)}{2AC}Nt^2$ ...(6)

Let (x,y,z) be a point on the instantaneous axis which pass through the origin and whose direction ratios are ω_1, ω_2 ω_3

$\frac{x}{\omega_1} = \frac{y}{\omega_2} = \frac{z}{\omega_3}$ and $\frac{x^2}{\omega_1^2} = \frac{y^2}{\omega_2^2} = \frac{z^2}{\omega_3^2}$ or $\frac{x^2 + y^2}{\omega^2} = \frac{z^2}{\omega_3^2}$

$\Rightarrow \omega_3^2 = [\omega^2 / z^2 + (x^2 + y^2)]$ and $(\omega_2 / \omega_1) = (y/x)$.

$\therefore (6)(\omega_2/\omega_1) = \tan[\{(C - A)/2AC\}N(C^2/N^2)\omega_3^2]$ $(\because \omega_3 = Nt/C)$

$\Rightarrow (y/x) = \tan\,[\{(C - A)\,C/2AN\}\,(\omega^2 z^2\,/\,x^2 + y^2)\}$

$\Rightarrow 2AN\,(x^2 + y^2)\tan^{-1}(y/x) = C\,(C - A)\,\omega^2 z^2.$

Example 4:

A thin ellipitic plate of semi axes a, b, (a>b) can turn freely about its centre which is fixed. It is set in motion with an angular velocity about an axis in its plane equally inclined to the axes of the ellipse. Show that the instantaneous axis will again be in the plane of the plate after a time,

$$2\int_0^{\lambda}(\lambda^4 - x^4)^{-1/2}\,dx \text{ where } \lambda^2 = \frac{n^2}{a^2}\frac{a^2 - b^2}{a^2 + b^2}$$

Solution:

Initially; we have

$\omega_1 = n\cos 45^\circ;\ \omega_2 = n\sin 45^\circ;\ \omega_3 = 0$

or $\omega_1 = \frac{n}{\sqrt{2}}, \omega_2 = \frac{n}{\sqrt{2}}, \omega_3 = 0$

Now Euler's equations of motion, under no forces, are

$$A\frac{d\omega_1}{dt} = (B - C)\omega_2\omega_3;\ B\frac{d\omega_2}{dt} = (C - A)\omega_3\omega_1$$

and $C\frac{d\omega_3}{dt} = (A - B)\omega_1\omega_2$

But for the elliptic plate, we have

$$A = \frac{Mb^2}{4}, B = \frac{Ma^2}{4}, \text{ and } C = A + B$$

$\Rightarrow A\frac{d\omega_2}{dt} = -A\omega_2\omega_3$, or $\dot{\omega}_1 = -\omega_2\omega_3$, ...(1)

$\therefore B\frac{d\omega_3}{dt} = B\omega_3\omega_1$, or $\dot{\omega}_2 = \omega_3\omega_1$, ...(2)

and $(A + B)\frac{d\omega_3}{dt} = (A - B)\omega_1\omega_2$ or $\dot{\omega}_3 = -\frac{2\lambda^2}{n^2}\omega_1\omega_2$ $(\because C = A + B)$

$$\left[\because \lambda^2 = \frac{n^2}{2}\frac{a^2 - b^2}{a^2 + b^2} = \frac{n^2 B - A}{2B + A}\right]$$

Dividing (2) by (3), we get

$$\frac{\dot{\omega}_2}{\dot{\omega}_3} = \frac{n^2}{2\lambda^2}\cdot\frac{\omega_3}{\omega_2} = 2\lambda^2\omega_2\dot{\omega}_2 = -n^2\omega_3\dot{\omega}_3$$

$\Rightarrow 2\lambda^2\omega\frac{2}{2} = -n^2\omega_3^2 + a$ where a is constant.

Initially. $\omega_2 = \frac{n}{\sqrt{2}}, \omega_3 = 0, \therefore a = \lambda^2 n^2$

$$\Rightarrow 2\lambda^2\omega_2^2 = \lambda^2 n^2 - n^2\omega_3^2 \Rightarrow 2\lambda^2\omega_2^2 = n^2(\lambda^2 - \omega_3^2) \quad ...(i)$$

Again, dividing (1) by (3), we have

$$\frac{\dot{\omega}_1}{\dot{\omega}_2} = \frac{n^2}{2\lambda^2}\frac{\omega_3}{\omega_1} \text{ or } 2\lambda^2\omega_1\dot{\omega}_1 = n^2\omega_3\dot{\omega}_3$$

$2\lambda^2\omega_1 = n^2\omega_3^2 + b$ integrating, where b is constant.

But initially $\omega_1 = \frac{n}{\sqrt{2}}, \omega_3 = 0, \quad \therefore b = \lambda^2 n^2$

$$\Rightarrow 2\lambda^2\omega_1^2 = n^2\omega_3^2 + \lambda^2 n^2 \text{ or } 2\lambda^2\omega_1^2 = n^2(\lambda^2 + \omega_3^2) \quad ...(ii)$$

Now (i) × (ii) $\Rightarrow 4\lambda^4\omega_1^2\omega_2^2 = n^4(\lambda^2 - \omega_3^4) \Rightarrow \frac{2\lambda^2}{n^2}\omega_1\omega_2 = \pm(\lambda^4 - \omega_3^4)^{1/2}$

Using (3), we get $\omega_3 = (\lambda^4 - \omega_3^4)^{1/2}$ ...(iii)

But ω_3 will be maximum when $\dot{\omega}_3 = 0$, or when $\lambda^4 - \omega_3^4 = 0$ or $\omega_3 = \lambda$

Now integrating (iii,) we get

[choose plus sing, for ω_3 as ω_3 increases from 0 to λ]

and t_2 time from (ω_3 = l) to ω_3 (= 0) is $-\int_\lambda^0 \frac{d\omega_3}{(\lambda^4 - \omega_3^{4})^{1/2}}$

$$= \int_0^\lambda \frac{d\omega_3}{(\lambda^4 - \omega_3^{4})^{1/2}}$$

[choose negative sign, for ω_3 as ω_3 decreases from λ to 0]

$\therefore$ Total time when the instantaneous axis will be again in the plane of the plate, is given by

$$t_1 + t_2 = 2\int_0^\lambda \frac{d\omega_3}{(\lambda^4 - \omega_3^4)^{1/2}} = 2\int_0^\lambda (\lambda^4 - z^4)^{-1/2} dx$$

Example 5:

A rigid body which is symmetric about an axis has one point fixed on this axis. Discuss the rotational motion of the body, assuming that there are no forces action other than the reaction forces at the fixed point.

Solution:

Let us assume the axis of symmetry coincident with one of the principal axes. Say the one having direction k. Then A = B and Euler's equations give:

$$A\dot{\omega}_1 + (C - A)\omega_3\omega_2 = 0 \qquad ...(1)$$

$$A\dot{\omega}_2 + (A - C)\omega_3\omega_1 = 0 \qquad ...(2)$$

and $$C\dot{\omega}_3 = 0 \qquad ...(3)$$

(3) $\Rightarrow \omega_3$ = constant = K say, so that (1) and (2) become after dividing by A, $\dot{\omega}_1 + \left\{\frac{C-A}{A}\right\}K\omega_2 = 0$ ...(4)

and A, $\dot{\omega}_2 + \left\{\frac{A-C}{A}\right\}K\dot{\omega}_1 = 0$ ...(5)

$$\therefore \ddot{\omega}_2 = -\left\{\frac{A-C}{A}\right\}K\dot{\omega}_1 = \left\{\frac{A-C}{A}\right\}K^2\left\{\frac{C-A}{A}\right\}\omega_2$$

$\Rightarrow \ddot{\omega}_2 + \kappa^2\omega_2 = 0$ where $\kappa = \left|\frac{A-C}{A}\right|K.$ ...(6)

Solving (6), we obtain $\omega_3 = \alpha \cos \kappa t + \beta \sin \kappa t$. ...(7)

Now have the time scale in such a way that t = 0 Þ $\omega_2 = 0$.

$\therefore$ (7) gives $\omega_2 = \beta \sin \kappa t$. $(\because \alpha = 0)$ ...(8)

Then from (5), we have $\dot{\omega}_2 = \left\{\frac{C-A}{A}\right\}K\omega_1 = \kappa\omega_1$

$\Rightarrow \beta\kappa \cos \kappa t = \kappa\omega_1$

$\Rightarrow \omega_1 = \beta \cos \kappa t$

$\therefore \vec{\omega} = \omega_1 i + \omega_2 j + \omega_3 k$

$= \beta \cos \kappa t \; i + \beta \sin \kappa t \; j + Kk$ ...(10)

and $\omega = |\vec{\omega}| = \sqrt{(\beta^2 + K^2)}$ = constant.

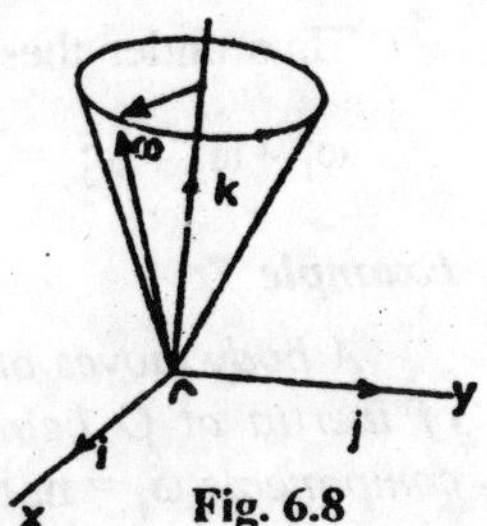

Fig. 6.8

This shows that the angular velocity is constant in magnitude equal to $\omega = \sqrt{(\beta^2 + K^2)}$ and processes round the k axis with frequency $f = \frac{\kappa}{2\pi} = \frac{|C-A|}{2\pi A}K$ as shown in the adjoining diagram,

Example 6:

A body under the action of no forces moves so that the resolved part of its angular velocity about one of the principal axes at the centre of gravity is constant. Show that the angular velocity of the body must be constant

Solution:

If ω_1, ω_2,ω_3, are the angular velocities about the axes the C.G. and A,B, C are the principal moments at the C.G., then Euler's equations of motion under no forces are

$A\dot{\omega}_1 - (B - C)\,\omega_2\omega_3 = 0$ ...(1)

$B\dot{\omega}_2 - (C - A)\,\omega_3\omega_1 = 0$ ...(2)

$C\dot{\omega}_3 - (A - B)\,\omega_1\omega_2 = 0$ ...(3)

Multiplying (1) by ω_1, (2) by ω_2 and (3) by ω_3 and adding we get

$A\omega_1\dot{\omega}_2 + B\,\omega_2\dot{\omega}_3 + C\,\omega_3\dot{\omega}_3 = 0,$

which on integration gives

$A\omega_1^2 + B\omega_2^2 + C\omega_3^2 = \text{constant.}$ ...(4)

Now as given in the question, let ω_1 = const, then two cases arise.

Case I. *When B = C*

Then from (1) we $\omega_2\omega_3 = 0$ get

$\because$ either $\omega_2 = 0$ or $\omega_3 = 0$.

Now, if $\omega_1 = 0$, then from (3), we get ω_3 = constant.

if $\omega_3 = 0$, then from (2), we get ω_2 = constant,

Thus under these conditions, we have

$\omega_1^2 + \omega_2^2 + \omega_3^2 = \textit{const.}$

Example 7:

A body moves about a point O under no forces, the principal moments of inertia at O being 3A, 5A and 6A. Initially the angular velocity has components $\omega_1 = n$, $\omega_2 = 0$, $\omega_3 = n$ *about the corresponding principal axes. Show that at any latter time, t* $\omega_2 = \dfrac{3n}{\sqrt{5}} \text{than}\left(\dfrac{nt}{\sqrt{5}}\right)$ *and that the body ultimately rotates about is mean axis.*

Solution:

Euler's equations of motion under no forces are

$A\dot{\omega}_1 - (B - C)\omega_2\omega_3 = 0; B\dot{\omega}_2 - (C - A)\omega_3\omega_1 = 0;$ ...(1)

and $C\dot{\omega}_3 - (A - B)\omega_1\omega 2 = 0$

Substituting in (1), the given values for A, B, C we get

$3A\dot{\omega}_1 - (5A - 6A)\omega_2\omega_3 = 0 \Rightarrow 3\omega_1 = -\omega_2\omega_3$ ...(2)

$5A\dot{\omega}_1 - (6A - 3A)\omega_3\omega_1 = 0 \Rightarrow 5\omega_2 = 3\omega_3\omega_1$ ...(3)

$6A\dot{\omega}_3 - (3A - 5A)\omega_1\omega_2 = 0 \Rightarrow 3\omega_3 = \omega_2\omega_2$ ...(4)

From (2) and (3), we get $9\omega_1\dot{\omega}_1 + 5\omega_1\dot{\omega}_2 = 0.$

which on integration yields $9\omega_1^2 + 5\omega_2^2 = a$ (says)

But initially $\omega_1 = n$ and $\omega_2 = 0$, $\therefore a = 9n^2$.

Thus we have $9_1^2 + 5\omega_2^2 = 9n^2$. ... (5)

From (2) (4) we get $\omega_1\dot{\omega}_3 - \omega_2\dot{\omega}_3 = 0\,0,$

which on integration gives $\omega_1^2 - \omega_3^2 = b$ (say)

Initially $\omega_1 = n$ and $\omega_3 = n$, $\therefore b = 0.$

which on integration gives $\omega_1^2 - \omega_3^2 = b$ (say)

Initially $\omega_1 = n$ and $\omega_3 = n$, $\therefore b = 0.$

Hence $\omega_1^2 = \omega_3^2$

Now equation (3) is,

$$5\dot{\omega}_2 = 3\omega_3\omega_1 = 3\omega_1^2 \Rightarrow 5\frac{d\omega_2}{dt} = \frac{1}{3}(9n^2 = 5\omega_2^2) \text{ since } \omega_1 = \omega_2$$

$$\Rightarrow t = 15\int\frac{d\omega_2}{9n^2 - 5\omega_2^2} = \int\frac{d\omega_2}{\frac{9}{5}n^2 - \omega_2^2} = \frac{\sqrt{5}}{n}\tanh^{-1}\left(\frac{\sqrt{5}}{3n}\omega_2\right)$$

$$\Rightarrow \omega_2 = \frac{3n}{\sqrt{5}}\tanh\left(\frac{nt}{\sqrt{5}}\right)$$

Further when $t \to \infty$, $\tanh\left(\frac{nt}{\sqrt{5}}\right) \to 1 \therefore \omega_2 \to \frac{3n}{\sqrt{5}}.$

Putting $\omega_2 = \frac{3n}{\sqrt{5}}$ in (5), we get $\omega_1 = 0$

and then from (6), we have $\omega_3 = 0$

i.e. the rotation ultimately is about the mean axis.

Example 8:

A body moves under no forces about a point O, the mean axis principal moments of inertia at O being 6A, 3A and A. Initially angular velocity of the body has the components $\omega_1 = n, \omega_2 = 0, \omega_3 = 3n$ *about the principal axes. Show that at any time t*

$$\omega_2 = -(\sqrt{5})\, n \tanh(\sqrt{5}nt)$$

and ultimately body rotates about the mean axis.

Solution:

Euler's equations of motion under no forces are

$A\dot{\omega}_1 - (B - C)\omega_2\omega_3 = 0;$

$B\dot{\omega}_2 - (C - A)\omega_3\omega_1 = 0;$ and $C\dot{\omega}_3 - (A - B)\omega_1\omega_2 = 0$

Substituting in these equations, the given values of A,B and C, we get

$$6A\dot{\omega}_1 - (3A - A)\omega_2\omega_3 = 0 \Rightarrow 3\dot{\omega}_1 = \omega_2\omega_3 \quad ...(1)$$

$$3A\dot{\omega}_2 - (A - 6A)\omega_3\omega_1 = 0 \Rightarrow 3\dot{\omega}_2 = -5\omega_3\omega_1 \quad ...(2)$$

$$A\dot{\omega}_3 - (6A - 3A)\omega_1\omega_2 = 0 \Rightarrow \dot{\omega}_3 = 3\omega_1\omega_2 \quad ...(3)$$

From (1) and (2), we get

$$5\omega_1\dot{\omega}_1 + \dot{\omega}_2\omega_2 0 \Rightarrow 5\omega_1^2 + \omega_2^2 = a \text{ (say)}$$

Initially $\omega_1 = n$ and $\omega_2 = 0$, $\quad \therefore a = 5n^2 \Rightarrow 5\omega_1^2 + \omega_2^2 = 5n^2$

Again from (1) and (3), we get

$$9\omega_1\dot{\omega}_1 - \omega_2\dot{\omega}_3 = 0 \Rightarrow 9\omega_1^2 - \omega_3^2 = b \text{ (say)}$$

Initially $\omega_1 = n$ and $\omega_3 = 3n$, $\therefore b = 0$.

Hence $9\omega_1^2 - \omega_3^2 = 0 \Rightarrow \omega_3 = 3\omega_1$

Using (5) in (2), we get

$$\dot{\omega}_2 = -5\omega_1^2 \Rightarrow \dot{\omega}_2 = -(5n^2 - \omega_2^2)$$

i.e. $\dfrac{d\omega_2}{dt} = -(5n^2 - \omega_2^2) \Rightarrow t = -\displaystyle\int \frac{d\omega_2}{5n^2 - \omega_2^2}$

$\therefore t = -\tanh^{-1}\dfrac{\omega_2}{n\sqrt{5}} + C$ But $C = 0$ since $\omega_2 = 0$ when $t = 0$.

Further as $t \to \infty$. $\tanh(n\sqrt{5}) \to 1, \because \omega_2 = -n\sqrt{5}$

Substituting this value of ω_2 in (4), we get $\omega_1 = 0$

And then from (5), we get $\omega_3 = 0$.

Thus we observe that the body ultimately rotates about its mean axis.

Example 9:

Obtain the direction cosines of a set of principal axes at O, one of the corners of the cube.

Solution:

Let O be a corner of the cube of edge 2a and G, the C.G. consider O as origin and three coterminous edges Ox, Oy, and Oz as the fixed axes. Hence co-ordinates of C.G. are (a.a,a). M.I. of the cube about any line through G is $\left(\frac{2}{3}\right)Ma^2(l^2+m^2+n^2)$ where l, m, n are the d.c.s and of the line, but $l^2 + m^2 + n^2 = 1$, hence the required m.i. becomes $\left(\frac{2}{3}\right)Ma^2$. Also the P.I. about any two perpendicular line through G is zero. Thus by parallel-axes theorem the P.I.'s about OG and any two perpendicular lines through O are zero. This implies that OG and any two perpendicular lines through O are the principal axes.

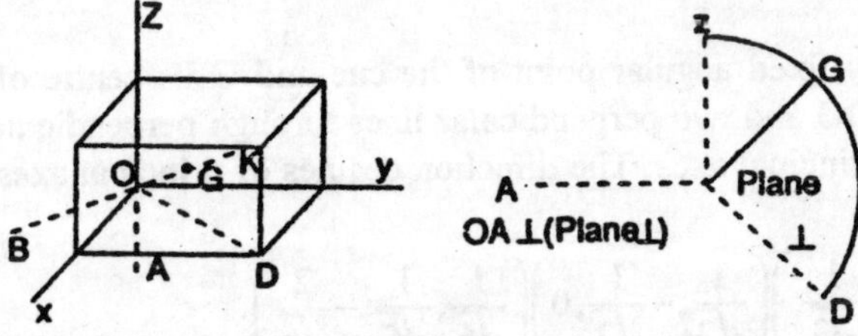

Fig. 6.9

Now consider a line OA ⊥ to the plane containing z-axis, OG, OD where OD is the diagonal of the base face of the cube. Then OA lies in the xy-plane and is ⊥ to OG and OD both. Therefore OA is another principal axis, the third principal axis OB is then evidently perpendicular to OA and OG. This suggests us that OA, OB and OG are principal axes at O. Let A,B,C be the M.I.'s of the cube about these principal axes, then we have

$$A = B = (2/3)Ma^2 + \sqrt{(3a^2)}\ M$$

$$= (11/3)\ Ma^2, C = (2/3)Ma^2, C = (2/3)Ma^2 \qquad ...(1)$$

Now, d.c.'s of the diagonal of the base face of the cube viz. of the line OD are $(1\sqrt{2}),(1\sqrt{2}),0$; dc'sof OZ are (0, 0, 1);

and dc's of OG are $(1\sqrt{3}),(1\sqrt{3}),(1\sqrt{3})$.

whence by solid geometry, the dc's of the line

OB(⊥ to OG and OA) are $(1\sqrt{2}),(1\sqrt{2}),0$

Again by solid geometry the dc's of the line

OB(⊥ to OG and OA) are $(1\sqrt{2}),(-1\sqrt{2}),0$

Thus the ds's of OA are $(1\sqrt{2}),(-1/\sqrt{2}),0$

the ds's of OB are $(1\sqrt{6}),(1\sqrt{6}),(-2/\sqrt{6});$

and the ds's of OG are $(1\sqrt{3}),(1/\sqrt{6}),(1/\sqrt{6}).$

Example 10:

A solid cube is in motion about an angular point, which is fixed. If there are no external forces and are the angular velocities about the edges through the fixed point, prove that $\omega_1+\omega_2+\omega_3 = cons.$ *and* $\omega_1^2+\omega_2^2+\omega_3^2 = const.$

Solution:

If O is any fixed angular point of the cue and G its centre of gravity. Then the line OG and two perpendicular lines through perpendicular to OG form a set of principal axes. The direction cosines of principal axes through O are

$$\left(\frac{1}{\sqrt{3}},\frac{1}{\sqrt{3}},\frac{1}{\sqrt{3}}\right)\left(\frac{1}{\sqrt{2}},-\frac{1}{\sqrt{2}},0\right)\left(\frac{1}{\sqrt{6}},\frac{1}{\sqrt{6}},-\frac{2}{\sqrt{6}}\right).$$

Obviously the angular velocities about OG and the other two principal axes respectively are

$$\frac{\omega_1+\omega_2+\omega_3}{\sqrt{3}};\frac{\omega_1-\omega_2}{\sqrt{2}};\frac{\omega_1+\omega_2-2\omega_3}{\sqrt{6}}$$

Now, in this case $A=\frac{2Ma^2}{3},B\frac{11Ma^2}{3},C\frac{11Ma^2}{3}$

Euler's equations of motion under no forces are

$$A\frac{d}{dt}\left(\frac{\omega_1+\omega_2+\omega_3}{\sqrt{3}}\right)-(B-C)\left(\frac{\omega_1-\omega_2}{\sqrt{2}}\right)\left(\frac{\omega_1+\omega_2-2\omega_3}{\sqrt{6}}\right)=0 \quad ...(1)$$

$$B\frac{d}{dt}\left(\frac{\omega_1-\omega_2}{\sqrt{2}}\right)-(C-A)\left(\frac{\omega_1+\omega_2-2\omega_3}{\sqrt{6}}\right)\left(\frac{\omega_1+\omega_2+\omega_3}{\sqrt{3}}\right)=0 \quad ...(2)$$

$$B\frac{d}{dt}\left(\frac{\omega_1+\omega_2-2\omega_2}{\sqrt{6}}\right)-(A-B)\left(\frac{\omega_1+\omega_2+2\omega_3}{\sqrt{3}}\right)\left(\frac{\omega_1-\omega_2}{\sqrt{2}}\right)=0 \quad ...(3)$$

Since B = C, therefore from (1), we have

$$\frac{d}{dt}(\omega_1+\omega_2+\omega_3)=0 \Rightarrow \omega_1+\omega_2+\omega_3=\text{const.}$$

Substituting the values of A,B,C in (2) and (3) respectively, we get

$$11(\dot{\omega}_1 - \dot{\omega}_2) = 3(\omega_1 + \omega_2 - 2\omega_3)(\omega_1 + \omega_2 + - 2\omega_3) \quad ...(2')$$

and $11(\dot{\omega}_1 + \dot{\omega}_2 - 2\dot{\omega}_3) = -9(\omega_1 + \omega_2 + 2\omega_3)(\omega_1 + \omega_2)$ ...(3')

Now dividing (2') by (3¢) and simplifying, we get

$$(\omega_1 + \omega_2 - 2\omega_3)(\dot{\omega}_1 + \dot{\omega}_2 - 2\dot{\omega}_3)(\omega_1 - \omega_2)(\dot{\omega}_1 - \dot{\omega}_2) = 0$$

Integrating it, we get

$$(\omega_1 + \omega_2 - 2\omega_3)^2 + 3(\omega_1 - \omega_2)^2 = \text{ const.}$$

or $6(\omega_1^2 + \omega_2^2 + \omega_3^2) - 2(\omega_1 + \omega_2 + \omega_3)^2 = \text{const.}$

or $6(\omega_1^2 + \omega_2^2 + \omega_3^2) - 2(\omega_1 + \omega_2 + \omega_3)^2 = \text{const.}$

or $\omega_1^2 + \omega_2^2 + \omega_3^2 = \text{const.}$

Example 11:

A rigid body rotates freely about its centre of mass under no forces. The body is rotating with angular velocity about the axis of greatest moment C when a small angular momentum AP is applied about the axis of least moment A. Show that the instantaneous axis moves in the body with period

$$\frac{2\pi}{T} \textit{ where } T^2 = \frac{(C-B)(C-A)}{AB}\omega^2.$$

Solution:

Euler's equations motion under no forces are

$$A\dot{\omega}_1 - (B - C)\omega_2\omega_3 = 0 \quad ...(1)$$

$$B\dot{\omega}_2 - (C - A)\omega_3\omega_1 = 0 \quad ...(2)$$

and $C\dot{\omega}_3 -- (A - B)\omega_1\omega_2 = 0$ ...(3)

Dividing (1) by (2), we get

$$A(C - A)\dot{\omega}_1\dot{\omega}_1 + B(C - B)\dot{\omega}_2\dot{\omega}_2 = 0$$

Integrating it, we have

$$A(C - A)\omega_1^2 + B(C - B)\omega_2^2 = a, \text{say} \quad ...(4)$$

Initially $A\omega_1 = AP \Rightarrow \omega_1 = p, \omega_2 = 0$ and $\omega_3 = \omega$

$\therefore\ A(C + A)p^2 = a$

Substituting the value that of the constant a in (4), we get

$$A(C - A)\omega_1^2 + B(C - B)\omega_2^2 = A(C - A)p^2 \quad ...(5)$$

Since it is given that C> B> A, hence both sides of (3) are positive, It also suggests that ω_1 and ω_2 will be very small corresponding to p. Thus $\omega_1\omega_2$ can be neglected.

Then $(3) \Rightarrow C\dot{\omega}_3 = 0 \Rightarrow \dot{\omega}_3 = \omega_3 = \text{const.} = \text{w}.$

Now consider the equation (1) *i.e.*

$$A\dot{\omega}_1 = - \Rightarrow (C-B)\omega_2\omega_3 = -(C-B)\omega_2\omega$$

$$\therefore A\ddot{\omega}_1 = -(C-BB)\omega\dot{\omega}_2 [\omega = \text{const.}]$$

$$\therefore A\ddot{\omega}_1 = -(C-B)\frac{(C-A)}{B}\omega^2\omega_1 \qquad \text{[using (2)]}$$

$$\Rightarrow \ddot{\omega}_1 = -\frac{(C-B)(C-A)\omega^2}{AB}\omega_1 = -T^2\omega_1$$

where $T^2 = \dfrac{(C-B)(C-A)}{AB}\omega^2.$

Example 12:

A rigid body rotates about a fixed point under the action of no forces. Investigate the following relations, the invariable line being taken as axis of z

$$\dot{\theta} = -G\sin\theta\cos\psi\sin\psi\left(\frac{1}{A}-\frac{1}{B}\right)$$

$$\dot{\phi} = G\left(\frac{\cos^2\phi}{A}+\frac{\sin^2\psi}{B}\right), \dot{\psi} + \cos\theta\dot{\phi} = \frac{G\cos\theta}{C}$$

where G denotes the angular momentum of the body and other symbols have their usual meanings.

Solution:

Let the fixed point about which the body rotate be O. Let OA, OB, OC be the principal axes at O. The components of angular momentum about OA, OB, OC respectively are given as $A\omega_1$, $B\omega_2$, $C\omega_3$ since G is the angular momentum about Oz, which makes an angle θ with OC, therefore we have

$C\omega_3 = G \cos \theta$, $A\omega_1 = - G \sin \theta \cos \psi$, $B\omega_2 = G \sin \theta \sin \psi$

Now Eulers geometrical equations are

$$\omega_1 = \dot{\theta}\sin\psi - \dot{\phi}\sin\theta\cos\phi \qquad ...(1)$$

$$\omega_2 = \dot{\theta}\cos\psi + \dot{\phi}\sin\theta\sin\phi \qquad ...(2)$$

$$\omega_3 = \dot{\psi} + \dot{\phi}\cos\theta$$

Now multiplying (1) by sin y, (2) by cos y and adding, we get

$$\omega_1 \sin\psi + \omega_2 \cos\psi = \dot{\theta}$$

or $\dot{\phi}\sin\theta = \omega_2 \sin\psi + \omega_1 \cos\psi$

$$= \frac{G\sin\theta\sin^2\psi}{B} + \frac{G\sin\theta\cos^2\psi}{A}$$

$$= G\sin\theta\left(\frac{\sin^2\psi}{B} + \frac{\cos^2\psi}{A}\right) \therefore \dot{\phi} = G\left(\frac{\sin^2\psi}{B} + \frac{\cos^2\psi}{A}\right) \quad ...(5)$$

From (3), we have

$$\dot{\psi} + \dot{\phi}\cos\theta = \omega_3 = \frac{G\cos\theta}{C} \therefore \dot{\psi} + \dot{\phi}\cos\theta = \frac{G\cos\theta}{C} \quad ...(6)$$

Thus the required relations are obtained.

Example 13:

On the assumption that the earth had once been rotating bout an axis through its centre of gravity not coincident with a principal axis and been subject to the acting of retarding couple whose magnitude at each instant was proportional to the angular velocity at that time and where axis was the instantaneous axis of rotation, find the component angular velocities about the principal axes and show that the instantaneous axis would approach ultimately coincide with the least axis.

Solution:

Euler's dynamical equations are

$$A\dot{\omega}_1 - (B - C)\omega_2\omega_3 = L, B\dot{\omega}_2 - (C - A)\omega_3\omega_1 = M,$$

$$C\dot{\omega}_3 - (A - B)\omega_1\omega_2 = N$$

But here $L = -\lambda\omega_2, M = -\lambda\omega_2, N = -\lambda\omega_3$

and A = B, therefore the above equations take the form as

$$A\dot{\omega}_1 = (A - C)\omega_2\omega_3 = -\lambda\omega_1 \quad ...(1)$$

$$A\dot{\omega}_2 = (C - A)\omega_3\omega_1 = -\lambda\omega_2 \quad ...(2)$$

$$C\dot{\omega}_3 = -\lambda\omega_3 \quad ...(3)$$

Solving the differential equation (3), we get

$$\omega_3 = pe^{-\lambda t/c} \text{ where p is a const.} \quad ...(4)$$

$$A\dot{\omega}_1 = (A - C)pe^{-\lambda t/c}\omega_2 - \lambda\omega_1 \quad ...(5)$$

$$A\dot{\omega}_2 = (C - A)pe^{-\lambda t/c}\omega_1 - \lambda\omega_2 \quad ...(6)$$

Multiplying (6) by i and adding to (5), we get

$$A(\dot{\omega}_1 + i\dot{\omega}_2) = (A - C)pe^{-\lambda t/c}(\omega_3 + i^3\omega_1) - \rho(\omega_1 + i\omega_2)$$

$$= (A - C)pe^{-\lambda t/c}(i^4\omega_2 + i^3\omega_1) - \lambda(\omega_1 + i\omega_2)$$

$$= i^3(A - C)pe^{-\lambda t/c}(\omega_1 + i\omega_3) - \lambda(\omega_1 + i\omega_2)$$

Putting $\omega_1 + i\omega_2 = u$, we get $\dot{u} = -\left[\frac{A-C}{A} ipe^{-\lambda t/c} + \frac{\lambda}{A}\right]u.$

i.e. $\frac{du}{dt} = -\left[\frac{A-C}{A} ipe^{-\lambda t/c} + \frac{\lambda}{A}\right]u. - \left[\frac{-C(A-C)}{\lambda A} ipe^{-\lambda t/c} + \frac{\lambda}{A}\right]u.$

Integrating it, we get $u = \alpha$ e

where α is const.

$$= \alpha e^{-(\lambda/A)t} e[iC(A - C)/\lambda A]pe^{-(\lambda t/c)}$$

$$\Rightarrow \omega_1 + i\omega_2 = \alpha_e^{-\lambda t/a}\left[\cos\left\{\frac{(A-C)C}{\lambda A} pe^{-\lambda t/c}\right\} + i\sin\left\{\frac{C(A-C)}{\lambda A} pe^{-\lambda t/c}\right\}\right]$$

Separating the real and imaginary parts, we get

$$\omega_1 = \alpha e^{-\lambda/A} \cos\left\{\frac{C(A-C)}{\lambda A} pe^{-\lambda t/C}\right\}, \text{ and}$$

$$\omega_2 = \alpha e^{-\lambda/A} \sin\left\{\frac{C(A-C)}{\lambda A} pe^{-\lambda t/C}\right\}.$$

Example 14:

If the earth be regarded as a solid of revolution, whose principal moments of inertia at the centre of gravity are A, A, C; show that its axis of rotation describes a cone of very small angle about the axis of the figure in period $\frac{A}{C-A}$ *sidereal days.*

Solution:

Euler's equations of motion under on forces are

$$A\dot{\omega}_1 - (B - C)\omega_2\omega_3 = 0, B\dot{\omega}_2 - (C - A)\omega_3\omega_1 = 0$$

$$C\dot{\omega}_3 - (A - B)\omega_1\omega_2 = 0.$$

But here principal moments of inertias are given as A, A and C, therefore the equations becomes

$$A\dot{\omega}_1 - (B - C)\omega_2\omega_3 = 0 \quad ...(1)$$

$$A\dot{\omega}_2 - (C - A)\omega_3\omega_1 = 0 \quad ...(2)$$

$$C\dot{\omega}_3 = 0 \quad ...(3)$$

Solving (3), we get ω_3 = const. ...(4)

Now if the earth rotates with angular velocity ω about an axis through centre of gravity and making an angle α with the axis of the figure, then initially, we have $\omega_1 = \omega \sin \alpha$, $\omega_2 = 0$, $\omega_3 = \omega \cos \alpha$

Thus the equation (4) becomes $\omega_3 = \omega \cos \alpha$,

Further dividing (1) by (2), we get

$\omega_1 \dot{\omega}_1 + \omega_2 \dot{\omega}_2 = 0 \quad \Rightarrow \omega_1^2 + \omega_2^2 = a$, where 'a' is const.

But initially $\omega_1 = \omega \sin \alpha$, $\omega_2 = 0 \quad \Rightarrow \omega_1^2 + \omega_2^2 = \omega^2 \sin^2 \alpha$

Now substituting the values of ω_2, ω_3 in (1) and differentiating, we get

$$A\dot{\omega}_1 - (A - C)\omega \cos a\omega_2 = 0$$

$$i.e.\ \ddot{\omega}_1 = \frac{A - C}{A}\omega \cos \alpha\, \dot{\omega}_2$$

$$= \frac{A - C}{A}\omega \cos \alpha . \frac{C - A}{A}\omega \cos \alpha \omega \qquad \text{[using (2)]}$$

$$\therefore \ddot{\omega}_1 = -\left(\frac{C - A}{A}\omega \cos \alpha\right)^2 \omega_1 \qquad \text{...(7)}$$

Now proportional direction cosines of the instantaneous axis are

$\omega_1, \omega_2, \omega_3$.

$\therefore$ angle between the instantaneous axis and the axis of the figure.

$$= \cos^{-1}\left\{\frac{\omega_3}{\sqrt{(\omega_1^2 + \omega_2^2 + \omega_3^2)}}\right\} = \cos^{-1}\left\{\frac{\omega \cos \alpha}{\sqrt{(\omega^2 \sin^2 \alpha + \omega^2 \cos^2 \alpha}}\right\}$$

$$= \cos^{-1}(\cos \alpha) = \alpha$$

It shows that instantaneous axis describes about the axis of the figure a right cone of semivertical angle α. The period of rotation is

$$= \frac{2\pi}{\frac{C - A}{A}\omega \cos \alpha} = \frac{2\pi}{\frac{(C - A)\omega'}{A}}, \text{ since a is small.}$$

$$= \frac{2\pi A}{(C - A)\omega} = \frac{A}{C - A}, \qquad \left[\because \text{sidereal day} = \frac{2\pi}{\omega}\right]$$

Example 15:

The principal moments of inertia of a body at the centre of mass are A, 3A, 6A. The body is so rotated that its angular velocities about the axes are 3n, 2n, n respectively. If in the subsequent motion under no forces ω_1,

ω_2, ω_3 *denote the angular velocities about the principal axes at time t, prove that* $\omega_1 = 3\omega_3 = \frac{9n}{\sqrt{5}}$ *sech u and* ω_3 *= 3 n tanh n where* $u = 3nt + \frac{1}{2}\log 5.$

Solution:

Since the body moves under no forces, therefore Euler's equations of motion are

$$A\dot{\omega}_1 - (B-C)\omega_2\omega_3 = 0,\ B\dot{\omega}_2 - (C-A)\omega_3\omega_1 = 0, \text{ and}$$

$$C\dot{\omega}_3 - (A-B)\omega_1\omega_2 = 0.$$

But here the principal moments are given as A, 3A and 6A, therefore the above equation becomes

$$A\dot{\omega}_1 - (3A-6A)\omega_2\omega_3 = 0 \Rightarrow \dot{\omega}_1 = -3\omega_2\omega_3 \quad ...(1)$$

$$3A\dot{\omega}_2 - (6A-A)\omega_3\omega_1 = 0 \Rightarrow 3\dot{\omega}_2 = -5\omega_3\omega_1 \quad ...(2)$$

$$6A\dot{\omega}_3 - (A-3A)\omega_1\omega_2 = 0 \Rightarrow 3\dot{\omega}_3 = -\omega_1\omega_2. \quad ...(3)$$

Now dividing (1) and (3), we get

$$\omega_1\dot{\omega}_1 - 9\omega_3\dot{\omega}_3 = 0$$

Intergrating $\omega_1^2 - 9\omega_3^2 = a$ (const.)

But initially $\omega_1 = 3n, \omega_3 = n$

Thus we have $\omega_1^2 - 9\omega_3^2 = 0 \Rightarrow \omega_1^2 = 9\omega_3^2 \Rightarrow \omega_1 = 3\omega_3.$ ...(4)

Again dividing (2) by (3), we get

$$\omega_2\dot{\omega}_2 + 5\omega_3\dot{\omega}_3 = 0 \Rightarrow \omega_2^2 + 5\omega_3^2 = b \text{ (const.)}$$

Initially $\omega_2 = 2n, \omega_3 = n \ \therefore\ b = 9n^2$

Hence $\omega_2^2 + 5\omega_3^2 = 9n^2.$ ...(5)

Now substituting $\omega_1 = 3\omega_3$ in (2), we have

$$3\dot{\omega}_2 = 15\omega_3^2 = 15\left[\frac{9n^2 - \omega_2^2}{5}\right] \text{ [using (5)] } \therefore \dot{\omega}_2 = (9n^2 - \omega_2^2)$$

i.e. $dt = \frac{d\omega_2}{9n^2 - \omega_2} \quad \therefore t = \frac{1}{3n}\tanh^{-1}\left(\frac{\omega_2}{3n}\right) + k.$

But when t = 0, $\omega_2 = 2n \ \therefore k = -\frac{1}{3}\tanh^{-1}\left(\frac{2}{3}\right)$

Hence $T = \frac{1}{3n}\tanh^{-1}\left(\frac{\omega_2}{3n}\right) - \frac{1}{3}\lg\sqrt{5}$ *

$$\therefore 3nt + \text{lon}\sqrt{5} = \tanh^{-1}\left(\frac{\omega_2}{3n}\right)$$

or $\omega_2 = 3n\tanh[3nt + \log\sqrt{5}] = 3n \tanh u.$

from (5), we have $5\omega_3^2 = 9n^2 - \omega_2^2 = 9n^2 - 9n^2 \tanh^2 u = 9n^2 \text{sech}^2 u$

$$\therefore \omega_3 = \frac{3n}{\sqrt{5}}\text{sech } u \Rightarrow \omega_1 = 3\omega_3 = \frac{9n}{\sqrt{5}}\text{sech } u$$

Example 16:

A rectangular parallelopiped whose edges are a, 2a, 3a, can turn about its centre and is set rotating about a line perpendicular to the mean axis and making an angle $\cos^{-1}\left(\frac{5}{8}\right)$ *with the least axis. Prove that ultimately the body will rotate about the mean axis.*

Solution:

If ω is the initial angular velocity, then we have

$$\omega_1 = \frac{5}{8}\omega, \omega_2 = 0, \omega_3 = \frac{\sqrt{(39)}}{8}, \text{since } \omega_1^2 + \omega_2^2 + \omega_3^2 = \omega^2.$$

Also $A = \frac{b^2 + c^2}{3} = \frac{(2a)^2 + (3a)^2}{3} = \frac{13a^2}{3}$

$$B = \frac{c^2 + a^2}{3} = \frac{(3a)^2 + (a)^2}{3}; C = \frac{a^2 + b^2}{3} = \frac{a^2 + (2a)^2}{3} = \frac{5a^2}{3}.$$

Now Euler's equations of motion under no forces are

$A\dot{\omega}_1 - (B - C)\omega_2\omega_3 = 0;\quad B\dot{\omega}_2 - (C - A)\omega_3\omega_1 = 0;$

$C\dot{\omega}_3 - (A - B)\omega_1\omega_2 = 0.$

Putting in the above equations, the values of A,B, C, we get

$$\frac{13}{3}a^2\dot{\omega}_1 - \left[\frac{10a^2}{3} - \frac{5a^2}{3}\right]\omega_2\omega_3 = 0 \Rightarrow 13\dot{\omega}_1 = 5\omega_2\omega_3 \quad \text{...(1)}$$

$$\frac{10a^2}{3}\dot{\omega}_2 - \left[\frac{5a^2}{3} - \frac{13a^2}{3}\right]\omega_3\omega_1 = 0 \Rightarrow 5\dot{\omega}_2 = -4\omega_3\omega_1 \quad \text{...(2)}$$

$$\frac{5a^2}{3}\dot{\omega}_3 - \left[\frac{13a^2}{3} - \frac{10a^2}{3}\right]\omega_1\omega_2 = 0 \Rightarrow 5\dot{\omega}_3 = 3\omega_1\omega_3 \quad \text{...(3)}$$

Dividing (1) by (2) and cross multiplying, we get

$$52\omega_1\dot{\omega}_1 + 25\dot{\omega}_2 = 0$$

which on integration gives $52\omega_1^2 + 25\omega_2^2 = k$ (const.)

But initially $\omega_1 = \frac{5}{8}\omega \;\; \omega_3 = 0 \qquad \therefore k = \frac{325}{16}\omega^2$.

Hence $52\omega_1^2 + 25\omega_2^2 = \frac{325}{16}\omega^2$.

Again dividing (1) by (3) and cross-multiplying, we have

$$39\omega_1\dot{\omega}_1 - 27\omega_3\dot{\omega}_3 = 0 \Rightarrow 39\omega_1^2 - 27\omega_3^2 = d \text{ (const.)}$$

But initially $\omega_1 = \frac{5}{8}\omega, \omega_3 = \frac{\sqrt{(39)}}{8}\omega \;\; \therefore d = 0$

$$\therefore 39\omega^2 - 2\omega_3^2 = 0 \Rightarrow \omega_3 = \frac{\sqrt{(39)}}{5}\omega_1.$$

Using (5) in (2), we have

$$\dot{\omega}_2 = -\frac{4}{5}.\frac{\sqrt{(39)}}{5}\omega_1^2 = -\frac{4\sqrt{(39)}}{25}\omega_1^2$$

$$= -\frac{4\sqrt{(39)}}{25 \times 52}\left[\frac{325}{16}\dot{\omega}_\pi - 25\omega_2^2\right]$$

$$= -\frac{\sqrt{3}}{25\sqrt{(13)}}\left[\frac{325}{16}\omega^2 - 25\omega_2^2\right]$$

$$\therefore \frac{\sqrt{3t}}{\sqrt{(13)}} = -\int \frac{d\omega_2}{\frac{13}{16}\omega^2 - \omega_2^2} = -\frac{4}{\omega\sqrt{(13)}}\tanh^{-1}\frac{4\omega_2}{\omega\sqrt{(13)}}$$

$$\therefore \omega_2 = -\frac{\omega\sqrt{(13)}}{4}\tanh^{-1}\left[\left(\frac{\sqrt{3}}{4}\right)\omega t\right]$$

But as $t \to \infty$, $\tanh\left[4\left(\frac{\sqrt{3}}{4}\right)\omega t\right] \to 1 \therefore \omega_2 = -\frac{\omega\sqrt{(13)}}{4}$

Making use of (4) and (5), we get $\omega_1 = 0$ and $\omega_3 = 0$.

So the body ultimately rotates about the mean axis.

Example 17:

A lamina rotating with uniform angular velocity an about an axis through its centre of gravity perpendicular to its plane has an additional angular velocity λn impressed upon it about the axis of least moment, (A <B<C)

where $\lambda^2 = (B + A) / (B - A)$. Prove that at time t, its angular velocities are λn sech nt, λn tanh nt, n sech nt.

Also show that it will ultimately revolve about the axis of mean moment.

Solution:

Euler's equations of motion under no forces are:

$A\dot{\omega}_1 - (B - C)\omega_2\omega_3 = 0;$

$B\dot{\omega}_2 - (C - A)\omega_3\omega_1 = 0;$

$C\dot{\omega}_3 - (A - B)\omega_1\omega_2 = 0.$

In this case C = A + B. Putting A + B for C in the above equations, we get

$$*\tanh^{-1}(x/a) = \frac{1}{2}\text{lon}\frac{a+x}{a-x} \Rightarrow \tanh^{-1}(2/3) = \frac{1}{2}\text{long}\left(\frac{3+2}{3-2}\right) = \log\sqrt{(5)}$$

$$A\dot{\omega}_1 + A\omega_2\omega_3 = 0 \Rightarrow \dot{\omega}_1 = -\omega_2\omega_3 \quad ...(1)$$

$$B\dot{\omega}_2 - B\omega_3\omega_1 = 0 \Rightarrow \dot{\omega}_2 = \omega_3\omega_1 \quad ...(2)$$

$$(A+B)\dot{\omega}_3 - (A-B)\omega_1\omega_3 = 0 \Rightarrow \dot{\omega}_3 = -\frac{1}{\lambda^2}\omega_1\omega_2$$

$$\left(\because \lambda^2 = \frac{B+A}{B-A}\right) \quad ...(3)$$

Now dividing (1) by (2) and then cross-multiplying, we get

$\omega_1\dot{\omega}_1 + \omega_2\dot{\omega}_2 = 0 \Rightarrow \omega_1^2 + \omega_2^2 = a$, where a is constant of integration.

But initially $\omega_1 = \lambda n,, \omega_2 = 0, \omega_3$ $\therefore$ a = $\lambda^2 n^2$

Hence $\omega_1^2 + \omega_2^2 = \lambda^2 n^2$ ...(4)

Again dividing (1) by (3) and then cross-multiplying, we have

$\omega_1\dot{\omega}_1 - \lambda^2\dot{\omega}_3\omega_3 = 0 \Rightarrow \omega_1^2 - \lambda^2\omega_3^2 = b,$

where b is a constant of integration.

Initially, we have $\omega_1 = \lambda n$, $\omega_2 = 0$, $\omega_3 = n$ $\therefore$ b = 0

Hence $\omega_1^2 - \lambda^2\omega_3^2 = 0 \Rightarrow \omega_1^2 = \lambda^2\omega_2^2 \Rightarrow \omega_1 = \lambda\dot{\omega}_3$

Further substituting the value of ω_3 from (5) in (2), we get

$\dot{\omega}_2 = \frac{1}{\lambda}\omega_1^2 = \frac{1}{\lambda}(\lambda^2 n^2 - \omega_2^2)$ [using (4)]

i.e. $\frac{d\omega_2}{dt} = \frac{1}{\lambda}(\lambda^2 n^2 - \omega_2^2) \therefore t = \int \frac{\lambda d\omega_2}{\lambda^2 n^2 - \omega_2^2} = \frac{\lambda}{\lambda n}\tanh^{-1}\left(\frac{\omega_2}{\lambda n}\right) + C,$

where C is a constant.

But when t = 0, $\omega_2 = 0$, $\therefore$ C = 0

So $t = \frac{1}{n}\tanh^{-1}\left(\frac{\omega_2}{\lambda n}\right) \Rightarrow \omega_2 = \lambda n \tanh(nt)$ ...(6)

Substituting this value of ω2 in (4), we get

$\omega_1^2 = \lambda^2 n^2 \tanh^2(nt) = [\lambda nswxh(nt)]^2 \Rightarrow \omega_1 = \lambda n \operatorname{sech}(nt)$ ...(7)

From (5) we have $\omega_2 =$ n sech (nt)

Further when $t \to \infty$, we have

$$\omega_1 = \lambda n \lim_{t\to\infty} \operatorname{sech}(nt) = \lambda n \lim_{t\to\infty} \frac{2}{e^{nt} - e^{-nt}} = 0$$

$$\omega_3 = \lambda n \lim_{t\to\infty} \tanh nt = \lambda n \lim_{t\to\infty} \frac{e^{nt} - e^{-nt}}{e^{nt} + e^{-nt}} = \lambda n \lim_{t\to\infty} \frac{1 - e^{-2nt}}{1 + e^{-ent}} = \lambda n$$

and $\omega_3 = \frac{1}{\lambda}\omega_1 = 0$. Thus ultimate values of angular velocities are 0, λn, 0. It show that, ultimately, the lamina revolves about the axis of mean moment.

Example 18:

A uniform elliptic disc is free to move about a focus and is set rotation with initial angular velocity Ω about an axis perpendicular to the corresponding latus rectum and making an angle θ with the plane of the disc. If cos 2θ = (A/B) *when A,B are the moments of inertia of the disc about the major axis and latus rectum respectively, prove that after* time t, the component angular velocity of the disc about the major axis will be

$$\Omega\sqrt{\left(\frac{A+B}{2B}\right)}\operatorname{sech}\left[\Omega t\left(\frac{B-A}{2B}\right)\right].$$

Solution:

The initial axis of rotation is perpendicular to the latus rectum and makes an angle θ with the major axis; will have direction cosines cos θ, cos (90 – θ), cos 90 *i.e.* cosθ, sin θ, 0. Corresponding to the set of principal axes, lactus rectum and a line through the focus and perpendicular to the plane of the disc. Since initial angular velocity is Ω therefore initially, we have

$$\omega_1 = \Omega\cos\theta, \omega_2 = 0, \omega_3 = \Omega\sin\theta$$

Further for lamina. We have C = A + B, therefore Euler's equations under no forces become

$$A\dot{\omega}_1 + A\omega_2\omega_3 = 0 \Rightarrow \dot{\omega}_1 = -\omega_2\omega_3 \quad ...(1)$$

$$B\dot{\omega}_2 - B\omega_3\omega_1 = 0 \Rightarrow \dot{\omega}_2 = -\omega_3\omega_1 \quad ...(2)$$

$$(A+B)\dot{\omega}_3 - (A-B)\omega_1\omega_2 = 0 \Rightarrow \dot{\omega}_3 = -\frac{B-A}{A+B}\omega_1\omega_2 \quad ...(3)$$

Dividing (1) by (2), we get $\omega_1\dot{\omega}_1 + \omega_2\dot{\omega}_2 + \omega_2\dot{\omega}_2 = 0 \Rightarrow \omega_1^2 + \omega_2^2 = a$

where a is a constant of integration. Since initially

$\omega_1 = \Omega\cos\theta, \omega_2 = 0$, therefore $\Omega^2\cos^2\theta$.

Hence $\omega_1^2 + \omega_2^2 = \Omega^2\cos^2\theta$ ...(4)

Again dividing (1) by (3), we get

$$\omega_1\dot{\omega}_1 - \frac{B+A}{B-A}\omega_3\dot{\omega}_3 = \Rightarrow \omega_1^2 - \frac{B+A}{B-A}\omega_3^2 = b$$

where b is a constant of integration. Initially

$\omega_1 = \Omega\cos\theta, \omega_3 = \Omega\sin\theta$

$$\therefore b = \Omega^2\left[\cos^2\theta - \frac{B+A}{B-A}\sin^2\theta\right] = \Omega^2\frac{(B-A)\cos^2\theta - (A+B)\sin^2\theta}{B-A}$$

$$= \frac{B(\cos^2\theta - \sin^2\theta - A}{B-A} = \frac{B\cos^2\theta - A}{B-A} = 0 \qquad [\because \cos 2\theta = (A/B)]$$

Hence $\omega^2 = \dfrac{B+A}{B-A}\omega_3^2$

Substituting the value of ω_3 from (5) in (2), we get

$$\dot{\omega}_2 = \sqrt{\left(\frac{B-A}{B+A}\right)}\omega_1^2 = \sqrt{\left(\frac{B-A}{B+A}\right)}\left[\Omega^2\cos^2\theta - \omega_2^2\right] \qquad [\text{using (4)}]$$

$$\therefore t = \sqrt{\left(\frac{B+A}{B-A}\right)}\int\frac{d\omega_2}{\Omega^2\cos^2\theta - \omega_2^2}$$

$$= \sqrt{\left(\frac{B+A}{B-A}\right)}\frac{1}{\Omega\cos\theta}\tanh^{-1}\left\{\frac{\omega_2}{\Omega\cos\theta}\right\}$$

the constant of integration vanish since $\omega_2 = 0$ when $t = 0$

$$= \frac{1}{\Omega}\sqrt{\left(\frac{B+A}{B-A}\right)}\sqrt{\frac{2B}{B+A}}\tanh^{-1}\left\{\frac{\omega_2}{\Omega}\left(\frac{2B}{B+A}\right)\right\}*$$

$$\therefore \omega_2 = \Omega\sqrt{\left(\frac{B+A}{2B}\right)}\tanh^{-1}\left[\Omega t\sqrt{\frac{B-A}{2B}}\right]$$

Substituting this value of ω_2 in (4) we get

$$\omega_1 = \Omega\sqrt{\left(\frac{B+A}{2B}\right)}\operatorname{sech}\left\{\Omega t\sqrt{\frac{B-A}{2B}}\right\}$$

Example 19:

A rigid body possesses an axis of symmetry OC and moves about O under a retarding couple $\lambda C w_3$ about OC; λ being a constant : A,A, C being the principal moments of inertia at O, and ω_1, ω_2, ω_3 being the angular velocity components about the principal axes, the third axis being OC, Initially the body is given an angular velocity ω about a line inclined at α to OC. Prove that ultimately the instantaneous axis will be perpendicular to OC.

Solution:

Initially we have $\omega_1 = 0$, ω_2, $= \omega \sin \alpha$, ω_3, $= \omega \cos \alpha$ Euler's general equations of motion are

$$A\dot{\omega}_1 - (B-C)\omega_2\omega_3 = L;$$

$$B\dot{\omega}_2 - (C-A)\omega_3\omega_1 = M;$$

$$C\dot{\omega}_3 - (A-B)\omega_1\omega_2 = N;$$

But $L = 0$, $M = 0$, $N = -\lambda C\omega_3$ and $B = A$

Therefore the above equations becomes

$$A\dot{\omega}_1 - (B-C)\omega_2\omega_3 = 0;$$

$$B\dot{\omega}_2 - (C-A)\omega_3\omega_1 = 0;$$

$$C\dot{\omega}_3 = -\lambda C\omega_3 \Rightarrow \dot{\omega}_1 = -\lambda\omega_3.$$

i.e. $\dfrac{d\omega_3}{dt} = -\lambda\omega_3 \Rightarrow \omega_3 = ke^{-\lambda t}$, where k is constant.

But when $t = 0$, $\omega_3 = \omega\cos\alpha \therefore k = \omega\cos\alpha$,

Hence $\omega_3 = \omega\cos\alpha e^{-\lambda t}$ ...(1)

Now when $t \to \infty, \omega_3 = \omega\cos\alpha \lim_{t\to\infty} e^{-\lambda} = \cos\alpha \lim_{t\to\infty e} \dfrac{i}{\lambda t} = 0$

It shows that ultimately instantaneous axis is perpendicular to OC.

Example 20:

A body having an axis of symmetry OC, moves about a fixed O under no forces, except a constant retarding complex-kC about the axis OC If A,A,

C are the moments of inertia about ω_1, ω_2, ω_3 the angular velocities about the principal axes OA, OB, OC, show that at time t,

$$\omega_1 = \Omega\cos\lambda t\left(\Omega - \frac{1}{2}kt\right), \omega_2 = -\omega\sin\lambda t\left(\Omega - \frac{1}{2}tk\right), \omega_3 = \Omega - kt$$

where $\lambda = \frac{A-C}{A}$, *the initial values of* ω_1, ω_2, ω_3 *being* Ω, 0, Ω *respectively.*

Solution:

In this case L = M = 0, N = – kC and $B \equiv A$

Putting these values in Euler's dynamical equations, we get

$$A\dot{\omega}_1\ (A-C)\omega_2\omega_3 = 0 \Rightarrow \dot{\omega}_1 = \lambda\omega_2\omega_3,\ \text{since}\ \lambda = \frac{A-C}{A} \quad ...(1)$$

$$A\dot{\omega}_2 - (C-A)\omega_3\omega_1 = 0 \Rightarrow \dot{\omega}_2 = -\lambda\omega_3\omega_1, \quad ...(2)$$

$C\dot{\omega}_3 = -kC \Rightarrow \dot{\omega}_3 = -k \Rightarrow \omega_3 = -kt + a$, where a is a constant of integration. Initially we have $\omega_3 = \Omega \therefore a = \Omega$.

Hence $\omega_3 = \Omega - kt$ ...(3)

Substituting this value of ω_3 in (1) and (2), we have

$$\omega_1 = \Omega\,(\Omega - kt)\omega_2 \quad ...(4)$$

and $\omega_2 = -\lambda(\Omega - kt)\omega_1$ ...(5)

Multiplying (5) by in and adding to (4), we get

$$\dot{\omega}_1 + i\dot{\omega}_2 = \lambda(\Omega - kt)[\omega_2 - i\omega_1] = -i\lambda(\Omega - kt)(\omega_1 + i\omega_2)]$$

Putting $\omega_1 + i\omega_2 = u$ so that $\dot{\omega}_1 + i\dot{\omega}_2 = \dot{u}$, we have

$$\dot{u} = -i\lambda(\Omega - kt)u \Rightarrow \frac{du}{u} = -i\lambda(\Omega - kt)dt$$

integrating, we get log $\dot{u} = -i\lambda(\Omega t - \frac{1}{2}kt^2) + b$ where b is a constant of integration.

But when $t \to 0$, $u = \omega_1 + i\omega_2 = \Omega + 0 = \Omega \therefore b = \log\Omega$

$$\therefore \log u - \log\Omega = -i\lambda(\Omega t - \frac{1}{2}kt^2) \Rightarrow \log\frac{u}{\Omega} = -i\lambda(\Omega t - \frac{1}{2}kt^2)$$

$$\Rightarrow u = \Omega e - i\lambda(\Omega t - \frac{1}{2}kt^2)$$

$$\Rightarrow \omega_1 + i\omega_2 = \Omega[\cos\{\lambda(\Omega t - \frac{1}{2}kt^2\} - t\sin\{\lambda(\Omega t - \frac{1}{2}kt^2)\}]$$

$$\Rightarrow \omega_1 = \Omega\cos\{\lambda t(\Omega - \frac{1}{2}kt)\} \text{ and } \Rightarrow \omega_2 = -\Omega\sin\{\lambda t(\Omega - \frac{1}{2}kt)\}$$

Hence we get the required values of $\omega_1, \omega_2, \omega_3$.

$$*\cos\ 2\theta = \frac{A}{B} \Rightarrow 2\cos^2\theta - 1 = \frac{A}{B} \Rightarrow \cos^2\theta\,\frac{B+A}{2B} \Rightarrow \cos\theta = \sqrt{\left(\frac{B+A}{2B}\right)}.$$

Example 21:

Show that in free motion of the body with an axis of symmetry C about its centre of gravity if n denotes the spin about the axis C and ψ *denotes the Euler's third angle, then* $A\dot{\psi}\text{sym} = (A - C)n$.

Solution:

Here B = A.

$\therefore$ Euler's equation of motion under no forces are

$$A\dot{\omega}_1 - (A - C)\omega_2\omega_3 = 0 \Rightarrow \dot{\omega}_1 = -\frac{(A-C)}{A}\omega_2\omega_3 \qquad ...(1)$$

$$A\dot{\omega}_2 - (C - A)\omega_3\omega_1 = 0 \Rightarrow \dot{\omega}_2 = -\frac{(A-C)}{A}\omega_3\omega_1 \qquad ...(2)$$

$$C\dot{\omega}_3 = 0 \Rightarrow \dot{\omega}_3 = 0 \Rightarrow \omega_3 = \text{const} = n \qquad ...(3)$$

Solving (1) and (2), we get

$$\omega_1\dot{\omega}_1 + \omega_2\dot{\omega}_2 = 0 \Rightarrow \omega_1^2 + \omega_2^2 = a, \text{ where a is const.}$$

Now the direction cosines of the invariable line are proportional to A ω_1, $A\omega_2$, $C\omega_3$ and the direction cosines of the axis of symmetry are 0, 0, 1. If θ is the angle between them

$$\therefore \cos\theta = \frac{C\omega_3}{\sqrt{[(A\omega_1)^2 + (A\omega_2)^2 + (C\omega_3)^2]}} \qquad \text{(Note B = A)}$$

$$= \frac{Cn}{\sqrt{[A^2(\omega_1^2 + \omega_2^2) + C^2n^2]}} \qquad ...(4)$$

It shows that $\cos\theta$ = const. $\Rightarrow \theta$ = const $\Rightarrow \dot{\theta} = 0$

Now substituting $\dot{\theta} = 0$ in Euler's geometrical equations, we get

$$\omega_1 = -\dot{\phi}\sin\dot{\theta}\cos\psi \qquad ...(5)$$

$$\omega_2 = \dot{\phi}\sin\dot{\theta}\sin\psi \qquad ...(6)$$

$$\omega_3 = \psi + \dot{\phi}\cos\theta$$

Squaring and adding (5) and (6), we get $\omega_1^2 + \omega_2^2 = \dot{\phi}^2 \sin^2\theta$

Substituting this value of $\omega_1^2 + \omega_2^2$ in (4), we get

$$\cos^2\theta = \frac{C^2n^2}{A^2\dot{\phi}^2\sin^2\theta + C^2n^2}$$

$$\Rightarrow (A^2\dot{\phi}^2\sin^2\theta + C^2n^2)\cos^2\theta = C^2n^2 = C^2n^2\sin^2\theta$$

$$\Rightarrow A^2\dot{\phi}^2\sin^2\theta\cos^2\theta$$

$$\Rightarrow \dot{\phi}^2\cos^2\theta = (C^2n^2/A^2) \Rightarrow (\omega_3 - \dot{\psi}) = Cn/A \qquad \text{[using (7)]}$$

$$\Rightarrow A(n - \dot{\psi}) = \Rightarrow (A - C)n = A\dot{\psi}$$

EXERCISES

1. Deduce Euler's Dynamical Equations
2. State Lagrange's equations and deduce Euler's equations from them, for a body turning about a fixed point.
3. State and prove Euler's Dynamical equations under the action of external forces.
4. A solid of revolution whose principal moments at the centre of inertia are A, A, C, (C>A) is set spinning with angular velocity ω about an axis passing through the centre of inertia and making aind angle i with the figure. Prove that the instantaneous axis of rotation describes in body a right cone of semi-vertical angle i in period $\frac{2\pi A \sec i}{(C-A)\omega}$, and that the axis of the figure describes a right cone in space of semi-vertical angle θ where tan θ (A/C) tan i, in the period $2\pi/\Omega$: where Ω sin ω sin i or $\Omega = (\omega/A)\sqrt{(A^2\sin^2 i + C^2\cos^2 i)}$.
5. A uniform circular disc free to turn about its centre is fixed, is set rotating with angular velocity ω about an axis which makes an angle 45° with the axis of the disc. Prove that in the subsequent motion the axis of the disc describes a right cone about an axis making an angle $\tan^{-1}\frac{1}{2}$ with the initial axis of rotation with constant velocity $\frac{1}{2}\omega^2\sqrt{(10)}$.

6. A uniform thin circular disc is set rotating with an angular velocity ω about an axis through the centre making an angle i with the normal. Prove that the semi-vertical angle θ of the come described by the axis of the disc is given by $\tan\theta = \left(\frac{1}{2}\right)\tan i$.

   If ω be the angular velocity, prove that the above cone is described in the period $2\pi/[\omega\sqrt{1+3\cos^2 i)}]$.

7. An elliptic lamina acted on by an external force F is set rotating about a line through its centre which makes equal with the major and minor axes and with the normal to its plane. Prove that, if e be the eccenricity of the ellipse and ω_1, ω_2, ω_3 the angular velocities about the major and minor axes and the lamina to the planes then.

   $\omega_1 = F\cos\theta$, $\omega_2 = F\sin\theta$, $\omega_2 = \theta\ F\sqrt{\{(1-e^2\sin^2\theta)/(2-2^2)\}}$, where F is a constant.